Test Bank

for

Starr, Evers, and Starr's

Biology Today and Tomorrow
With Physiology

Second Edition

Larry G. Sellers
Louisiana Tech University

THOMSON

BROOKS/COLE

Australia • Brazil • Canada • Mexico • Singapore • Spain • United Kingdom • United States

Thomson Higher Education
10 Davis Drive
Belmont, CA 94002-3098
USA

For more information about our products,
contact us at:
Thomson Learning Academic Resource Center
1-800-423-0563

For permission to use material from this text or product, submit a request online at
http://www.thomsonrights.com.
Any additional questions about permissions can be submitted by email to **thomsonrights@thomson.com.**

Test Bank Contents

Preface

This book contains more than 3400 test bank questions to accompany Starr's *Biology Today and Tomorrow*. The test bank questions are available on disk through the Faculty Support Department of Brooks/Cole or your local Brooks/Cole representative.

We hope you find these questions useful, and we welcome any comments that will help to improve them.

Several instructors contributed to the test bank; therefore it represents a consensus of the kind of questions that are most suitable for students.

All questions are ranked according to level of difficulty (E = Easy, M = Moderate, and D = Difficult). (On the disk version of the test bank, because of the requirements of the test-generator program, 1 = Easy, 3 = Moderate, and 5 = Difficult.) Each rank is represented by about a third of the total questions. The test bank includes the following categories:

1. **Multiple-choice** questions

2. **Matching** questions

3. **Classification** questions, which use the same group of answers for a series of questions.

4. **Select the Exception** questions, which require the student to select the exception from four or five given answers.

5. **Problems**, which appear only in the genetics chapter.

6. **Labeling** of figures exercises appear in most of the chapters.

CHAPTER 1
INVITATION TO BIOLOGY

Multiple-Choice Questions

M   1. The study of biology is important because
*   a. it provides an understanding of life.
    b. it is essential for humans to understand how organisms think.
    c. it is the most difficult and comprehensive of the sciences.
    d. it explains the nature of the universe.
    e. it provides a basis for religious belief.

LIFE'S LEVELS OF ORGANIZATION

E   2. Which is the smallest unit of life that can exist as a separate entity?
*   a. a cell
    b. a molecule
    c. an organ
    d. a population
    e. an ecosystem

D   3. Living organisms are members of ALL of the levels listed below; however, rocks can only be components of
    a. the community.
    b. the population.
    c. the ecosystem.
    d. the biosphere.
*   e. both the ecosystem and the biosphere.

OVERVIEW OF LIFE'S UNITY

E   4. Which of the following would NOT be a key characteristic of "life"?
    a. organization into cells
    b. response to environmental change
    c. reproduction
*   d. inability to change
    e. use of energy

E   5. Living organisms are different from nonliving objects because they
    a. react to environmental stimuli.
    b. exhibit massive complexity.
    c. possess molecules of deoxyribonucleic acid.
    d. exhibit multiple levels of organization.
*   e. all of these

M   6. Nonliving entities would NOT possess
    a. energetic interactions.
*   b. DNA.
    c. atoms.
    d. elements.
    e. any of these

M   7. The DNA molecule is most similar functionally to a
    a. pair of scissors.
    b. flashlight battery.
*   c. computer memory chip.
    d. ballpoint pen.
    e. craft kit of ceramic tiles.

E   8. The ability to acquire, store, transfer, or utilize energy is called
    a. biochemistry.
    b. photosynthesis.
*   c. metabolism.
    d. respiration.
    e. phosphorylation.

E   9. Homeostasis provides what kind of environment?
    a. positive
*   b. constant
    c. limiting
    d. changing
    e. chemical and physical

D   10. Which of the following phrases would most likely be used in a discussion of homeostasis?
    a. respond to environmental stimuli
*   b. limited range of variation
    c. rapid energy turnover
    d. cycle of elements
    e. structural and functional units of life

D   11. Metabolic reactions would most likely be described during a discussion of
*   a. energy transfer.
    b. cellular organization.
    c. responses to environmental stimuli.
    d. perpetuation of the species.
    e. none of these

E   12. Each cell is able to maintain a constant internal environment. This is called
    a. metabolism.
*   b. homeostasis.
    c. physiology.
    d. adaptation.
    e. evolution.

M   13. About twelve to twenty-four hours after the previous meal, a person's blood-sugar level normally varies from 60 to 90 milligrams per 100 milliliters of blood, though it may rise to 130 mg/100 ml after meals high in carbohydrates. That the blood-sugar level is maintained within a fairly narrow range despite uneven intake of sugar is due to the body's ability to carry out
    a. adaptation.
    b. inheritance.
    c. metabolism.
*   d. homeostasis.
    e. all of these

M   14.   All organisms are somewhat similar in
   a.   their requirements for energy.
   b.   their participation in one or more nutrient cycles.
   c.   their ultimate dependence on the sun.
   d.   their interaction with other forms of life.
*   e.   all of these

D   15.   Which of the following would NOT be characteristic of living organisms?
   a.   complex structural organization
   b.   dependence on other organisms for energy and resources
   c.   reproductive capacity
*   d.   uniformity of size and form
   e.   capacity to change

IF SO MUCH UNITY, WHY SO MANY SPECIES?

M   16.   Which of the following do not depend *directly* on sunlight for energy?
   I.   producers
   II.   consumers
   III.   decomposers
   a.   I only
*   b.   II and III only
   c.   II only
   d.   III only
   e.   I and III

E   17.   A two-part scientific name consists of which of the following?
   I.   domain name
   II.   genus name
   III.   species name
   a.   I only
   b.   II only
   c.   III only
   d.   I and II
*   e.   II and III

E   18.   The plural for genus is
   a.   genus.
   b.   geni.
*   c.   genera.
   d.   genuses.
   e.   genae.

E   19.   Members of what group are single cells of considerable internal complexity?
   a.   animals
*   b.   protistans
   c.   fungi
   d.   plants
   e.   eubacteria

E   20.   Members of what group are multicellular producers?
   a.   animals
   b.   protistans
   c.   fungi
*   d.   plants
   e.   eubacteria

E   21.   Which of the following are mostly decomposers?
   a.   plants
*   b.   fungi
   c.   animals
   d.   archaea
   e.   protistans

E   22.   Which of the following is NOT a eukaryote?
   a.   fungi
*   b.   bacteria
   c.   plants
   d.   animals
   e.   protistans

AN EVOLUTIONARY VIEW OF DIVERSITY

M   23.   Hereditary information must
   a.   be unchanging most of the time.
   b.   pass from one generation to the next.
   c.   control a large number of different characteristics.
   d.   provide for the rare change in information.
*   e.   all of these

E   24.   A mutation is a change in
   a.   homeostasis.
   b.   the developmental pattern in an organism.
   c.   metabolism.
*   d.   hereditary information.
   e.   the life cycle of an organism.

M   25.   Evolution occurs at what level of organization?
   a.   organism
   b.   molecule
   c.   organ
*   d.   population
   e.   ecosystem

D   26.   Which of the following statements is NOT true?
   a.   Diversity is the result of evolution.
   b.   The characteristics of any living organism are under the control of chemicals.
*   c.   The diversity of living organisms makes life processes unpredictable, even using scientific methods.
   d.   Organisms are similar in that their structure, organization, and interactions arise from matter and energy.
   e.   The behavior of individual organisms is dependent upon their evolutionary history.

D   27.   The diversity of structure, function, and behavior in living organisms is primarily the result of
   a.   reproduction.
   b.   heredity.
*   c.   evolution.
   d.   metabolism in living organisms.
   e.   homeostasis.

D   28. Which of the following *ultimately* accounts for variation in genetic traits?
     a. copying of DNA molecules
   * b. genetic mutation
     c. asexual reproduction
     d. ecological succession
     e. homeostatic mechanisms

D   29. An adaptive trait is a trait that has
     a. mutated.
   * b. survival value.
     c. decreased in frequency in a population.
     d. harmful biological effects.
     e. the potential to produce variation.

E   30. The animals used by Darwin to show variation in domesticated forms were
   * a. pigeons.
     b. chickens.
     c. pigs.
     d. dogs.
     e. cats.

M   31. The principal point of Darwin's theory of evolution by natural selection was that
     a. long-term heritable changes in organisms are caused by use and disuse.
     b. mutations that adapt an organism to a given environment always arise in the greatest frequency in the organisms that occupy that environment.
     c. mutations are caused by all sorts of environmental influences.
   * d. survival of characteristics in a population depends on competition between organisms, especially between members of the same species.
     e. changes in organisms can be predicted by analysis of their DNA.

M   32. Which premise used by Darwin in his theory is INCORRECTLY stated below?
     a. More offspring are produced than will usually survive to reproduce.
     b. Members of populations show heritable variation.
     c. Some varieties have a better chance to survive and reproduce.
   * d. Organisms that possess advantageous traits have a decreased chance of producing offspring.
     e. Some traits become more common because their bearers contribute more offspring to the next generation.

M   33. The explanation for the diversity seen in nature is
     a. sexual dimorphism; that is, different characteristics are based upon sexual differences.
     b. divine creation of the many different forms of life.
     c. found in the science of classifying organisms.
   * d. natural selection.
     e. unknown at this time.

D   34. Which of the following statements is NOT true?
     a. Natural selection is based upon differing reproduction and survival.
     b. For populations to evolve, there must be variation.

   * c. All variations found in a population are heritable.
     d. A population undergoes evolution when the frequency of its genes changes.
     e. Over time, some genetic traits are more adaptive than others.

THE NATURE OF BIOLOGICAL INQUIRY

M   35. Of the following, which is the first explanation of a problem? (It is sometimes called an "educated guess.")
     a. principle
     b. law
     c. theory
     d. fact
   * e. hypothesis

E   36. Hypotheses are
     a. often in the form of a statement.
     b. sometimes generalizations.
     c. sometimes crude attempts to offer a possible explanation for observations.
     d. used to make predictions.
   * e. all of these

E   37. In order to arrive at a solution to a problem, a scientist usually devises one or more
     a. laws.
     b. theories.
   * c. experiments.
     d. principles.
     e. facts.

M   38. Which represents the *lowest* degree of certainty?
   * a. hypothesis
     b. conclusion
     c. fact
     d. principle
     e. theory

M   39. Which represents the *highest* degree of certainty?
     a. hypothesis
     b. fact
     c. principle
   * d. prediction
     e. theory

THE POWER OF EXPERIMENTAL TESTS

M   40. The control in an experiment
     a. makes the experiment less valid.
     b. is an additional copy for statistical purposes.
     c. reduces the experimental errors.
     d. minimizes experimental inaccuracy.
   * e. allows a standard of comparison for the experimental group.

M   41. As a result of experimentation,
     a. more hypotheses may be developed.
     b. more questions may be asked.
     c. a new biological principle could emerge.
     d. entire theories may be modified or discarded.
   * e. all of these

M 42. In an experiment, the control group is
   a. not subjected to experimental error.
   b. exposed to experimental treatments.
   c. maintained under strict laboratory conditions.
   * d. treated exactly the same as the experimental group, except for the one independent variable.
   e. statistically the most important part of the experiment.

E 43. The choice of whether a particular organism belongs to the experimental group or the control group should be based on
   a. age.
   b. size.
   * c. chance.
   d. designation by the experimenter.
   e. sex.

E 44. Which of the following could be changed based on new evidence?
   a. hypothesis
   b. theory
   c. prediction
   d. experiment
   * e. all of these

THE SCOPE AND LIMITS OF SCIENCE

E 45. Science is based on
   a. faith.
   b. authority.
   * c. evidence.
   d. force.
   e. consensus.

M 46. Which of the following is NOT used in the development of science?
   a. evaluation of data
   * b. personal conviction
   c. prediction
   d. systematic observation
   e. experiments

E 47. All of the following will strengthen a theory EXCEPT
   a. repetitions of experiments.
   b. increased observations.
   c. time.
   * d. faith.
   e. confirmation by many scientists.

E 48. The validity of scientific discoveries CANNOT be based on
   a. morality.
   b. aesthetics.
   c. philosophy.
   d. economics.
   * e. any of these

Classification Questions

Answer questions 49–52 by matching the descriptions to the most appropriate function, process, or trait listed below.
   a. metabolism
   b. reproduction
   c. photosynthesis
   d. growth
   e. homeostasis

M 49. a process found only in plants and some bacteria

E 50. characteristic most organisms exhibit that tends to buffer the effects of environmental change

M 51. the capacity to acquire, store, and use energy

E 52. process in which one generation replaces another

Answers: 49. c   50. e   51. a   52. b

Answer questions 53–59 by matching the descriptions with the most appropriate kingdom listed below.
   a. archaea
   b. protistans
   c. plants
   d. fungi
   e. animals

E 53. multicellular producers

E 54. prokaryotic

M 55. unicellular organisms of considerable internal complexity

M 56. multicellular consumers

E 57. oldest living organisms

M 58. unicellular producers

M 59. multicellular decomposers

Answers: 53. c   54. a   55. b   56. e
              57. a   58. b   59. d

Selecting the Exception

E 60. Four of the five answers listed below are necessary characteristics to the life of an individual organism. Select the exception.
   a. metabolism
   b. homeostasis
   c. development
   d. heredity
   * e. diversity

M 61. Four of the five answers listed below are characteristics of life. Select the exception.
   * a. ionization
   b. metabolism
   c. reproduction
   d. growth
   e. development

E   62. Four of the five answers listed below are aspects of the scientific method. Select the exception.
        a. observation
        b. hypothesis
        c. experimentation
    *   d. philosophy
        e. conclusion

M   63. Four of the five answers listed below are terms associated with the scientific method. Select the exception.
    *   a. faith
        b. theory
        c. experiment
        d. prediction
        e. hypothesis

D   64. Four of the five answers listed below are deductions made by Charles Darwin. Select the exception.
        a. Natural selection is a result of differential reproduction.
        b. Much of biological variation is heritable.
        c. More offspring are produced than can survive.
    *   d. Mutations produce changes in inheritance.
        e. Some variations of heritable traits improve chances of survival.

CHAPTER 2
MOLECULES OF LIFE

Multiple-Choice Questions

ATOMS AND THEIR INTERACTIONS

M **1.** Which is NOT an element?
* a. water
b. oxygen
c. carbon
d. chlorine
e. hydrogen

M **2.** Which is the smallest portion of a substance that retains the properties of an element?
* a. atom
b. compound
c. ion
d. molecule
e. mixture

E **3.** The atom that represents the greatest weight in the human body is
a. hydrogen.
b. carbon.
c. nitrogen.
* d. oxygen.
e. phosphorus.

M **4.** Radioactive isotopes
a. are electrically unbalanced.
b. behave the same chemically and physically but differ biologically from other isotopes.
c. are the same physically and biologically but differ from other isotopes chemically.
* d. have an excess number of neutrons.
e. are produced when substances are exposed to radiation.

E **5.** Which is NOT a compound?
a. salt
b. a carbohydrate
* c. carbon
d. a nucleotide
e. methane

E **6.** The negative subatomic particle is
a. the neutron.
b. the proton.
* c. the electron.
d. both the neutron and proton.
e. both the proton and electron.

E **7.** The positive subatomic particle is
a. the neutron.
* b. the proton.
c. the electron.
d. both the neutron and proton.
e. both the proton and electron.

E **8.** The neutral subatomic particle is
* a. the neutron.
b. the proton.
c. the electron.
d. both the neutron and proton.
e. both the proton and electron.

E **9.** The nucleus of an atom contains
* a. neutrons and protons.
b. neutrons and electrons.
c. protons and electrons.
d. protons only.
e. neutrons only.

E **10.** Which components of an atom are negatively charged?

   I. electrons

   II. protons

   III. neutrons

* a. I only
b. II only
c. III only
d. I and II
e. II and III

E **11.** Which components of an atom do not have a charge?

   I. electrons

   II. protons

   III. neutrons

a. I only
b. II only
* c. III only
d. I and II
e. II and III

E **12.** All atoms of an element have the same number of
a. ions.
* b. protons.
c. neutrons.
d. electrons.
e. protons and neutrons.

D **13.** Tracer isotopes
a. are used only in plants.
b. work differently than nontracers in reactions.
* c. are detected by their radioactivity.
d. have an unbalanced electrical charge.
e. are not found in nature.

D 14. Which of the following statements is NOT true?
   a. All isotopes of an element have the same number of electrons.
   b. All isotopes of an element have the same number of protons.
* c. All isotopes of an element have the same number of neutrons.
   d. All radioactive isotopes are unstable.
   e. All isotopes of an element have the same atomic number.

M 15. Radioactive isotopes have
   a. excess electrons.
   b. excess protons.
* c. excess neutrons.
   d. insufficient neutrons.
   e. insufficient protons.

M 16. In the chemical shorthand ^{14}C, the fourteen represents the number of
   a. excess neutrons.
* b. protons plus neutrons.
   c. electrons.
   d. protons plus electrons.
   e. radioactive particles.

M 17. By analogy, the orbitals and atomic nucleus may be said to most resemble a
   a. merry-go-round.
   b. sundial.
* c. solar system.
   d. nest of mixing bowls.
   e. wave of water currents.

D 18. Magnesium has 12 protons. How many electrons are in its third energy level?
* a. 2
   b. 4
   c. 6
   d. 8
   e. 10

D 19. Magnesium has 12 protons. How many electrons are in its first energy level?
* a. 2
   b. 4
   c. 6
   d. 8
   e. 10

D 20. Magnesium has 12 protons. How many electrons are in its second energy level?
   a. 2
   b. 4
   c. 6
* d. 8
   e. 10

D 21. Oxygen, with an atomic number of 8, has _?_ electrons in the first energy level and _?_ electrons in the second energy level.
   a. 1; 7
* b. 2; 6
   c. 3; 5
   d. 4; 4
   e. 5; 3

M 22. Which statement is NOT true?
   a. Electrons closest to the nucleus are at the lowest energy level.
   b. No more than two electrons can occupy a single orbital.
* c. Electrons are unable to move out of the assigned orbital space.
   d. The innermost orbital holds two electrons.
   e. At the second energy level there are four possible orbitals with a total of eight electrons.

E 23. Water is an example of a(n)
   a. atom.
   b. ion.
* c. compound.
   d. mixture.
   e. element.

E 24. Which includes the other four?
   a. atoms
* b. molecules
   c. electrons
   d. elements
   e. protons

M 25. Which statement is FALSE?
   a. A molecule is made of at least two atoms.
   b. Compounds are made of elements.
   c. Two atoms of oxygen make a molecule of oxygen.
* d. Proportions of elements in compounds vary according to their source in nature.
   e. Elements are found in compounds and molecules.

M 26. A molecule is
* a. a combination of two or more atoms.
   b. less stable than its constituent atoms separated.
   c. electrically charged.
   d. a carrier of one or more extra neutrons.
   e. none of these

BONDS IN BIOLOGICAL MOLECULES

E 27. What is formed when an atom loses or gains an electron?
   a. mole
* b. ion
   c. molecule
   d. bond
   e. reaction

D 28. Which of the following is NOT accurate concerning ionization?
   a. When one atom loses an electron, another must gain.
 * b. When an atom loses an electron, it becomes negatively charged.
   c. Ionic bonds form between ionized atoms.
   d. In the compound NaCl, Na loses an electron to become positive.
   e. In an ion, the number of protons and electrons is unequal.

M 29. The bond in table salt (NaCl) is
   a. polar.
 * b. ionic.
   c. covalent.
   d. double.
   e. nonpolar.

D 30. In _?_ bonds, atoms share electrons equally.
 * a. nonpolar covalent
   b. polar covalent
   c. double covalent
   d. triple covalent
   e. unstable covalent

E 31. Electrons are shared in bonds called
   a. covalent.
   b. polar.
   c. nonpolar.
   d. ionic.
 * e. all of these except "ionic"

D 32. The shape (or tertiary form) of large molecules is often controlled by what kind of bonds?
 * a. hydrogen
   b. ionic
   c. covalent
   d. inert
   e. single

D 33. A hydrogen bond is
   a. a sharing of a pair of electrons between a hydrogen and an oxygen nucleus.
   b. a sharing of a pair of electrons between a hydrogen nucleus and either an oxygen or a nitrogen nucleus.
 * c. an attractive force that involves a hydrogen atom and an oxygen or a nitrogen atom that are either in two different molecules or within the same molecule.
   d. none of these
   e. all of these

D 34. Which of the following is NOT true of hydrogen bonds?
   a. They are quite weak.
   b. The hydrogen is slightly positive.
   c. They are common in macromolecules.
 * d. They form in salts such as NaCl.
   e. They always involve hydrogen.

WATER'S LIFE-GIVING PROPERTIES

M 35. Hydrophobic molecules are _?_ water.
   a. attracted to
   b. absorbed by
 * c. repelled by
   d. mixed with
   e. polarized by

D 36. Which of the following is TRUE of water?
   a. The oxygen end is slightly electropositive.
 * b. Hydrogen bonds hold water molecules together.
   c. Water covers about one-half of the Earth's surface.
   d. Hydrophobic interactions attract water molecules.
   e. Solvent properties are greatest with nonpolar molecules.

D 37. Water is an excellent solvent because
   a. it forms spheres of hydration around charged substances and can form hydrogen bonds with many substances.
   b. it has a high heat-containing property.
   c. of its cohesive properties.
   d. it is a liquid at room temperature.
 * e. all of these

D 38. Glucose dissolves in water because it
   a. ionizes.
   b. is a polysaccharide.
 * c. is polar and forms many hydrogen bonds with the water molecules.
   d. has a very reactive primary structure.
   e. is an isotope.

D 39. Water has the ability to retard heat gain and loss due to its
   a. hydrophilic interactions.
   b. evaporation.
 * c. hydrogen bonds.
   d. crystal structure.
   e. liquidity.

M 40. The column of water extending in tubes from plant roots to leaves is due mostly to
 * a. cohesion.
   b. evaporation.
   c. ionization.
   d. hydrophobic interactions.
   e. all of these

ACIDS AND BASES

M 41. A salt will dissolve in water to form
   a. acids.
   b. gases.
 * c. ions.
   d. bases.
   e. polar solvents.

M 42. A reaction of an acid and a base will produce water and
   a. a buffer.
 * b. a salt.
   c. gas.
   d. solid precipitate.
   e. solute.

E 43. Which of the following represents H^+?
 * a. hydrogen ion
   b. acid
   c. base
   d. hydroxyl ion
   e. acceptor

M 44. Which of the following would NOT be used in connection with the word "acid"?
   a. excess hydrogen ions
   b. contents of the stomach
 * c. magnesium hydroxide
   d. HCl
   e. pH less than 7

D 45. A pH of 10 is how many times as basic as a pH of 7?
   a. 2
   b. 3
   c. 10
   d. 100
 * e. 1,000

D 46. A solution with a pH of 8 has how many times fewer hydrogen ions than a solution with a pH of 6?
   a. 2
   b. 4
   c. 10
 * d. 100
   e. 1,000

D 47. Which of the following is NOT true?
   a. Acids release hydrogen ions.
   b. In a neutral solution, the amounts of hydrogen and hydroxyl ions are almost equal.
 * c. Salts precipitate out of solution and have no function in cells.
   d. Polar water molecules are attracted to water.
   e. Hydrogen bonding between water molecules gives water its temperature-stabilizing and cohesive properties.

M 48. Cellular pH is kept near a value of 7 because of
   a. salts.
 * b. buffers.
   c. acids.
   d. bases.
   e. water.

MOLECULES OF LIFE—FROM STRUCTURE TO FUNCTION

E 49. The three most common atoms in your body are
 * a. hydrogen, oxygen, and carbon.
   b. carbon, hydrogen, and nitrogen.
   c. carbon, nitrogen, and oxygen.
   d. nitrogen, hydrogen, and oxygen.
   e. carbon, oxygen, and sulfur.

M 50. Carbon usually forms how many bonds with other atoms?
   a. 2
   b. 3
 * c. 4
   d. 5
   e. 6

E 51. The word "organic" signals the presence of
 * a. carbon.
   b. oxygen.
   c. nitrogen.
   d. sulfur.
   e. hydrogen.

M 52. An —OH group is a(n) _?_ group.
   a. carboxyl
 * b. hydroxyl
   c. amino
   d. methyl
   e. ketone

M 53. A —CH_3 group is a(n) _?_ group.
   a. carboxyl
   b. hydroxyl
   c. amino
 * d. methyl
   e. ketone

M 54. An —NH_2 group is a(n) _?_ group.
   a. carboxyl
   b. hydroxyl
 * c. amino
   d. methyl
   e. ketone

M 55. A —COOH group is a(n) _?_ group.
 * a. carboxyl
   b. hydroxyl
   c. amino
   d. methyl
   e. ketone

M 56. The formation of large polymers from smaller repeating units is known as what kind of reaction?
   a. oxidation
   b. reduction
 * c. condensation
   d. hydrolysis
   e. decarboxylation

E 57. The breakdown of large molecules by the enzymatic addition of water is an example of what kind of reaction?
   a. oxidation
   b. reduction
   c. condensation
 * d. hydrolysis
   e. decarboxylation

E 58. A condensation reaction typically produces
   a. monomers.
   b. salts.
 * c. polymers.
   d. simple sugars.
   e. amino acids.

M 59. Which reaction results in the breakdown of a molecule into two smaller ones?
   a. synthesis
 * b. cleavage
   c. condensation
   d. polymerization
   e. both cleavage and condensation

D 60. Condensation and hydrolysis are accomplished in cells by
   a. bonding attraction.
 * b. the action of enzymes.
   c. spontaneous action.
   d. functional group interactions.
   e. all of these

M 61. The relatively unimportant by-product(s) of many condensation reactions is (are)
   a. carbon dioxide.
   b. aldehyde groups.
   c. enzymes.
   d. alcohols.
 * e. water.

THE TRULY ABUNDANT CARBOHYDRATES

E 62. Which of the following could be used to describe a monomer of carbohydrates?
   a. glycogen
   b. nucleotide
   c. simple sugar
   d. monosaccharide
 * e. both simple sugar and monosaccharide

E 63. Which substance is the most common in cells?
 * a. carbohydrates
   b. salts and minerals
   c. proteins
   d. fats
   e. nucleic acids

E 64. A large biological molecule is composed of smaller units called
   a. polymers.
   b. isomers.
 * c. monomers.
   d. isotopes.
   e. dimers.

M 65. Which of the following is composed of a 1:2:1 ratio of carbon to hydrogen to oxygen?
 * a. carbohydrate
   b. protein
   c. lipid
   d. nucleic acid
   e. steroid

D 66. Oligosaccharides include
   a. transport molecules in plants.
   b. storage compounds in both plants and animals.
   c. side chains on proteins.
   d. monomers to form polysaccharides.
 * e. the most plentiful sugar in plants.

D 67. Glucose and fructose are different
   a. in the number of carbons they possess.
   b. in their relationship to the sucrose molecules.
 * c. in the way that their atoms are arranged.
   d. in the number of double bonds they possess.
   e. both in the way that their atoms are arranged and in the number of double bonds they possess.

M 68. Fructose and glucose are
   a. ring forms.
   b. structurally different.
   c. monosaccharides.
   d. simple sugars.
 * e. all of these

M 69. Glucose and ribose
   a. have the same number of carbon atoms.
   b. have the same structural formulas.
   c. are the two components of sucrose.
 * d. are monosaccharides.
   e. are molecules whose atoms are arranged the same way.

M 70. Sucrose is composed of
   a. two molecules of fructose.
   b. two molecules of glucose.
 * c. a molecule of fructose and a molecule of glucose.
   d. a molecule of fructose and a molecule of galactose.
   e. two molecules of fructose.

M 71. The combination of glucose and galactose forms
   a. fructose.
   b. maltose.
 * c. lactose.
   d. sucrose.
   e. mannose.

E 72. Plants store their excess carbohydrates in the form of
   * a. starch.
   b. glycogen.
   c. glucose.
   d. cellulose.
   e. fats.

M 73. Glycogen is a polysaccharide used for energy storage by
   * a. animals.
   b. plants.
   c. protistans.
   d. monerans.
   e. both animals and protistans.

M 74. Cellulose is
   * a. a material found in cell walls.
   b. a component of plasma membranes.
   c. a plant protein.
   d. formed by hydrolysis.
   e. the most complex of the organic compounds.

M 75. Which is NOT a monosaccharide?
   a. glucose
   b. fructose
   c. deoxyribose
   * d. starch
   e. ribose

M 76. Which of the following includes all the others?
   a. sucrose
   b. glucose
   c. cellulose
   d. glycogen
   * e. carbohydrate

M 77. Which of the following CANNOT be used to describe some aspect of polysaccharides?
   a. energy storage
   b. straight or branched chain
   c. glucose subunits
   * d. insoluble in water
   e. complex

M 78. A polysaccharide
   a. is composed of many monosaccharides that have been linked together.
   b. may be straight and unbranched or highly branched.
   c. is most likely made of glucose molecules if it is one of the natural polysaccharides.
   d. is commonly cellulose, glycogen, and starch in nature.
   * e. all of these

D 79. Chitin is a polysaccharide with _?_ atoms attached to the glucose backbone.
   a. magnesium
   b. phosphorus
   c. potassium
   * d. nitrogen
   e. sulfur

GREASY, FATTY—MUST BE LIPIDS

M 80. Which of the following is more soluble in a nonpolar solvent (such as acetone) than in water?
   a. lipids
   b. polysaccharides
   c. fats
   d. sterols
   * e. all of these except polysaccharides

M 81. Triglycerides are
   a. carbohydrates.
   b. nucleotides.
   c. proteins.
   * d. neutral fats.
   e. amino acids.

M 82. Oils are
   a. liquid at room temperatures.
   b. unsaturated fats.
   c. found only in animals.
   d. complex carbohydrates.
   * e. both liquid at room temperature and unsaturated fats.

E 83. Which of the following are lipids?
   a. sterols
   b. triglycerides
   c. oils
   d. waxes
   * e. all of these

D 84. Sterols
   a. are used in the synthesis of amino acids.
   b. consist of four carbon rings.
   c. may have different numbers, types, and positions of functional groups attached to them.
   d. are key components of eukaryotic cell membranes.
   * e. all of these choices are true except "are used in the synthesis of amino acids"

D 85. Long-chain fatty acids attached to long-chain alcohols is a characteristic of
   a. triglycerides.
   b. phospholipids.
   c. sterols.
   * d. waxes.
   e. glycoproteins.

M 86. Unsaturated fatty acids
   * a. have fewer hydrogens than fatty acids.
   b. are more characteristic of animal fats than plant fats.
   c. contribute to the possibility of arteriosclerosis.
   d. have no double bonds.
   e. are solid at room temperature.

D 87. If the cuticle were removed from an apple while leaving the skin intact,
*   a. the apple would lose water and dehydrate.
   b. the apple would undergo fungal decomposition.
   c. nothing would happen.
   d. the apple would begin to swell as it absorbs moisture from the air.
   e. all of these

M 88. An example of a compound with saturated fatty acids is
   a. olive oil.
   b. corn oil.
*   c. butter.
   d. linoleic acid.
   e. soybean oil.

M 89. Lipids
*   a. serve as food reserves in many organisms.
   b. include cartilage and chitin.
   c. include fats consisting of one fatty-acid molecule and three glycerol molecules.
   d. are composed of monosaccharides.
   e. none of these

E 90. Cell membranes are characterized by the presence of
   a. triglycerides.
*   b. phospholipids.
   c. unsaturated fats.
   d. steroids.
   e. fatty acids.

D 91. All sterols have
   a. the same number of double bonds.
   b. double bonds in the same positions.
*   c. four rings of carbon to which are attached other atoms.
   d. the same functional groups.
   e. the same number and positions of double bonds.

PROTEINS—DIVERSITY IN STRUCTURE AND FUNCTION

D 92. Primary protein structure is dependent on
   a. hydrophobic interactions.
   b. hydrogen bonds.
*   c. bonds between carbon and hydrogen.
   d. covalent linkages between carbon and oxygen.
   e. all of these

D 93. Proteins may function as
   a. structural units.
   b. hormones.
   c. storage molecules.
   d. transport molecules.
*   e. all of these

D 94. The "R" group found in amino acids consists of
   a. an amine group.
   b. a hydroxyl group.
   c. a carboxyl group.
*   d. additional atoms.
   e. an amine group and a carboxyl group.

E 95. Amino acids are the building blocks for
*   a. proteins.
   b. steroids.
   c. lipids.
   d. nucleic acids.
   e. carbohydrates.

E 96. What kind of bond exists between two amino acids in a protein?
*   a. peptide
   b. ionic
   c. hydrogen
   d. amino
   e. sulfhydroxyl

M 97. The sequence of amino acids is the _?_ structure of proteins.
*   a. primary
   b. secondary
   c. tertiary
   d. quaternary
   e. stereo

E 98. Amino acids are linked by what kind of bonds to form the primary structure of a protein?
   a. disulfide
   b. hydrogen
   c. ionic
*   d. peptide
   e. none of these

M 99. The secondary structure of proteins can be
   a. helical.
   b. sheetlike.
   c. globular.
   d. the sequence of amino acids.
*   e. both helical and sheetlike.

M 100. The interaction of four polypeptide chains in a hemoglobin molecule is _?_ structure.
*   a. quaternary (fourth level)
   b. secondary (second level)
   c. primary (first level)
   d. tertiary (third level)
   e. quintinery (fifth level)

D 101. Denaturation of proteins may result in all EXCEPT one of the following. Which one is it?
   a. breakage of hydrogen bonds
   b. loss of three-dimensional structure
*   c. removal of R groups from amino acids
   d. alteration of enzyme activity
   e. endangerment of cell's life

WHY IS PROTEIN STUCTURE SO IMPORTANT?

E **102.** The sixth amino acid in normal hemoglobin is glutamate, but it is replaced by _?_ in sickle-cell anemia.
   a. histidine
   b. proline
   c. leucine
   * d. valine
   e. threonine

M **103.** Which of the following is NOT a known dysfunction in the expression of sickle-cell anemia?
   a. loss of shape of red blood cells with insufficient oxygen
   b. rheumatism
   c. brain damage
   * d. excessive absorption of oxygen causing the cell to swell
   e. enlarged spleen

NUCLEOTIDES AND THE NUCLEIC ACIDS

E **104.** Nucleotides are used in
   a. proteins.
   b. steroids.
   c. lipids.
   * d. ATP, NAD^+, and FAD.
   e. carbohydrates.

M **105.** Which of the following is NOT found in every nucleic acid?
   * a. ribose
   b. phosphate group
   c. single-ring base
   d. double-ring base
   e. All of these are characteristic of every nucleotide.

D **106.** The nucleotide associated with chemical messages is
   * a. cyclic AMP.
   b. FAD.
   c. NAD^+.
   d. ATP.
   e. all of these

D **107.** Flavin adenine dinucleotide and nicotinamide adenine dinucleotide are examples of
   a. functional nucleotides.
   * b. transport nucleotides (coenzymes).
   c. structural nucleotides.
   d. nuclear proteins.
   e. chemical messengers.

M **108.** The nucleotide most readily available in energy transfers is
   a. cyclic AMP.
   b. FAD.
   c. NAD^+.
   * d. ATP.
   e. all of these

E **109.** Nucleotides contain what kind of sugars?
   a. three-carbon
   b. four-carbon
   * c. five-carbon
   d. six-carbon
   e. seven-carbon

M **110.** DNA
   a. is one of the adenosine phosphates.
   b. is one of the nucleotide coenzymes.
   * c. stores and retrieves heritable information in all cells.
   d. translates protein-building instructions into actual protein structures.
   e. none of these

D **111.** Which molecule is INCORRECTLY matched with its component parts?
   a. fat: fatty acids
   * b. starch: riboses
   c. protein: amino acids
   d. glycogen: glucoses
   e. nucleic acids: nucleotides

Matching Questions

M **112.** Matching. Choose the one most appropriate answer for each.
   1. ___ enzymes
   2. ___ glucose
   3. ___ nucleotide coenzymes
   4. ___ phospholipids
   A. a six-carbon sugar
   B. energy carriers such as NAD^+ and FAD
   C. principal components of cell membranes
   D. speed up metabolic reactions
   E. DNA and RNA

Answers: 1. D   2. A   3. B   4. C

Classification Questions

The various energy levels in an atom of magnesium have different numbers of electrons. The magnesium nucleus contains 12 protons. Use the following numbers to answer questions 113–115.
   a. 1
   b. 2
   c. 3
   d. 6
   e. 8

D **113.** number of electrons in the first energy level

D **114.** number of electrons in the second energy level

D **115.** number of electrons in the third energy level

Answers: 113. b   114. e   115. b

The following are types of chemical bonds. Answer questions 116–120 by matching the descriptions with the most appropriate bond type.

    a. hydrogen
    b. ionic
    c. covalent

M **116.** the bond between the atoms of table salt

M **117.** the bond type holding several molecules of water together

M **118.** the bond between the oxygen atoms of gaseous oxygen

M **119.** the bond that breaks when salts dissolve in water

M **120.** atoms connected by this kind of bond share electrons

Answers: 116. b   117. a   118. c

             119. b   120. c

The following are chemical functional groups that may be part of a biologically active molecule. Answer questions 121–131 by matching the items with the most appropriate group.

    a. —COOH
    b. —CH$_3$
    c. —NH$_2$
    d. —OH

    e. $>$C$=$O

    f.

    g. —CHO

E **121.** the amine group

E **122.** the carboxyl group

M **123.** the group that is acidic on amino acids

M **124.** the group that occurs repeatedly in sugars; composed of two elements

E **125.** the methyl group

E **126.** the hydroxyl group

E **127.** the ketone group

M **128.** the group on the amino-terminal end of proteins

M **129.** the group on the carboxyl-terminal end of proteins

M **130.** a group composed of three different elements; found in sugars

M **131.** the group typical of energy carriers such as ATP

Answers: 121. c   122. a   123. a   124. d
           125. b   126. d   127. e   128. c
           129. a   130. g   131. f

The following are basic building blocks of macromolecules. Answer questions 132–139 by matching the items with the most appropriate building block.

    a. amino acids
    b. glucose
    c. glycerol
    d. fatty acids
    e. nucleotides

E **132.** the basic unit of proteins

E **133.** the basic unit of DNA

E **134.** the basic unit of RNA

E **135.** the basic unit of cellulose

E **136.** the basic unit of glycogen

E **137.** the basic unit of starch

M **138.** the monomeric unit of a polypeptide chain

M **139.** Which two units combine in various ways to form lipids?
    a. a and b
    b. a and c
    c. b and c
    d. b and d
    e. c and d

Answers: 132. a   133. e   134. e   135. b
           136. b   137. b   138. a   139. e

Selecting the Exception

D **140.** Four of the five answers listed below are related by a unifying characteristic. Select the exception.
    a. ionic bond
    b. covalent bond
    c. polar bond
    d. hydrogen bond
  * e. cluster of nonpolar groups

M **141.** Four of the five answers listed below are alkaline (pH above 7). Select the exception.
    a. milk of magnesia
    b. household ammonia
    c. baking soda
    d. phosphate detergent
  * e. wine

M **142.** Four of the five answers listed below are acidic (pH below 7). Select the exception.
    a. vinegar
    b. oranges
  * c. soap
    d. lemon juice
    e. beer

D 143. Four of the five answers listed below are characteristics of water. Select the exception.
   a. stabilizes temperature
   b. is a common solvent
   c. has cohesion and surface tension
 * d. produces salts
   e. repels hydrophobic substances

M 144. Four of the five answers listed below are related by a common chemical similarity. Select the exception.
   a. cellulose
 * b. hydrochloric acid
   c. amino acid
   d. protein
   e. nucleic acid

M 145. Four of the five answers listed below are related as members of the same group. Select the exception.
   a. glucose
   b. fructose
 * c. cellulose
   d. ribose
   e. deoxyribose

D 146. Four of the five answers listed below are related as members of the same group. Select the exception.
   a. lactose
   b. sucrose
   c. maltose
   d. table sugar
 * e. fructose

D 147. Four of the five answers listed below are carbohydrates. Select the exception.
 * a. glycerol
   b. cellulose
   c. starch
   d. sucrose
   e. glycogen

D 148. Four of the five answers listed below are polysaccharides. Select the exception.
   a. chitin
   b. cellulose
 * c. hemoglobin
   d. starch
   e. glycogen

M 149. Four of the five answers listed below are lipids. Select the exception.
   a. triglyceride
   b. wax
   c. butter
 * d. insulin
   e. steroid

M 150. Four of the five answers listed below are saturated fats. Select the exception.
   a. butter
   b. lard
 * c. peanut oil
   d. animal fat
   e. adipose tissue

D 151. Four of the five answers listed below are amino acids. Select the exception.
   a. glycine
 * b. adenine
   c. phenylalanine
   d. valine
   e. tyrosine

D 152. Four of the five answers listed below are functional groups. Select the exception.
 * a. R group
   b. amino group
   c. carboxyl group
   d. hydroxyl group
   e. aldehyde group

Labeling

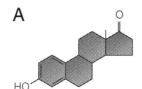

A

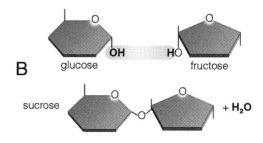

B

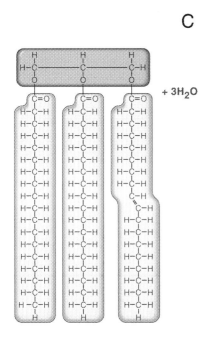

C

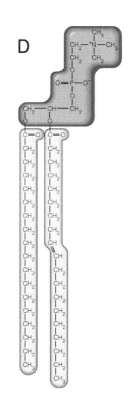

D

+ 3H₂O

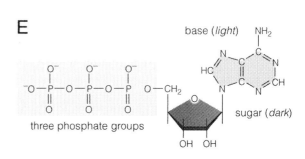

E

three phosphate groups

base (*light*)

sugar (*dark*)

E **153.** In figure "E" the sugar is
   a. ribose.
   * b. deoxyribose.

E **154.** The formation of the molecule in figure "B" is the result of
   a. hydrolysis.
   b. cleavage.
   * c. condensation.
   d. ionization.
   e. randomization.

E **155.** In figure "D" the polar portion of the molecule is
   * a. upper "head."
   b. lower "tails."

E **156.** In figure "C" the unsaturated fatty acid is
   a. on the left.
   b. in the middle.
   * c. on the right.

E **157.** The molecule in figure "A" is
   a. polar.
   b. a protein.
   c. ionized.
   * d. a sterol.
   e. water soluble.

CHAPTER 3
HOW CELLS ARE PUT TOGETHER

Multiple-Choice Questions

WHAT IS "A CELL"?

E 1. One of the generalizations of the cell theory is that
   a. all cells have a nucleus.
   b. all cells divide by meiosis.
   * c. all living organisms are made up of cells.
   d. cells arise through spontaneous generation.
   e. growth is solely the result of cell division.

M 2. Which of these cell features is absent in a bacterial cell?
   a. plasma membrane
   b. nucleoid
   c. cytoplasm
   * d. nucleus
   e. DNA

E 3. All cells except bacteria and archaea
   a. are eukaryotes.
   b. possess a nucleus.
   c. use organelles for compartmentalization.
   d. possess a nucleus and use organelles for compartmentalization.
   * e. are eukaryotes, possess a nucleus, and use organelles for compartmentalization.

M 4. If a cell did not have ribosomes, it would be unable to
   a. extract energy from glucose.
   b. synthesize glucose.
   c. store food in the form of fat.
   * d. form proteins.
   e. utilize oxygen.

MOST CELLS ARE *REALLY SMALL*

D 5. If the volume of a cell increases, its surface area will
   a. decrease.
   b. remain the same.
   c. increase proportionately.
   d. increase to a greater degree.
   * e. increase to a lesser degree.

D 6. Volume increases by the _?_ of the diameter, and surface area increases by the _?_.
   a. square; doubling
   b. square; cube
   * c. cube; square
   d. cube; cube
   e. none of these

M 7. Cells are of small size because of considerations of
   a. weight.
   b. complexity.
   * c. diffusion.
   d. space.
   e. division.

D 8. Elephants are large animals because they
   a. have bigger cells.
   b. possess expandable cells.
   * c. are made of a greater number of cells.
   d. have bigger cells and are made of a greater number of cells.
   e. have bigger cells that are expandable and of greater number.

E 9. The highest magnification generally used to study the internal structure of cells is provided by the
   * a. transmission electron microscope.
   b. compound light microscope.
   c. phase contrast microscope.
   d. scanning electron microscope.
   e. binocular dissecting microscope.

THE STRUCTURE OF CELL MEMBRANES

M 10. An analysis of a plasma or nuclear membrane would yield
   a. cellulose.
   b. suberin and cutin.
   * c. phospholipids and proteins.
   d. microtubules and microfilaments.
   e. all of these

E 11. The phospholipid molecules of most membranes have
   a. a hydrophobic head and a hydrophilic tail.
   b. a hydrophobic head and a hydrophobic tail.
   c. a hydrophobic head and two hydrophobic tails.
   * d. a hydrophilic head and two hydrophobic tails.
   e. none of these

E 12. Hydrophobic interactions of the tails of phospholipids can produce
   * a. a lipid bilayer.
   b. hydrolysis of the fatty acids.
   c. a protein membrane.
   d. a cytoskeleton.
   e. a nonpolar membrane.

D   13. Which of the following statements is TRUE?
   a. When lipids and water are mixed, it is the water molecules that isolate themselves into droplets.
   b. When lipids and water are mixed, the lipids dissolve and enter into a solution.
   * c. Lipids are classified as nonpolar substances and will not mix with water.
   d. Polar substances are able to pass through a plasma membrane more readily than nonpolar substances.
   e. All portions of a phospholipid molecule found in a membrane are classified as nonpolar.

D   14. A hypothetical "microbullet" shot through a phospholipid bilayer would pass the components in which order?
   a. tail >>> tail >>> head >>> head
   b. head >>> tail >>> head >>> tail
   c. tail >>> head >>> head >>> tail
   * d. head >>> tail >>> tail >>> head
   e. head >>> head >>> tail >>> tail

D   15. If a plasma membrane were compared to a sandwich, _?_ would be considered the filling.
   a. cholesterol
   b. protein
   c. hydrophilic heads
   * d. hydrophobic tails
   e. carbohydrates

D   16. Unsaturated tails tend to _?_ at the sites of their double bonds.
   a. dissolve
   * b. kink or bend
   c. separate
   d. react with ions
   e. expand

D   17. The relative impermeability of membranes to water-soluble molecules is a result of
   a. the nonpolar nature of water molecules.
   b. the presence of large proteins that extend through both sides of membranes.
   c. the presence of inorganic salt crystals scattered through some membranes.
   d. the presence of cellulose and chemicals such as cutin, lignin, pectin, and suberin in the membranes.
   * e. the presence of phospholipids in the lipid bilayer.

D   18. In an attempt to visualize the fluid mosaic model of a membrane, we could describe the _?_ as floating in a sea of _?_.
   a. lipid; protein
   b. phospholipids; carbohydrate
   * c. proteins; lipid
   d. fats; water
   e. glycolipids; sterols

M   19. A membrane is more "fluid" than solid because
   a. phospholipid tails prevent close packing.
   b. proteins can shift positions.
   c. water is the main component.
   * d. phospholipid tails prevent close packing into a solid layer
   e. phospholipid tails prevent close packing, proteins can shift positions, and water is the main component.

M   20. Which statement is TRUE of plasma membranes?
   * a. They have protein molecules on their surfaces that identify them.
   b. They are essentially impermeable.
   c. They are basically static, nonchanging structures.
   d. They are hydrophilic barriers between cells.
   e. They function primarily through the activity of their carbohydrates.

D   21. A transport protein is most analogous to a
   a. wall partition.
   * b. subway train.
   c. light switch.
   d. voice identification device.
   e. television receiver.

M   22. Most of the active functions of plasma membranes are carried out by
   a. cholesterol.
   * b. proteins.
   c. hydrophilic heads.
   d. hydrophobic tails.
   e. carbohydrates.

D   23. A water-soluble hormone (signaling molecule) would most likely bind to which of the following membrane proteins?
   a. active transporter
   b. recognition
   * c. receptor
   d. passive transporter
   e. communication

A CLOSER LOOK AT PROKARYOTIC CELLS

E   24. Which are examples of prokaryotes?
   a. protozoa
   * b. bacteria
   c. algae
   d. fungi
   e. mosses

M   25. Prokaryotic cells do NOT have
   a. ribosomes.
   * b. a nucleus housing DNA.
   c. cytoplasm.
   d. a plasma membrane.
   e. ribosomes or membrane-bound nuclei.

E   26.   Prokaryotes
            a. have nucleoid regions.
            b. are unicellular.
            c. have cell walls.
            d. are bacteria.
        *   e. all of these

M   27.   On which of the following are polypeptide chains
           constructed?
            a. Golgi bodies
            b. mitochondria
            c. chloroplasts
        *   d. ribosomes
            e. endoplasmic reticula

M   28.   A mutant bacterial strain lacking cytoplasmic
           ribosomes would be incapable of
            a. carbohydrate synthesis.
            b. respiration.
            c. DNA programming.
        *   d. protein synthesis.
            e. diffusion.

A CLOSER LOOK AT EUKARYOTIC CELLS

M   29.   Which of the following organelles is correctly
           matched with its function?
            a. nucleus: protein synthesis
            b. ER: heredity
        *   c. Golgi bodies: packaging
            d. mitochondria: digestion
            e. chloroplasts: storage of lipids

D   30.   The organelle that pinches off portions of its
           membrane to form a vesicle used for storage or
           transport is the
            a. mitochondrion.
            b. chloroplast.
            c. nucleolus.
        *   d. Golgi body.
            e. ribosome.

E   31.   An organelle found inside the nucleus is a
            a. plastid.
            b. vacuole.
            c. microvillus.
        *   d. nucleolus.
            e. basal body.

M   32.   Which of the following terms CANNOT be used to
           characterize eukaryotic chromosomes?
            a. DNA plus proteins
            b. duplicated
            c. condensed
        *   d. bathed in cytoplasm
            e. "colored bodies"

M   33.   Which of the following is NOT technically a part of
           the endomembrane system?
        *   a. nucleus
            b. endoplasmic reticulum
            c. lysosomes
            d. Golgi bodies
            e. vesicles

E   34.   A system of canals, tubes, and sacs that transport
           molecules inside the cytoplasm describes
            a. Golgi bodies.
            b. ribosomes.
            c. mitochondria.
            d. lysosomes.
        *   e. endoplasmic reticula.

M   35.   The endoplasmic reticulum
        *   a. serves as the internal transportation system of a
               cell.
            b. is the inner membrane of the mitochondria.
            c. is characterized by the presence of ribosomes
               throughout.
            d. manufactures ATP.
            e. stores DNA.

E   36.   Which of the following are sometimes referred to as
           rough or smooth, depending on the structure?
            a. Golgi bodies
            b. ribosomes
            c. mitochondria
            d. lysosomes
        *   e. endoplasmic reticula

M   37.   Which of the following are primary cellular assembly
           sites for the production of polypeptide chains?
            a. Golgi bodies
        *   b. ribosomes
            c. mitochondria
            d. lysosomes
            e. smooth endoplasmic reticula

M   38.   Which of the following are the primary structures for
           the packaging of cellular secretions for export from
           the cell?
        *   a. Golgi bodies
            b. ribosomes
            c. mitochondria
            d. lysosomes
            e. endoplasmic reticula

E   39.   Which of the following contain enzymes and are the
           main organelles of intracellular digestion?
            a. Golgi bodies
            b. ribosomes
            c. mitochondria
        *   d. lysosomes
            e. endoplasmic reticula

M 40. Which of the following cell organelles is responsible for disposal of hydrogen peroxide?
   a. Golgi bodies
   b. ribosomes
   c. mitochondria
   d. lysosomes
 * e. peroxisomes

M 41. Which of the following are the primary cellular sites for the recapture of energy from organic compounds?
   a. Golgi bodies
   b. ribosomes
 * c. mitochondria
   d. lysosomes
   e. endoplasmic reticula

M 42. Which of the following contain enzymes used in the formation of ATP?
   a. Golgi bodies
   b. ribosomes
 * c. mitochondria
   d. lysosomes
   e. endoplasmic reticula

M 43. Energy stored in which of the following molecules is converted by mitochondria to a form DIRECTLY usable by the cell?
   a. water
 * b. organic compounds
   c. NAD^+
   d. nucleic acids
   e. carbon dioxide

D 44. In contrast to the membrane of the nucleus, the double membrane of a mitochondrion
   a. is riddled with holes.
   b. is not permeable.
 * c. creates two compartments.
   d. separates DNA from cytoplasm.
   e. has two lipid bilayers.

D 45. Starch is stored in
 * a. plastids.
   b. vacuoles.
   c. lysosomes.
   d. microvilli.
   e. any of these

M 46. Fluid-filled sacs that may store food, ions, or water in cells are called
   a. plastids.
 * b. vacuoles.
   c. microvilli.
   d. nucleoli.
   e. Golgi bodies.

D 47. Which of the following are found in BOTH plant and animal cells?
   a. nucleus, Golgi body, chloroplasts
 * b. ribosomes, mitochondria, plasma membranes
   c. centrioles, cell walls, nucleolus
   d. vacuoles, nucleolus, starch grains
   e. starch grains, chloroplasts, vacuoles

D 48. Which of the following can achieve the largest size individually in any plant cell?
   a. plastids
 * b. vacuoles
   c. chloroplasts
   d. nucleoli
   e. microfilaments

M 49. Only plant cells possess
   a. a central vacuole.
   b. plastids.
   c. grana.
   d. stroma.
 * e. all of these

WHERE DID ORGANELLES COME FROM?

D 50. Which of the following is the primary advantage of the eukaryotic nuclear envelope?
   a. providing residence for ribosomes
 * b. allowing isolation of DNA from foreign DNA and cellular machinery
   c. providing pore entry places
   d. enabling faster cell division
   e. enabling larger cell size

D 51. If a biologist said that the human body might be getting its power from "bacteria," he would be referring to
   a. energy cells that utilize bacteria for producing energy.
   b. bacteria in our intestinal tract that digest food to supply us with energy.
 * c. the mitochondria in our cells that may have originated as endosymbiotic bacteria.
   d. the *E. coli* throughout the human body that produce ATP.
   e. the bacteria on the skin that can trap the sun's energy for our use.

D 52. Which of the following is thought to be the descendant of ancient bacteria that were engulfed by a cell?
   a. nuclei
   b. Golgi bodies
   c. ER
 * d. mitochondria
   e. lysosomes

THE DYNAMIC CYTOSKELETON

M 53. Structural features which contain proteins that help to control the shapes of cells are
   a. plastids.
   b. vacuoles.
   c. microvilli.
   d. nucleoli.
 * e. microfilaments.

E　**54.** Cell components used to move chromosomes during cell division are the
a. cilia.
b. flagella.
*　c. microtubules.
d. microfilaments.
e. Golgi bodies.

E　**55.** Which organelle is whiplike in structure and function?
a. microfilament
b. intermediate filament
c. microvillus
*　d. flagellum
e. microtubule

E　**56.** Motor proteins are active in
a. microtubules.
b. Golgi bodies.
c. ribosomes.
d. cilia.
*　e. both microtubules and cilia.

D　**57.** Cilia and flagella
a. are found only in cells that are actively moving.
b. are found only in sex cells and unicellular organisms.
*　c. have basically the same internal movement mechanisms.
d. may also function as receptor sites for certain hormones.
e. are found only in one-celled organisms.

CELL SURFACE SPECIALIZATIONS

M　**58.** Which of the following is NOT found as a part of ALL cells?
a. cell membrane
*　b. cell wall
c. ribosomes
d. DNA
e. RNA

D　**59.** A cell wall
*　a. provides skeletal support for plants.
b. controls what enters and leaves a cell.
c. replaces the plasma membrane of animal cells in plant cells.
d. is found in all eukaryotes.
e. is not a part of bacteria cells.

D　**60.** Which of the following junctions permit(s) cytoplasmic interconnections between cells?
a. gap junctions
b. plasmodesmata
c. adhering junctions
*　d. only gap junctions and plasmodesmata
e. gap junctions, plasmodesmata, and adhering junctions

D　**61.** Plasmodesmata are related to
a. gap junctions in animal cells.
b. tight junctions in bacteria.
*　c. wall junctions in plants.
d. adhering junctions.
e. both tight junctions in bacteria and adhering junctions.

Matching Questions

M　**62.** Matching. Choose the one most appropriate answer for each.
1. ___ microtubules
2. ___ chloroplasts
3. ___ Golgi bodies
4. ___ DNA molecules
5. ___ RNA molecules
6. ___ central vacuoles
7. ___ lysosomes
8. ___ mitochondria
9. ___ nucleoli
10. ___ ribosomes

A. contain enzymes for intracellular digestion
B. assemble amino acids into polypeptide chains
C. receive and process new substances that arrive in vesicles from the ER
D. break down organic compounds in the ATP-forming reaction of aerobic respiration

E. construction sites where subunits of ribosomes are built from RNA and proteins
F. transcribe, translate hereditary instructions into specific proteins
G. increase cell surface area; stores metabolic substances
H. encode hereditary information
I. help distribute chromosomes to the new cells during cell division
J. organelles of photosynthesis, storage, or both

Answers:　1. I　　2. J　　3. C　　4. H
5. F　　6. G　　7. A　　8. D
9. E　　10. B

Classification Questions

The following items are organelles found in animal cells. Answer questions 63–71 with reference to these organelles.

    a. ribosome
    b. mitochondrion
    c. lysosome
    d. Golgi body
    e. endoplasmic reticulum

E   63.   This organelle is the site of polypeptide assembly.

M   64.   The cellular digestion and disposal of biological molecules occurs inside this organelle.

M   65.   Aerobic respiration occurs in and on this organelle.

M   66.   RNA carries out the genetic code translation process in association with ribosomes on this organelle.

M   67.   The packaging of secretory proteins occurs in association with this structure.

M   68.   This organelle is involved in lipid production and protein transport.

D   69.   The hemoglobin of mammals and birds is synthesized on this tiny, two-part organelle.

E   70.   Sugar metabolism occurs in association with this organelle.

D   71.   DNA synthesis occurs in the nucleus. Its breakdown can occur in this organelle.

Answers   63. a   64. c   65. b   66. e

            67. d   68. e   69. a   70. b

            71. c

Selecting the Exception

M   72.   Four of the five statements listed below are portions of a well-known theory. Select the exception.
    a. Cells are the structural and functional components of living things.
    b. Cells arise from preexisting cells.
    c. All organisms are composed of cells.
    d. Cells are the basic living unit of organization of living things.
*   e. All cells have a nucleus.

M   73.   Four of the five answers listed below are familiar organelles in the cytoplasm. Select the exception.
*   a. nucleolus
    b. mitochondrion
    c. ribosome
    d. Golgi body
    e. chloroplast

M   74.   Four of the five answers listed below are organelles found in eukaryotic cells. Select the exception.
    a. mitochondrion
    b. Golgi body
*   c. nucleoid
    d. lysosome
    e. vacuole

D   75.   Four of the five answers listed below are composed of membranes. Select the exception.
    a. endoplasmic reticulum
    b. thylakoid
    c. plasma membrane
*   d. chromosome
    e. nuclear envelope

D   76.   Four of the five answers listed below are chloroplast features. Select the exception.
    a. stroma
    b. thylakoid
*   c. microtubule
    d. pigment
    e. ATP

D   77.   Four of the five answers listed below are identified with plasma membrane extensions. Select the exception.
*   a. chloroplast
    b. cilia
    c. microtubule
    d. motor protein
    e. cytoskeleton

D   78.   Four of the five answers listed below are types of intercellular connections. Select the exception.
    a. tight junctions
    b. gap junctions
    c. plasmodesmata
    d. adhering junctions
*   e. intermediate microfilaments

M   79.   Four of the five answers listed below are surrounded by membranes. Select the exception.
    a. mitochondrion
*   b. ribosome
    c. chloroplast
    d. vacuole
    e. lysosome

M   80.   Four of the five answers listed below are characteristics of the plasma membrane. Select the exception.
    a. phospholipid
    b. fluid mosaic
    c. lipid bilayer
*   d. inert and impermeable
    e. hydrophobic tails

Labeling

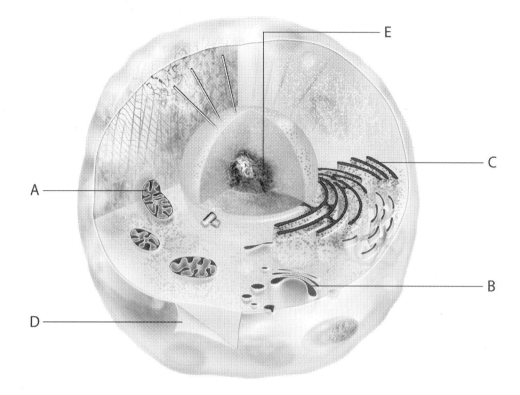

E **81.** On the generalized animal cell figure, choose the letter of the organelle in which ATP-forming reactions of aerobic respiration occur.

E **82.** On the generalized animal cell figure, choose the letter of the organelle on which the ribosomes serve as sites for protein (polypeptide) assembly.

E **83.** On the generalized animal cell figure, choose the letter of the organelle where proteins and lipids are modified and sorted for export.

E **84.** On the generalized animal cell figure, choose the letter of the area where chromatin is located.

E **85.** On the generalized animal cell figure, choose the letter of the cell part that selectively controls the entry and exit of materials.

D **86.** On the generalized animal cell figure, choose the letter of the cell part that includes a double membrane, that is, four layers of phospholipids.

M **87.** On the generalized animal cell figure, choose the letter of the cell part that is a portion of the endomembrane system AND attached to the nucleus.

M **88.** On the generalized animal cell figure, choose the letter of the cell part whose surface increases by the square as the cell volume increases.

Answers: 81. A 82. C 83. B 84. E

85. D 86. A 87. C 88. D

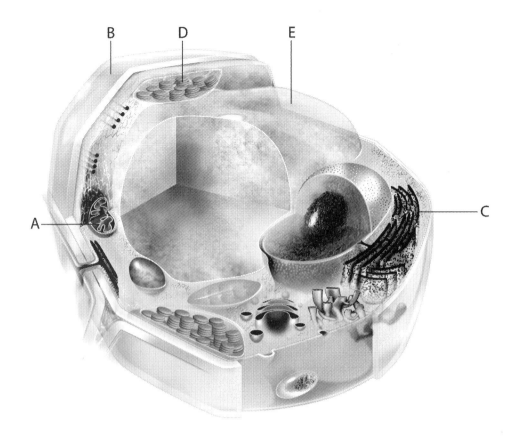

E **89.** On the generalized plant cell figure, choose the
letter that identifies the cell wall.

E **90.** On the generalized plant cell figure, choose the
letter that identifies the central vacuole.

E **91.** On the generalized plant cell figure, choose the
letter that identifies the rough ER.

E **92.** On the generalized plant cell figure, choose the
letter that identifies the chloroplast.

E **93.** On the generalized plant cell figure, choose the
letter that identifies the mitochondrion.

M **94.** On the generalized plant cell figure, choose the
letter that identifies the cell part that performs
photosynthetic activity.

M **95.** On the generalized plant cell figure, choose the
letter that identifies a cell part that would contain
lignin.

Answers: 89. B   90. E   91. C   92. D

93. A   94. D   95. B

CHAPTER 4
HOW CELLS WORK

Multiple-Choice Questions

INPUTS AND OUTPUTS OF ENERGY

M   1.   Energy
  a. cannot be trapped from sunlight by fungi and heterotrophic organisms.
  b. involves ATP in living organisms.
  c. is the ability to do work.
  d. usage is governed by the laws of energy.
  * e. all of these

D   2.   According to the first law of thermodynamics,
  a. although energy in the universe is constant, energy in an earthly system may increase temporarily.
  b. the amount of energy in the universe is constant.
  c. chemical reactions do not create or destroy energy.
  d. energy can change from one form to another.
  * e. all of these

D   3.   The second law of thermodynamics holds that
  a. matter can be neither created nor destroyed.
  b. energy can be neither created nor destroyed.
  * c. energy disperses spontaneously.
  d. energy transformations create a more orderly universe.
  e. energy and matter are the same thing.

D   4.   The second law of thermodynamics states that
  a. energy can be transformed into matter and, because of this, we can get something for nothing.
  b. energy can be destroyed only during nuclear reactions, such as those that occur inside the sun.
  c. if energy is gained by one region of the universe, another place in the universe also must gain energy in order to maintain the balance of nature.
  * d. energy that is available to do work in the universe is decreasing.
  e. energy can be created out of nothing.

D   5.   Which of the following statements is FALSE?
  a. The universe has a defined amount of energy.
  b. One form of energy can be converted to other forms of energy.
  c. Whenever energy conversions occur, some energy is lost.
  * d. Once energy is utilized, it is not seen in any other form.
  e. There are differences in the quality of energy.

E   6.   Essentially, the first law of thermodynamics says that
  a. one form of energy cannot be converted into another.
  b. randomness is increasing in the universe.
  * c. energy can be neither created nor destroyed.
  d. energy cannot be converted into matter or matter into energy.
  e. all of these

D   7.   Which of the following is an application of the first law of thermodynamics?
  a. The level of randomness increases as time passes.
  b. Living organisms represent an exception to the laws of thermodynamics.
  * c. Energy in the universe does not increase or decrease.
  d. Fungi and plants do not make their own energy but derive it from somewhere else.
  e. The amount of energy found in the compounds on one side of an equation is equal to that on the other side.

D   8.   Which statement is TRUE?
  a. Living organisms are exempt from the laws of thermodynamics.
  * b. The amount of energy in the web of life is greatest among the plants that capture solar energy.
  c. The universe is "running down."
  d. As members at the top of the food chain, all the humans have more energy than all the plants.
  e. When plants trap energy, they convert it into light.

D   9.   The energy used by living organisms
  a. is declining through time.
  * b. is derived by breaking bonds that hold the atoms in organic molecules together.
  c. involves ionic bonds more often than covalent bonds.
  d. is available only from glucose when it undergoes respiration.
  e. tends to accumulate in a food chain.

M   10.   Which reaction is NOT an exergonic reaction?
  * a. protein synthesis
  b. digestion
  c. fire
  d. respiration
  e. movement

D 11. Endergonic reactions
    a. have more energy in the reactants than in the products.
*   b. have more energy in the products than in the reactants.
    c. are illustrated by the breakdown of glucose.
    d. are the mechanisms used by animals to provide energy for biological reactions.
    e. have more energy in the products than in the reactants and are illustrated by the breakdown of glucose.

D 12. Which of the following statements about exergonic reactions is NOT true?
    a. They release energy.
    b. Glucose metabolism is an example.
*   c. Their products have more energy than the reactants.
    d. There is an energy loss.
    e. Bonds are broken.

E 13. ATP contains
    a. alanine.
    b. arginine.
*   c. ribose.
    d. tyrosine.
    e. glucose.

E 14. ATP contains
*   a. adenine.
    b. cytosine.
    c. uracil.
    d. thymine.
    e. guanine.

M 15. ATP is called the "energy currency" of the cell because it
    a. looks like money.
    b. accumulates in the body and is stored for emergency use.
    c. can be made into nucleic acids.
*   d. can be reused when it is energized during phosphorylation.
    e. is never out-of-date.

M 16. The removal of electrons from a compound is known as
    a. dehydration.
*   b. oxidation.
    c. reduction.
    d. phosphorylation.
    e. a nonreversible chemical reaction.

INPUTS AND OUTPUTS OF SUBSTANCES

D 17. Metabolism involves
    a. the cell's capacity to acquire energy.
    b. cellular processes used in accumulation of materials.
    c. reactions that break apart nutrients to release energy.
    d. disposal of materials.
*   e. all of these

D 18. Which of the following statements is TRUE?
    a. The products of a reaction can have less energy than the reactants.
    b. The products of a reaction can have more energy than the reactants.
    c. Reversible reactions tend to approach an equilibrium.
    d. Many reactions are reversible.
*   e. all of these

D 19. Chemical equilibrium for a particular reaction will not be achieved if
    a. more reactants are added.
    b. products are removed.
    c. additional enzyme is added.
    d. more reactants are added or products are removed.
*   e. more reactants are added, products are removed, or additional enzyme is added.

M 20. Chemical reactions will reach an equilibrium under which of the following conditions?
    a. There is sufficient time.
    b. The reactions are reversible.
    c. Product remains after it is formed.
    d. There are sufficient reactants.
*   e. all of these

M 21. A chemical equilibrium
    a. means the concentration of reactants and products is the same.
*   b. means the rate of opposing reactions is equal.
    c. means highly spontaneous reactions are less likely to occur than when the system is not at equilibrium.
    d. means both reactions are typically proceeding against concentration gradients.
    e. only occurs in endergonic reactions.

M 22. A biosynthetic pathway can be characterized as
*   a. endergonic.
    b. exergonic.
    c. degradative.
    d. releasing energy.
    e. producing ATP.

E 23. An orderly sequence of reactions with specific enzyme-mediated reactions occurring at each step is the definition of
    a. energy carriers.
*   b. metabolic pathways.
    c. the induced-fit model.
    d. intermediary compounds.
    e. activation.

E 24. Substances that enter a reaction are termed
    a. intermediates.
    b. enzymes.
    c. energy carriers.
*   d. reactants.
    e. end products.

HOW ENZYMES MAKE SUBSTANCES REACT

D   25.   Which of the following may show enzymatic activity?

           I. lipids   **II. proteins**   **III. RNA**

          a. I only
          b. II only
          c. III only
          d. I and II
    *   e. II and III

E   26.   Which of the following is NOT true of enzyme behavior?

          a. Enzyme shape may change during catalysis.
          b. The active site of an enzyme orients its substrate molecules, thereby promoting interaction of their reactive parts.
          c. All enzymes have an active site where substrates are temporarily bound.
    *   d. Each enzyme can catalyze a wide variety of different reactions.
          e. Enzymes make reactions occur at a faster rate.

E   27.   Enzymes

          a. are very specific.
          b. act as catalysts.
          c. are organic molecules.
          d. have special shapes that control their activities.
    *   e. all of these

M   28.   Enzymes

          a. control the speed of a reaction.
          b. change shapes to facilitate certain reactions.
          c. may place physical stress on the bonds of the substrate.
          d. may require cofactors.
    *   e. all of these

D   29.   Which of the following statements is FALSE?

          a. Enzymes catalyze reversible reactions in either direction.
          b. Enzymes are highly specific.
          c. Most enzymes are protein molecules.
    *   d. Enzymes allow some reactions to occur that would never occur without their help.
          e. Although enzymes may be modified during their involvement with the substrate, they revert to their original characteristics when the reaction is over.

M   30.   For an enzyme to function, what kind of energy must be provided?

          a. combination
    *   b. activation
          c. thermal
          d. electrical
          e. solar

M   31.   Activation energy

          a. is less when enzymes are present.
          b. allows greater interaction of substrate with the active site.
          c. is needed to begin a reaction.
          d. is less when enzymes are present and is needed to begin a reaction.
    *   e. is less when enzymes are present, allows greater interaction of substrate with the active site, and is needed to begin a reaction.

M   32.   Enzymes

    *   a. sometimes use cofactors.
          b. are usually molecules of RNA.
          c. are nonspecific with regard to substrate.
          d. enable some reactions to occur that would never happen without the availability of enzymes.
          e. will mediate a reversible reaction in one direction only.

E   33.   In enzyme-catalyzed reactions, "substrate" is a synonym for

          a. end products.
          b. by-products.
          c. enzymes.
    *   d. reactants.
          e. cofactors

D   34.   The active site of an enzyme

          a. is where the coenzyme is located.
          b. is a specific bulge or protuberance on an enzyme.
    *   c. is a groove or crevice in the structure of the enzyme into which the substrate fits.
          d. will react with only one substrate no matter how many molecules may resemble the shape of the substrate.
          e. rigidly resists any alteration of its shape.

M   35.   Enzymatic reactions can be controlled by

          a. the amount of substrates available.
          b. the concentration of products.
          c. temperature.
          d. modification of reactive sites by substances that fit into the enzyme and, later, their reactive site.
    *   e. all of these

D   36.   Inhibitors of enzyme-catalyzed reactions act by

          a. forming clusters of reactants that are unable to break free.
          b. tying up ATP supplies.
    *   c. binding to the enzyme's active site.
          d. tying up ATP supplies and binding to the enzyme's active site.
          e. forming clusters of reactants that are unable to break free, tying up ATP supplies, and binding to the enzyme's active site.

M   37.   Enzymes may be controlled by

          a. hormones.
          b. pH.
          c. inhibitors.
          d. the presence of cofactors.
    *   e. all of these

E   38. Enzymes may be controlled by
         a. temperature.
         b. the presence of chemicals that fit into allosteric
             sites.
         c. feedback inhibition.
         d. current metabolic conditions in the cell.
     *   e. all of these

M   39. Which of the following statements is FALSE?
         a. Enzymes are highly specific and act on chemicals
             called substrates.
         b. Enzymes act as catalysts and speed up chemical
             reactions within cells.
     *   c. Heavy metals such as cadmium and mercury
             function as coenzymes or activators of enzymes
             so they can function.
         d. Most enzymes are proteins.
         e. Enzymes can become denatured by pH extremes.

M   40. Allosteric inhibition is generally a result of
         a. excess substrates.
     *   b. an allosteric inhibitor.
         c. a change in the temperature of the system.
         d. a lack of coenzymes.
         e. pH inhibition.

DIFFUSION AND METABOLISM

D   41. Which of the following can affect the rate of diffusion
         through a semipermeable membrane?
         I.   steeper concentration gradients
         II.   higher temperatures
         III.   molecular size
         a. I only
         b. II only
         c. I and II
         d. II and III
     *   e. I, II, and III

D   42. The rate of diffusion through a semipermeable
         membrane will be lowest when which of the following
         is (are) true?
         I.   Concentration gradients are steep.
         II.   Temperatures are low.
         III.   Solutes are small molecules.
         a. I only
     *   b. II only
         c. I and III
         d. II and III
         e. I, II, and III

M   43. A concentration gradient ceases to exist when
         a. all the molecules have moved from high
             concentration to low.
         b. the membrane pores close.
         c. the temperature drops.
     *   d. there is no net movement.
         e. bulk flow intervenes.

E   44. In simple diffusion,
         a. the rate of movement of molecules is controlled
             by temperature and pressure.
         b. the movement of individual molecules is random.
         c. the movement of molecules of one substance is
             independent of the movement of any other
             substance.
         d. the net movement is away from the region of
             highest concentration.
     *   e. all of these

M   45. Oxygen and carbon dioxide, as well as other small
         molecules, cross the plasma membrane through the
         process(es) of
         a. osmosis.
     *   b. diffusion.
         c. endocytosis and exocytosis.
         d. active transport.
         e. facilitated diffusion.

WORKING WITH AND AGAINST DIFFUSION

E   46. Movement of a molecule *against* a concentration
         gradient is
         a. simple diffusion.
         b. facilitated diffusion.
         c. osmosis.
     *   d. active transport.
         e. bulk flow.

M   47. The method of movement that requires the expenditure
         of ATP molecules is
         a. simple diffusion.
         b. facilitated diffusion.
         c. osmosis.
     *   d. active transport.
         e. bulk flow.

E   48. The sodium-potassium pump is an example of
         a. simple diffusion.
         b. facilitated diffusion.
         c. osmosis.
     *   d. active transport.
         e. bulk flow.

M   49. The energy-driven motors used in active transport are
         a. calcium ions in the calcium pump.
     *   b. proteins.
         c. ATP molecules.
         d. carbohydrates.
         e. lipids.

WHICH WAY WILL WATER MOVE?

D   50.   If a single-celled freshwater organism, such as a protistan, is transferred to saltwater, which of the following is likely to happen?
    a.   The cell bursts.
    b.   Salt is pumped out of the cell.
*   c.   The cell shrinks.
    d.   Enzymes flow out of the cell.
    e.   There is no effect.

M   51.   Which statement is TRUE?
    a.   A cell placed in an isotonic solution will swell.
*   b.   A cell placed in a hypotonic solution will swell.
    c.   A cell placed in a hypotonic solution will shrink.
    d.   A cell placed in a hypertonic solution will remain the same size.
    e.   A cell placed in a hypotonic solution will remain the same size.

D   52.   Which statement is TRUE?
*   a.   The movement of solvent occurs from a hypotonic solution to an isotonic solution.
    b.   The net movement from an isotonic to a hypotonic solution involves the movement of solute molecules only.
    c.   The concentration of the solute is greater in an isotonic solution than in a hypertonic solution.
    d.   The concentration of the solvent is greater in a hypertonic solution than in an isotonic solution.
    e.   Osmosis involves only hypertonic solutions.

D   53.   The net direction that an ion or molecule moves is
    a.   dependent upon the size of the molecule.
    b.   unpredictable because movement is random.
    c.   controlled by the temperature of the medium.
    d.   controlled by the membranes in the vicinity.
*   e.   the result of concentration differences.

E   54.   A red blood cell will break open when placed in which of the following kinds of solution?
*   a.   hypotonic
    b.   hypertonic
    c.   isotonic
    d.   any of the above
    e.   none of these

M   55.   Wilting of a plant occurs
    a.   if the plant is placed in an isotonic solution.
    b.   if there is a rise in turgor pressure.
    c.   as a result of facilitated diffusion.
*   d.   when a plant with flexible cell walls is placed in a hypertonic solution.
    e.   when the plant stands in the sun and absorbs too much heat.

M   56.   Wilting is counteracted by
*   a.   water pressure within the cell.
    b.   osmotic pressure.
    c.   concentration gradients.
    d.   diffusion.
    e.   metabolic pressure within a cell.

M   57.   Which of the following is NOT a form of active transport?
    a.   sodium-potassium pump
    b.   endocytosis
    c.   exocytosis
*   d.   bulk flow
    e.   none of these

D   58.   Which statement is NOT true of bulk flow?
    a.   As in blood flow, it is faster than diffusion.
*   b.   It explains massive movement on a microscopic scale, but movement over large distances in animals is more likely due to diffusion.
    c.   It involves the movement of the molecules of different substances together.
    d.   It accounts for the movement of sap in the vascular tissues of plants.
    e.   When present, materials of different substances move in the same direction in response to pressure gradients.

M   59.   Bulk flow differs from osmosis in that bulk flow
*   a.   involves molecules that are not all alike.
    b.   goes against pressure gradients.
    c.   is intracellular.
    d.   is the reverse of osmosis.
    e.   is used only by plants.

CELL BURPS AND GULPS

D   60.   Which of the following is NOT a form of passive transport?
    a.   osmosis
    b.   facilitated diffusion
    c.   bulk flow
*   d.   exocytosis
    e.   none of these

M   61.   White blood cells use _?_ to remove foreign particles from the blood.
    a.   simple diffusion
    b.   bulk flow
    c.   osmosis
*   d.   phagocytosis
    e.   facilitated diffusion

M   62.   The action of a white blood cell engulfing a bacterium could be described by which of the following terms?
    a.   receptor-mediated exocytosis
    b.   phagocytosis only
    c.   exocytosis only
    d.   endocytosis only
*   e.   phagocytosis or endocytosis

M   63.   Exocytotic vesicles develop from the membranes of which of the following structures?
    a.   mitochondria
*   b.   Golgi bodies
    c.   lysosomes
    d.   vacuoles
    e.   phagocytes

Matching Questions

M   **64.** Matching. Choose the one most appropriate answer for each.

    1. ___ active site
    2. ___ allosteric enzyme
    3. ___ adenosine triphosphate
    4. ___ electron transfer chains
    5. ___ catalyst
    6. ___ antioxidant
    7. ___ denaturation
    8. ___ equilibrium
    9. ___ feedback inhibition
    10. ___ phosphorylation

    A. rate of forward reaction equals rate of reverse reaction
    B. catalysts making reactions occur much faster than they would on their own
    C. attaching a phosphate group by forming a higher energy bond
    D. an excess of end-product molecules alters the shape of the first enzyme in the pathway and shuts off that metabolic pathway
    E. part of an enzyme that binds to the substrate
    F. by binding a regulatory molecule, it changes the activity of a metabolic pathway
    G. lowers the activation energy of a reaction
    H. the currency in a cell's economy
    I. neutralize free radicals
    J. a permanent loss of protein structure

Answers: 1. E   2. F   3. H   4. B

          5. G   6. I   7. J   8. A

          9. D   10. C

Classification Questions

Questions 65–69 ask about membrane permeability. Answer them in reference to the following five processes:

    a. simple diffusion
    b. bulk flow
    c. osmosis
    d. active transport
    e. endocytosis

E   **65.** This process is used by white blood cells to ingest bacteria.

E   **66.** This process specifically moves water molecules across a differentially permeable membrane.

E   **67.** This process explains the movement of any kind of molecule from areas of higher concentration to areas of lower concentration.

E   **68.** This process is the tendency of molecules to move more rapidly because they move together.

M   **69.** This process explains the movement of molecules against a concentration gradient.

Answers: 65. e   66. c   67. a

          68. b   69. d

Selecting the Exception

E   **70.** Four of the five answers listed below are related to the second law of thermodynamics. Select the exception.
    a. Increased state of disorder.
  * b. Energy can be neither created nor destroyed.
    c. The amount of available energy in a closed system declines with time.
    d. Energy is lost as it is transferred or transformed to another form.
    e. Spontaneous flow of energy from high- to low-quality forms occurs.

M   **71.** Four of the five answers listed below apply to conditions in which energy is released. Select the exception.
  * a. endergonic reaction
    b. respiration
    c. metabolism
    d. second law of thermodynamics
    e. exergonic reaction

M   **72.** Four of the five answers listed below are related by their description of enzyme properties. Select the exception.
    a. cofactors
    b. active sites
    c. activation energy
  * d. substrate
    e. catalyst

D   **73.** Four of the five answers listed below affect the rate of an enzymatic reaction. Select the exception.
    a. pH
    b. temperature
    c. concentrations
    d. buildup of product
  * e. presence of hormones

D   **74.** Four of the five answers listed below are metabolic processes. Select the exception.
    a. protein synthesis
  * b. cell division
    c. digestion
    d. phosphorylation
    e. oxidation-reduction

D   **75.**   Four of the five answers listed below are parts of a common molecule. Select the exception.
         a.   phosphate group
         b.   adenine
*   c.   deoxyribose
         d.   ribose
         e.   hydrogen

M   **76.**   Four of the five answers listed below are factors affecting simple diffusion. Select the exception.
         a.   temperature
         b.   pressure
*   c.   characteristic of the membrane
         d.   size of the molecules
         e.   concentration gradient

M   **77.**   Four of the five answers listed below result when a cell is placed in a hypertonic solution. Select the exception.
         a.   wilting
         b.   cell membranes falling away from cell walls
*   c.   cells swell up
         d.   limpness
         e.   shriveling

D   **78.**   Four of the five answers listed below are related by energy requirements. Select the exception.
         a.   cell wall pressure
         b.   osmosis
         c.   bulk flow
*   d.   active transport
         e.   diffusion

D   **79.**   Four of the five answers listed below are related by energy requirements. Select the exception.
         a.   active transport
         b.   endocytosis
*   c.   facilitated diffusion
         d.   exocytosis
         e.   sodium-potassium pump

Labeling

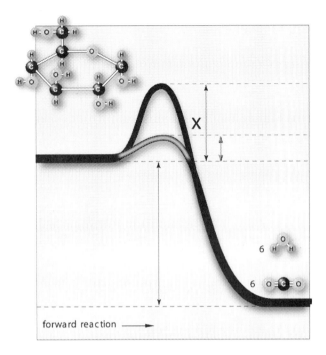

E   **80.**   The molecule structure in the upper left represents
    a. product.
*   b. reactant.
    c. intermediate.
    d. enzyme.
    e. activator.

E   **81.**   The amount of energy symbolized by the line "X" would be
    a. product energy.
    b. activation energy with enzyme.
*   c. activation energy without enzyme.
    d. reactant energy.
    e. energy released in the reaction.

CHAPTER 5
WHERE IT STARTS—PHOTOSYNTHESIS

Multiple-Choice Questions

THE RAINBOW CATCHERS

E   **1.** Plants need which of the following to carry on photosynthesis?
    a. H_2O
    b. CO_2
    c. O_2
    d. CO
   * e. H_2O and CO_2.

E   **2.** The ultimate energy source for food production is
    a. the grocery store.
    b. the soil.
    c. certain green plants.
   * d. the sun.
    e. various metabolic pathways found in all living organisms.

E   **3.** The conversion of solar energy to chemical energy occurs during
    a. glycolysis.
   * b. photosynthesis.
    c. respiration.
    d. fermentation.
    e. chemosynthesis.

E   **4.** The carbon source for organisms that derive their energy from photosynthesis is
    a. carbon monoxide.
   * b. carbon dioxide.
    c. hydrocarbons.
    d. methane.
    e. glucose.

M   **5.** The membrane that forms a compartment inside the stroma is the
   * a. thylakoid.
    b. stroma.
    c. lamella.
    d. mitochondrion.
    e. tracheid.

M   **6.** Which of the following is NOT associated with the light-dependent reactions?
    a. ATP
    b. thylakoids
    c. chlorophyll
   * d. stroma
    e. water

E   **7.** Carotenoid pigments reflect (do not absorb) which color of light?
    a. red
    b. yellow
    c. orange
    d. green
   * e. all but "green"

LIGHT-DEPENDENT REACTIONS

D   **8.** The oxygen released in photosynthesis comes from
    a. carbon dioxide.
    b. glucose.
    c. an unknown compound.
   * d. water.
    e. atmospheric oxygen.

M   **9.** When light excites chlorophyll, the chlorophyll molecule
    a. changes to carotene.
    b. becomes agitated and moves rapidly.
    c. becomes radioactive.
   * d. absorbs the energy and moves an electron to a higher energy level.
    e. becomes ionized.

M   **10.** The first event of photosynthesis is the
    a. hydrolysis of water.
    b. synthesis of sugar.
   * c. transfer of an electron from chlorophyll.
    d. manufacture of ATP.
    e. synthesis of NADPH.

M   **11.** When a molecule is excited by heat or light,
    a. it may lose an electron.
    b. it may gain an electron.
   * c. an electron from an inner energy level may move to a higher level.
    d. an electron from an outer energy level may move to an inner level.
    e. an electron may be ejected from the nucleus of the atom.

M   **12.** The first event in photosynthesis is the
    a. formation of phosphoglyceric acid.
   * b. donation of an electron from the photosystem to an acceptor.
    c. fixation of carbon dioxide.
    d. breakdown of the thylakoid membrane.
    e. formation of phosphoglyceraldehyde.

M   **13.** Chlorophyll reflects (does not absorb) which color of light?
    a. red
    b. yellow
    c. orange
   * d. green
    e. blue

M   **14.** Where in a plant cell is chlorophyll found?
    a. on the outer chloroplast membrane
    b. inside the mitochondria
    c. in the stroma
   * d. at the thylakoid membrane
    e. in the nucleus

M   15.   Photosystems are mainly
    *   a.   groupings of energy-trapping molecules.
          b.   enzymes for splitting water.
          c.   clusters of ATP molecules.
          d.   sugar assembly sites.
          e.   assemblies of thylakoids.

D   16.   Which of the following is most descriptive of an
          electron transfer chain?
          a.   It generates energy from nothing.
          b.   It is a mechanism used by cells to dispose of
               unused electrons.
          c.   It transfers electron energy, stepwise, from one
               compound to another.
    *   d.   It transfers energy, stepwise, from one compound
               to another.
          e.   It requires activation by sunlight.

E   17.   The cyclic pathway functions mainly to
          a.   fix CO_2.
          b.   produce O_2.
    *   c.   make ATP.
          d.   reduce NADP.
          e.   split H_2O.

M   18.   In the cyclic pathway,
    *   a.   ATP alone forms.
          b.   ATP and NADPH form.
          c.   oxygen is a by-product.
          d.   water participates in the process.
          e.   two photosystems are involved.

E   19.   The final hydrogen acceptor in the noncyclic pathway
          of ATP formation is
          a.   FAD.
          b.   PGA.
    *   c. $NADP^+$.
          d.   FMN.
          e.   PEP.

M   20.   The electrons that are passed to $NADP^+$ during the
          noncyclic pathway were obtained from
    *   a.   chlorophyll.
          b. CO_2.
          c.   glucose.
          d.   sunlight.
          e.   ATP.

E   21.   An important electron and hydrogen acceptor in the
          noncyclic pathway is
    *   a. $NADP^+$.
          b.   ADP.
          c. O_2.
          d. H_2O.
          e.   none of these

M   22.   The splitting of water in photosynthesis
          a.   releases oxygen.
          b.   results in accumulation of H^+ inside the
               thylakoid.
          c.   releases electrons.
          d.   helps to fill an electron "hole" in photosystem II.
    *   e.   all of these

D   23.   The products of the light-dependent reactions of
          photosynthesis
    *   a.   are used in the light-independent reactions.
          b.   are complex carbohydrates and proteins.
          c.   are stored in the vacuoles of the cell.
          d.   are oxygen and glucose.
          e.   are used in the light-independent reactions and are
               stored in the vacuoles of the cell.

D   24.   The enzymes associated with the light-dependent
          reactions of photosynthesis are located
          a.   on the outer membranes of the chloroplast.
          b.   in the liquid portion of the chloroplast.
    *   c.   on the thylakoid membrane.
          d.   throughout the cytoplasm.
          e.   on the plasma membrane.

M   25.   The light-dependent reactions of photosynthesis
    *   a.   involve splitting of water.
          b.   occur in mitochondria.
          c.   consist of the fixation of carbon dioxide.
          d.   produce phosphoglyceric acid as their first stable
               compound.
          e.   none of these

M   26.   The products of the light-dependent reactions in
          photosynthesis
          a.   are complex carbohydrates.
          b.   are not used in the light-independent reactions.
    *   c.   include ATP molecules and oxygen.
          d.   are phosphoglyceraldehyde molecules that may be
               converted into glucose and/or ribulose
               bisphosphate.
          e.   are complex carbohydrates and are
               phosphoglyceraldehyde molecules that may be
               converted into glucose and/or ribulose
               bisphosphate.

M   27.   Plant cells produce molecules of O_2
          a.   by splitting carbon dioxide.
          b.   during respiration.
          c.   by splitting ribulose bisphosphate.
    *   d.   by splitting molecules of water.
          e.   by breaking down glucose.

D   28.   In the noncyclic pathway of ATP formation, which
          event occurs last?
          a.   excitation of P700
          b.   photolysis of water
    *   c.   formation of NADPH
          d.   ATP synthesis
          e.   transfer of electron to P680

D   29.   In the noncyclic pathways,
          a.   there is a one-way flow of electrons from
               photosystem I to photosystem II.
          b.   ATP alone is produced.
    *   c.   hydrogen ions accumulate in the thylakoid
               compartments.
          d.   only electrons are transferred to hydrogen
               acceptors.
          e.   water is not involved in any of the reactions.

D 30. Which of the following is formed last in the transfer of solar energy?
   a. photosystem molecules
   b. electron transfer system
   c. photosystem II
   d. photosystem I
 * e. NADPH

D 31. Hydrogen ion flow out of the thylakoid compartments
   a. occurs between photosystems I and II.
   b. is called the hydrogen transfer system.
 * c. provides energy to produce ATP molecules.
   d. causes excitation of chlorophyll molecules.
   e. requires the intermediary action of acceptor molecules.

M 32. ATP is formed when _?_ the thylakoid compartment.
   a. hydrogen ions enter
   b. electrons leave
 * c. hydrogen ions leave
   d. electrons enter
   e. water is split in

LIGHT-INDEPENDENT REACTIONS

D 33. Actual assembly of sugars during photosynthesis
   a. occurs during light-independent reactions.
   b. takes place in the stroma.
   c. requires chlorophyll.
 * d. occurs during light-independent reactions and takes place in the stroma.
   e. occurs during light-independent reactions, takes place in the stroma, and requires chlorophyll.

M 34. Which of the following is NOT one of the chemicals produced in the synthesis (light-independent) reactions?
 * a. NADPH
   b. phosphoglyceric acid (PGA)
   c. phosphoglyceraldehyde (PGAL)
   d. glucose
   e. ribulose bisphosphate

E 35. All EXCEPT which condition must be present for light-independent reactions to occur?
   a. presence of carbon dioxide
 * b. exposure of the plant to light
   c. presence of ribulose bisphosphate
   d. presence of ATP and NADPH
   e. presence of required enzymes

E 36. The light-independent reactions were discovered by
   a. M. D. Hatch.
   b. Andrew Benson.
   c. Melvin Calvin.
   d. Robert Hill.
 * e. both Andrew Benson and Melvin Calvin.

E 37. The first stable compound produced from CO_2 in the light-independent reactions is
 * a. phosphoglycerate (PGA).
   b. ribulose bisphosphate (RuBP).
   c. phosphoglyceraldehyde (PGAL).
   d. glucose.
   e. phosphoenol pyruvate.

M 38. The carbon dioxide acceptor in the Calvin-Benson cycle is
   a. phosphoglycerate (PGA).
 * b. ribulose bisphosphate (RuBP).
   c. phosphoglyceraldehyde (PGAL).
   d. glucose.
   e. phosphoenol pyruvate.

M 39. Which of the following chemicals has five carbon atoms?
   a. phosphoglycerate (PGA)
 * b. ribulose bisphosphate (RuBP)
   c. phosphoglyceraldehyde (PGAL)
   d. glucose
   e. phosphoenol pyruvate

D 40. The light-independent reactions of photosynthesis
 * a. fix carbon dioxide into a stable organic compound.
   b. involve the liberation of oxygen.
   c. cannot occur in light.
   d. are known as photolysis.
   e. all of these

M 41. For each six atoms of carbon dioxide fixed in the light-independent reaction, how many molecules of PGAL (phosphoglyceraldehyde) are produced?
   a. 2
   b. 3
   c. 6
 * d. 12
   e. 15

D 42. How many molecules of PGAL (phosphoglyceraldehyde) are used to regenerate the six molecules of RuBP (ribulose bisphosphate)?
   a. 3
   b. 6
 * c. 10
   d. 12
   e. 18

D 43. In the Calvin-Benson cycle, which of the following can donate phosphate?
   a. NADPH
 * b. ATP
   c. RuBP
   d. ATP and RuBP only
   e. NADPH, ATP, and RuBP

D 44. Which of these chemicals has six carbon atoms?
   a. phosphoglycerate (PGA)
   b. ribulose bisphosphate (RuBP)
   c. phosphoglyceraldehyde (PGAL)
 * d. glucose
   e. oxaloacetate

M 45. Which of the following chemicals has the most energy?
  a. phosphoglycerate (PGA)
  b. ribulose bisphosphate (RuBP)
  c. phosphoglyceraldehyde (PGAL)
  * d. glucose
  e. oxaloacetate

E 46. In most complex plants, the excess glucose is stored as
  a. glucose.
  * b. starch.
  c. sucrose.
  d. glycogen.
  e. cellulose.

D 47. Plants manufacture glucose
  a. for exclusive use by animals.
  * b. to function as the beginning of more complex molecules.
  c. as a by-product produced as the plant manufactures oxygen.
  d. during the process known as photorespiration.
  e. via the tricarboxylic acid cycle.

M 48. Which of the following chemicals has four carbon atoms?
  a. phosphoglycerate (PGA)
  b. ribulose bisphosphate (RuBP)
  c. phosphoglyceraldehyde (PGAL)
  d. glucose
  * e. oxaloacetate

M 49. Which is a C_4 plant?
  a. corn, a grass plant
  b. pine
  c. cactus
  d. crabgrass
  * e. all except pine

M 50. The C_4 pathway involves
  a. RuBP.
  b. FAD.
  * c. oxaloacetate.
  d. ATP.
  e. water.

M 51. Which of the following would NOT be true of CAM plants?
  a. fix carbon only once
  b. live in desert environments
  * c. fix carbon mostly during the day
  d. open stomata only at night
  e. grow slowly

E 52. Plants need which of the following to carry on photosynthesis?
  * a. carbon dioxide and water
  b. nitrogen and hydrogen
  c. oxygen and carbon dioxide
  d. water and oxygen
  e. ribose and carbon dioxide

PASTURES OF THE SEAS

E 53. Which of the following would NOT be considered a photoautotroph?
  a. protists
  * b. insects
  c. corn
  d. certain bacteria
  e. algae

E 54. Which of the following would be at the lowest level (beginning) of an ocean food chain?
  a. krill
  b. whales
  * c. protists
  d. crustaceans
  e. birds

E 55. Which of the following would release oxygen in their usual metabolic processes?
  a. krill
  b. whales
  * c. protists
  d. crustaceans
  e. birds

E 56. Which of the following act like "sponges" taking in vast amounts of carbon dioxide?
  a. krill
  b. whales
  * c. protists
  d. crustaceans
  e. birds

D 57. Animals obtain their energy and carbon from
  a. the sun and atmosphere directly.
  * b. chemical compounds formed by autotrophs.
  c. inorganic sources.
  d. chemical compounds formed by autotrophs and inorganic sources.
  e. the sun and atmosphere directly, chemical compounds formed by autotrophs, and inorganic sources.

Matching Questions

M **58.** Matching. Choose the one most appropriate answer for each.

1. ___ cyclic pathway of ATP formation
2. ___ noncyclic pathway of ATP formation
3. ___ carbon dioxide fixation
4. ___ the PGA to PGAL conversion
5. ___ the formation of glucose

       A. uses ribulose bisphosphate; produces PGA
       B. uses ATP and NADPH
       C. detaches two phosphate groups
       D. produces ATP and NADPH
       E. uses an electron transfer chain to produce ATP only

Answers: 1. E   2. D   3. A   4. B
              5. C

Classification Questions

The processes listed below represent major chemical pathways in the photosynthetic process. Answer questions 59–63 with reference to these five processes.

      a. light-dependent reactions
      b. chemosynthetic reactions
      c. carbon dioxide fixation
      d. Calvin-Benson cycle
      e. C$_4$ pathway

D **59.** This leads to the formation of glucose-6-phosphate (sugar phosphate) from two molecules of phosphoglyceraldehyde.

M **60.** In this process, carbon dioxide is incorporated first into an unstable intermediate compound and then into phosphoglycerate.

E **61.** This yields NADPH as well as ATP.

M **62.** This is a carbon-fixing system that precedes the Calvin-Benson cycle in some plants.

M **63.** PGAL molecules are formed from the reaction of PGA molecules with ATP and NADPH in this pathway.

Answers: 59. d   60. c   61. a
               62. e   63. d

The five reactions listed below occur during the noncyclic pathway of ATP formation. Use them to answer questions 64–68.

      a. reduction of NADP
      b. phosphorylation of ADP
      c. pulling electrons from water
      d. oxidation of chlorophyll
      e. reduction of chlorophyll

D **64.** This process releases electrons to fill "holes" in chlorophyll in noncyclic ATP formation.

D **65.** When light energy is absorbed by a leaf, the first result will be this.

D **66.** The final step that occurs during noncyclic ATP formation is this.

M **67.** High-energy phosphate bonds are formed during this process.

D **68.** Oxygen is released following this process.

Answers: 64. c   65. d   66. a
               67. b   68. c

Selecting the Exception

E **69.** Four of the five answers listed below are heterotrophs. Select the exception.
      a. fungus
*   b. carrot
      c. earthworm
      d. lobster
      e. parasite

D **70.** Four of the five answers listed below are part of the light-independent reactions. Select the exception.
*   a. water
      b. carbon dioxide
      c. ribulose bisphosphate
      d. phosphoglyceraldehyde
      e. phosphoglycerate

D **71.** Four of the five answers listed below are participants in photosynthesis. Select the exception.
      a. photosystem
      b. light
*   c. mitochondrion
      d. chloroplast
      e. thylakoid

E **72.** Four of the five answers listed below are wavelengths absorbed by chloroplast pigments. Select the exception.
      a. red
*   b. green
      c. blue
      d. violet
      e. yellow

D **73.** Four of the five answers listed below are processes associated with light-dependent reactions. Select the exception.
      a. splitting of water
      b. ATP synthase
*   c. fixing carbon dioxide
      d. photosystem I and II
      e. noncyclic ATP formation

D **74.** Four of the five answers listed below are processes associated with light-independent reactions. Select the exception.
      a. uses ATP and NADPH
      b. involves RuBP
      c. produces PGA
      d. is called the Calvin-Benson cycle
*   e. requires light

Labeling

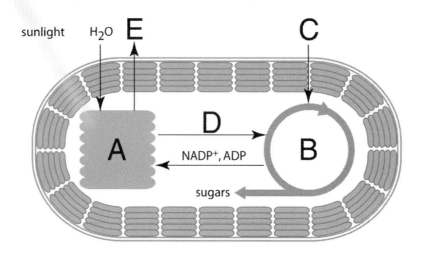

E   **75.**   The reactions that produce glucose are represented by the letter _?_.

E   **76.**   The reactions at letter "A" are
       a.   driven by ATP.
       b.   generating water.
       c.   using NADPH.
   *   d.   dependent on light.
       e.   called the Calvin-Benson cycle.

E   **77.**   What is the product labeled "E"?
       a.   carbon dioxide
       b.   chlorophyll
       c.   glucose
       d.   water
   *   e.   oxygen

E   **78.**   Carbon dioxide enters the reactions at letter _?_.

E   **79.**   What is generated at letter "D"?
       a.   oxygen
   *   b.   ATP
       c.   glucose
       d.   inorganic phosphate
       e.   ADP

E   **80.**   The entire structure pictured above is a
       a.   cell.
   *   b.   chloroplast.
       c.   thylakoid.
       d.   mitochondrion.
       e.   nucleus.

Answers: 75.   B   78.   C

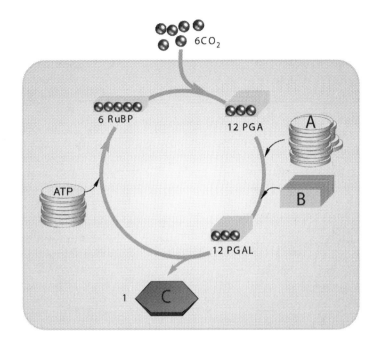

E **81.** This series of reactions is called
    a. glycolysis.
    b. light-dependent reactions.
    c. an electron transport chain.
  * d. the Calvin-Benson cycle.
    e. the Krebs cycle.

E **82.** The product at letter "C" is
  * a. glucose.
    b. protein.
    c. ADP.
    d. water.
    e. oxygen.

E **83.** Hydrogens and electrons are contributed by NADPH at letter _?_.

E **84.** Energy from ATP is represented by letter _?_.

Answers: 83. B   84. A

CHAPTER 6
HOW CELLS RELEASE CHEMICAL ENERGY

Multiple-Choice Questions

OVERVIEW OF ENERGY-RELEASING PATHWAYS

M   1.   All living organisms
a.   generate ATP.
b.   utilize oxygen.
c.   have a well-defined nucleus.
d.   produce carbon dioxide.
*   e.   generate ATP and produce carbon dioxide.

M   2.   When molecules are broken apart in respiration,
a.   the heat produced is used to drive biological reactions.
b.   the oxygen in the compounds that are broken apart is used as an energy source.
*   c.   the energy released is channeled into molecules of ATP.
d.   ATP is converted into ADP.
e.   ADP is released as a waste product.

D   3.   Cellular respiration
*   a.   is the mechanism that evolved to enable living organisms to utilize energy stored in glucose.
b.   occurs only in animal cells because plants carry on photosynthesis.
c.   utilizes fat as its primary energy source.
d.   occurs at the same rate throughout all cells of the body.
e.   is the only cellular mechanism that yields ATP.

D   4.   Cellular respiration
a.   is the exact reverse of photosynthesis.
b.   involves the physical exchange of gases.
*   c.   is a mechanism for tapping the energy found in the bonds between atoms forming organic compounds.
d.   can occur only if there is a supply of glucose available because no other compound is involved in cellular respiration.
e.   occurs only in animal cells.

E   5.   ATP is
*   a.   the energy currency of a cell's economy.
b.   produced by the destruction of ADP.
c.   expended in the process of photosynthesis.
d.   produced during the phosphorylation of any organic compound.
e.   a sugar.

M   6.   ATP is to the cell as _?_ is (are) to the financial community.
*   a.   printed currency
b.   checks
c.   credit
d.   gold reserves
e.   automated tellers

M   7.   ATP
a.   can be produced by photosynthesis.
b.   is produced in the degradation of organic compounds such as glucose.
c.   is generated in anaerobic respiration.
d.   is released in aerobic respiration.
*   e.   all of these

D   8.   Plant cells are capable of
a.   photosynthesis.
b.   ATP production.
c.   glucose breakdown.
d.   aerobic respiration.
*   e.   all of these

M   9.   Aerobes use _?_ as the final electron acceptor at the end of transport chains.
a.   hydrogen
b.   carbon
*   c.   oxygen
d. H_2O
e. NAD^+

M   10.   Most plants and animals use _?_ as their final hydrogen acceptor in cellular respiration.
*   a.   oxygen
b.   sulfur
c.   nitrogen
d.   magnesium
e.   phosphorus

E   11.   Which of the following liberates the most energy in the form of ATP?
*   a.   aerobic respiration
b.   anaerobic respiration
c.   alcoholic fermentation
d.   lactate fermentation
e.   All liberate the same amount, but through different means.

D   12.   Which of the following has the greatest total energy?
a.   cAMP
b.   ADP
c.   ATP
*   d.   glucose
e.   NADPH

M   13.   The correct operational sequence of the three processes listed below is:

I. glycolysis   II. ETP   III. Krebs cycle

a.   I >>> II >>> III
b.   II >>> I >>> III
c.   III >>> I >>> II
d.   II >>> III >>> I
*   e.   I >>> III >>> II

GLYCOLYSIS—GLUCOSE BREAKDOWN STARTS

M 14. Before a glucose molecule can be broken down to release energy,
   a. one ATP molecule must be added to glucose.
 * b. two phosphate groups must be attached to glucose.
   c. three ATP molecules must be added to glucose.
   d. one ATP molecule must be taken away from glucose.
   e. two ATP molecules must be taken away from glucose.

D 15. For glycolysis to begin,
   a. glucose must enter the mitochondria.
 * b. there must be an input of energy from ATP.
   c. oxygen must be available.
   d. some hydrogen acceptors must be available.
   e. heat must be supplied.

M 16. Glycolysis depends upon a continuous supply of glucose and
   a. NADP.
   b. pyruvate.
 * c. NAD^+.
   d. NADH.
   e. H_2O.

M 17. Glycolysis
   a. occurs in the mitochondria.
   b. happens to fats.
   c. results in the production of pyruvate.
   d. occurs in the cytoplasm.
 * e. results in the production of pyruvate and occurs in the cytoplasm.

D 18. In the breakdown of glucose, a phosphorylated six-carbon compound is split into two three-carbon compounds, which are named
 * a. phosphoglyceraldehyde (PGAL).
   b. pyruvate.
   c. acetyl-CoA.
   d. lactate.
   e. acetaldehyde.

M 19. The conversion of PGAL to pyruvate is accompanied by
   a. anaerobic respiration.
   b. photophosphorylation.
   c. the electron transfer chain.
 * d. substrate-level phosphorylation.
   e. the Krebs cycle.

D 20. The use of two ATP molecules at the beginning of glycolysis is comparable to _?_ in financial language.
   a. dividends
   b. a credit
   c. a debt
 * d. an investment
   e. liquidity

M 21. How many ATP molecules (net yield) are produced per molecule of glucose degraded during glycolysis?
   a. 1
 * b. 2
   c. 4
   d. 36
   e. 38

D 22. Substrate-level phosphorylation
 * a. occurs during glycolysis.
   b. requires the presence of oxygen.
   c. is a precursor for the phosphorylation of glucose.
   d. is the source for the majority of the ATP produced in aerobic respiration.
   e. does not occur during fermentation.

M 23. The end product of glycolysis is
   a. acetyl-CoA.
   b. oxaloacetate.
 * c. pyruvate.
   d. citrate.
   e. both a and b

M 24. The process by which a small amount of the energy in a glucose molecule is released as it is converted into two small organic acid molecules is called
   a. photolysis.
 * b. glycolysis.
   c. oxidative phosphorylation.
   d. substrate-level phosphorylation.
   e. the Krebs cycle.

M 25. Pyruvate can be regarded as the end product of
 * a. glycolysis.
   b. acetyl-CoA formation.
   c. electron transport phosphorylation.
   d. the Krebs cycle.
   e. the TCA cycle.

SECOND AND THIRD STAGES OF AEROBIC RESPIRATION

E 26. The Krebs cycle takes place in the
   a. ribosomes.
   b. cytoplasm.
   c. nucleus.
 * d. mitochondria.
   e. chloroplasts.

D 27. The chemical that enters the mitochondria from the cytoplasm to continue respiration is
   a. phosphoglyceraldehyde (PGAL).
   b. oxaloacetate.
   c. phosphoglycerate (PGA).
 * d. pyruvate.
   e. citrate.

D   28.   Which of the following compounds produces carbon dioxide during the breakdown of glucose in aerobic respiration?
a. phosphoglycerate
* b. pyruvate
c. ATP
d. NADH
e. fructose bisphosphate

D   29.   Krebs cycle reactions and electron transfer phosphorylation are
a. in the mitochondrion and ER, respectively.
* b. in separate parts of the mitochondrion.
c. inside and outside the mitochondrion, respectively.
d. in the same mitochondrial compartment.
e. cytoplasmic reactions.

E   30.   The breakdown of pyruvate in the Krebs cycle results in the release of
a. energy.
b. carbon dioxide.
c. oxygen.
d. hydrogen ions.
* e. all of these except oxygen

D   31.   During the Krebs cycle,
a. substrate-level phosphorylation occurs.
b. oxaloacetate is regenerated.
c. electrons and H^+ are transferred to coenzymes NAD^+ and FAD.
d. molecules of carbon dioxide are formed.
* e. all of these

D   32.   During which phase of aerobic respiration is ATP produced directly by substrate-level phosphorylation?
a. glucose formation
b. ethanol production
c. acetyl-CoA formation
* d. the Krebs cycle
e. all of these

D   33.   Which is capable of being reduced during both glycolysis and the Krebs cycle?
* a. NAD^+
b. FAD^+
c. ADP
d. NADH
e. $NADP^+$

D   34.   To break down a glucose molecule completely, how many "turns" of the Krebs cycle are required?
* a. 2
b. 3
c. 4
d. 6
e. 12

M   35.   The first intermediate produced after the entry of acetyl-CoA into the Krebs cycle is
a. pyruvate.
b. acetyl-CoA.
c. fructose bisphosphate.
d. oxaloacetate.
* e. citrate.

M   36.   The last intermediate produced in the Krebs cycle before the entry of the next acetyl-CoA is
a. pyruvate.
b. acetyl-CoA.
c. fructose bisphosphate.
* d. oxaloacetate.
e. citrate.

M   37.   Which of the following marks the transition from glycolysis to the Krebs cycle?
* a. acetyl-CoA formation
b. conversion of PGAL to PGA
c. regeneration of reduced NAD^+
d. oxidative phosphorylation
e. substrate-level phosphorylation

D   38.   The most abundant acceptor for hydrogen released in the Krebs cycle is
a. TPN.
b. FMN.
* c. NAD^+.
d. FAD.
e. cytochrome oxidase.

M   39.   When glucose is used as the energy source, the largest amount of ATP is produced in
a. glycolysis.
b. acetyl-CoA formation.
c. the Krebs cycle.
d. substrate-level phosphorylation.
* e. electron transfer phosphorylation.

M   40.   The greatest number of ATP molecules is produced in
a. glycolysis.
b. alcoholic fermentation.
c. anaerobic electron transfer.
* d. electron transfer phosphorylation.
e. the Krebs cycle.

E   41.   What is the name of the process by which reduced NAD^+ transfers electrons to oxygen?
a. glycolysis
b. acetyl-CoA formation
c. the Krebs cycle
* d. electron transfer phosphorylation
e. substrate-level phosphorylation

D   42.   The electron transfer chain of cellular respiration is located
* a. on the inner membrane of the mitochondria.
b. on the inner membrane of the chloroplasts.
c. in the fluid part of the chloroplast.
d. throughout the cytoplasm of the cell.
e. on the plasma membrane.

M 43. The ultimate electron acceptor in aerobic respiration is
   a. NAD^+.
   b. CO_2.
   c. ADP.
   d. $NADP^+$.
 * e. O_2.

M 44. The energy used to generate most of the ATP formed in aerobic respiration is released when electrons are passed from NADH to
 * a. oxygen.
   b. acetyl CoA.
   c. FADH.
   d. CO_2.
   e. NADPH.

D 45. The generation of hydrogen ion concentration gradients across the membranes of mitochondria produces ATP by means of
   a. glycolytic pathways.
   b. negative ion generators.
   c. phosphate pumps.
 * d. ATP synthases.
   e. none of these

M 46. During electron transport phosphorylation, which ions accumulate in the outer compartment of the mitochondria?
   a. calcium
 * b. hydrogen
   c. oxygen
   d. phosphorus
   e. sodium

D 47. The amount of energy released from a glucose molecule is dependent on what happens to
   a. carbon atoms.
   b. oxygen atoms.
 * c. hydrogen atoms.
   d. phosphorus atoms.
   e. water molecules.

ANAEROBIC ENERGY-RELEASING PATHWAYS

D 48. The bacteria that cause botulism CANNOT live in the presence of
   a. carbon dioxide.
 * b. oxygen.
   c. glucose.
   d. alcohol.
   e. ATP.

D 49. If fermentation follows glycolysis,
   a. CO_2 will be one of the products as pyruvate is converted to lactate.
 * b. the two NADH molecules produced during glycolysis will (depending on the organism) be used to reduce pyruvate to either lactate or ethanol and CO_2.
   c. ATP will be required to convert pyruvate to either lactate or ethanol and CO_2.
   d. oxidative phosphorylation occurs either on the plasma membrane or on derivatives of the plasma membrane.
   e. ATP produced during glycolysis will be used up in the production of alcohol.

M 50. Under anaerobic conditions, muscle cells produce
   a. ethyl alcohol.
   b. acetaldehyde.
   c. pyruvate.
 * d. lactate.
   e. citrate.

D 51. Fermentation
 * a. may occur in a muscle under anaerobic conditions.
   b. produces more ATP than is liberated in the hydrogen transfer series.
   c. breaks down glucose in reaction with oxygen.
   d. is restricted to yeasts.
   e. requires the use of oxygen in muscle cells.

E 52. Cheese, yogurt, and buttermilk are produced by bacteria that form
   a. ethyl alcohol.
   b. acetaldehyde.
   c. pyruvate.
 * d. lactate.
   e. citrate.

D 53. If you were searching for fermenters, you are least likely to find them in
   a. the guts of farm animals.
   b. marshes.
 * c. mountain streams.
   d. sediments of lakes and oceans.
   e. canned foods.

M 54. Lactate production in muscle cells is
   a. temporary.
   b. due to oxygen deficiency.
   c. an NAD regenerator.
   d. temporary and due to oxygen deficiency.
 * e. temporary, due to oxygen deficiency, and an NAD regenerator.

ALTERNATIVE ENERGY SOURCES IN THE BODY

E 55. The main source of energy in the human diet is
   a. fats.
 * b. carbohydrates.
   c. proteins.
   d. nucleotides.
   e. steroids.

M 56. Which of the following statements is TRUE?
    a. In aerobic respiration, ATP is released in the very first reaction.
    b. The process of glycolysis is restricted to anaerobic organisms.
    c. Ribose is a substitute for glucose in some pathways.
    d. Glycolysis occurs free in the mitochondria.
  * e. Enzymes lower the activation energy for each step in the chemical reactions in respiration.

E 57. Excess glucose in the human diet can result in accumulations of
    a. pyruvate.
    b. NADH.
  * c. fat.
    d. lactate.
    e. ATP.

E 58. After a meal,
    a. ATP production slows.
  * b. insulin levels rise.
    c. blood glucose levels remain constant.
    d. glycogen is used.
    e. glucagon levels rise.

CONNECTIONS WITH PHOTOSYNTHESIS

M 59. The early atmosphere was filled with oxygen by organisms capable of
    a. the Krebs cycle.
    b. the cyclic pathway.
    c. electron transfer phosphorylation.
  * d. the noncyclic pathway.
    e. the Calvin-Benson cycle.

M 60. Which statement is FALSE?
    a. Some ancient species survived because their metabolic pathways detoxified oxygen.
    b. Oxygen produced by early autotrophs oxidized iron.
  * c. CO_2 and H_2O serve as raw materials for aerobic respiration.
    d. Photoautotrophs utilize waste products of aerobic respiration.
    e. Carbon and oxygen flow through the processes of photosynthesis and aerobic respiration.

Matching Questions

M 61. Matching. Choose the one most appropriate answer for each.
  1. ___ glycolysis
  2. ___ fermentation
  3. ___ acetyl-CoA formation
  4. ___ the Krebs cycle
  5. ___ electron transfer phosphorylation
    A. produces NADH and CO_2; changes pyruvate
    B. produces ATP, NADH, and CO_2
    C. splits glucose into two pyruvate molecules
    D. regenerates NAD^+ as pyruvate; is converted to ethanol or lactate
    E. uses a membrane-bound system that produces a higher ATP yield

Answers: 1. C   2. D   3. A
           4. B   5. E

Classification Questions

Use the five processes listed below for questions 62–66.
    a. glycolysis
    b. aerobic respiration
    c. anaerobic electron transfer
    d. alcoholic fermentation
    e. lactate fermentation

E 62. In this process the energy yield is equal to two molecules of ATP and the final product is ethanol.

E 63. In this process the final product is lactate.

M 64. This process yields the most energy.

D 65. This process involves electron transfer phosphorylation.

M 66. This process precedes the Krebs cycle.

Answers: 62. d   63. e   64. b
           65. b   66. a

Use the five compounds listed below for questions 67–71.

    a. ethanol
    b. pyruvate
    c. lactate
    d. citrate
    e. acetaldehyde

M   **67.** This compound is utilized in alcoholic fermentation and lactate fermentation.

M   **68.** This compound is the most likely end product of a human runner experiencing an oxygen debt.

D   **69.** This compound is a product of yeast fermentation.

E   **70.** This compound is the end product of glycolysis.

M   **71.** This compound is an end product of anaerobic respiration in exercising muscle.

Answers: 67. b   68. c   69. a

                70. b   71. c

Selecting the Exception

D   **72.** Four of the five answers listed below are hydrogen acceptors. Select the exception.
    a. oxygen
    b. NADP+
 *   c. ATP
    d. NAD^+
    e. FAD

D   **73.** Four of the five answers listed below are compounds associated with anaerobic respiration. Select the exception.
    a. pyruvate
    b. lactic acid
    c. ethanol
 *   d. oxaloacetic acid
    e. acetaldehyde

D   **74.** Four of the five answers listed below are degradation processes for carbon compounds. Select the exception.
 *   a. Calvin-Benson cycle
    b. Krebs cycle
    c. fermentation
    d. respiration
    e. glycolysis

Labeling

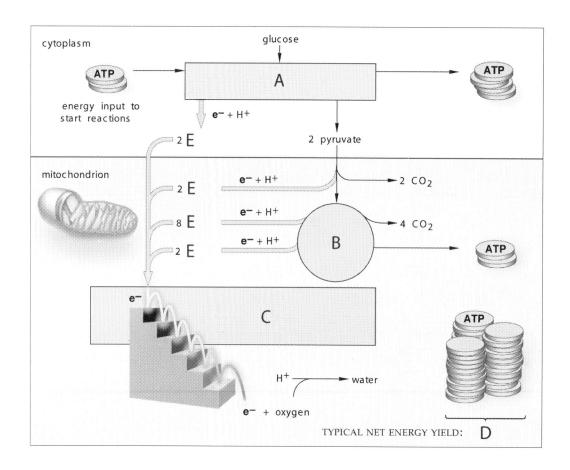

E   **75.** All of the lines labeled "E" represent
     a. FADH$_2$.
     b. NADH.
     c. NADPH.
    * d. either FADH$_2$ or NADH.
     e. none of these choices.

E   **76.** The glycolysis reactions are represented by the letter
     _?_.

E   **77.** Electron transfer phosphorylation is represented by the letter _?_.

E   **78.** The net ATP yield (at letter "D") from the complete metabolism of one glucose molecule is
     a. 32.
     b. 4.
    * c. 36.
     d. 64.
     e. 28.

E   **79.** The Krebs cycle is represented by the letter _?_.

M   **80.** The net ATP yield from the process at letter "A" is
     a. 32.
    * b. 2.
     c. 4.
     d. 6.
     e. 28.

D   **81.** If oxygen is not available for the process at "C," then the pyruvate
     a. will be converted directly to ATP.
     b. enters the endoplasmic reticulum to be changed to protein.
     c. is released from the cell.
    * d. can be changed to lactate.
     e. disappears from the cytoplasm.

Answers: 76. A   77. C   79. B

CHAPTER 7

HOW CELLS REPRODUCE

Multiple-Choice Questions

OVERVIEW OF CELL DIVISION MECHANISMS

M   1.   When a cell undergoes mitosis,
         a. the daughter cells have identical genes.
         b. the daughter cell has genes identical to those of the mother cell that produced it.
         c. the amount of cytoplasm in the mother cell and in each of the daughter cells is equal.
         d. there is an exact duplication and division of all of the organelles between daughter cells.
    *   e. the daughter cells have identical genes and each daughter cell has genes identical to those of the mother cell that produced it.

D   2.   When a eukaryotic cell divides, the daughter cells
         a. manufacture all the organelles from material in the cytoplasm.
    *   b. receive enough of the organelles to start up the new cells and produce additional organelles as needed.
         c. produce individual organelles that attach to the spindle fibers and are distributed just like chromosomes.
         d. produce an equal number of organelles distributed to each cell.
         e. get cellular organelles by an unknown process.

D   3.   Which of the following is NOT an example of a clone?
         a. a pair of identical twins
         b. a group of rooted plant cuttings from a single plant
         c. the cells produced by the asexual reproduction of a single-celled organism
    *   d. the offspring produced by two parents
         e. the buds on a flowering plant

D   4.   Which of the following statements is TRUE?
         a. Once a person reaches maturity, cell division stops unless it is to repair a wound.
         b. Cell division in an adult organism signifies cancer.
    *   c. Most cells throughout the body retain the ability to divide and replace themselves.
         d. Growth continues on throughout the life of an adult human.
         e. All cells retain the ability to divide even after the organism reaches maturity.

M   5.   Strictly speaking, mitosis and meiosis are divisions of the
         a. entire cells.
         b. cytoplasm.
    *   c. chromosomes.
         d. entire cells and chromosomes.
         e. entire cells, cytoplasm, and chromosomes.

M   6.   Which of the following is NOT associated with meiosis?
         a. reduction of number of chromosomes
    *   b. somatic cells
         c. sexual reproduction
         d. sperm and egg
         e. germ cells

M   7.   Eukaryotic DNA molecules
         a. have no proteins.
         b. have small amounts of protein at each end of the DNA molecules.
         c. have large amounts of protein at each end of the DNA molecules.
         d. have miniscule amounts of protein dispersed among the DNA molecules.
    *   e. have large amounts of protein dispersed among the DNA molecules.

D   8.   Which process is absolutely necessary for sexual reproduction to occur in a life cycle but is not necessarily required for organisms that only reproduce asexually?
         a. prokaryotic fission
         b. mitosis
    *   c. meiosis
         d. cytokinesis
         e. karyokinesis

E   9.   Chromatids that are attached at the centromere are called what kind of chromatids?
         a. mother
         b. daughter
    *   c. sister
         d. programmed
         e. either mother or daughter

E   10.   Proteins that resemble spools on which DNA molecules are wound are called
         a. kinetochores.
         b. centrioles.
         c. motor proteins.
    *   d. histones.
         e. spindles.

M   11.   A portion of a DNA molecule wound around a spool of histone protein is called a
         a. centromere.
    *   b. nucleosome.
         c. spindle.
         d. furrow.
         e. cell cycle.

E   12. When chromosomes become visible during prophase of mitosis, it is the result of
         a. uncoiling.
         b. DNA synthesis.
    *   c. condensation.
         d. chromatid duplication.
         e. addition of proteins to the DNA.

M   13. The number of DNA molecules present in a duplicated chromosome is
         a. 1.
         b. undetermined.
         c. half that of an unduplicated chromosome.
    *   d. 2.
         e. 4.

D   14. Which of these statements concerning the centromere is NOT true?
         a. It appears to join duplicated DNAs.
    *   b. It anchors proteins to DNA.
         c. Its position along the chromosome varies.
         d. It is visible as a constriction on the chromosome.
         e. It is where sister chromatids attach to each other.

D   15. Which statement is TRUE of the behavior of chromosomes in mitosis?
         a. Each new cell receives half of the number of chromosomes in the original cell.
    *   b. Each new cell receives copies of all the original chromosomes.
         c. If the original number of chromosomes was 46, each new cell will have 23.
         d. The sister chromosomes are not identical due to breakages in the DNA.
         e. All chromosomes are duplicated except the sex chromosomes.

INTRODUCING THE CELL CYCLE

M   16. DNA replication occurs
    *   a. between the gap phases of interphase.
         b. immediately before prophase of mitosis.
         c. during prophase of mitosis.
         d. during prophase of meiosis.
         e. at any time during cell division.

E   17. The chromosomes and genes are actually replicated during
         a. anaphase.
         b. metaphase.
    *   c. interphase.
         d. prophase.
         e. telophase.

E   18. Chromosomes are duplicated during what portion of the cell cycle?
         a. M
         b. D
         c. G_1
         d. G_2
    *   e. S

D   19. During the "gap" phases of the cell cycle, most of the activity is directed toward
         a. DNA replication.
         b. nuclear membrane synthesis.
         c. resting for the next step.
         d. sorting the chromosomes.
    *   e. growth and making the proteins that drive mitosis.

M   20. The interval before the onset of DNA replication is
    *   a. the G_1 stage.
         b. the G_2 stage.
         c. the M stage.
         d. the S stage.
         e. all stages.

MITOSIS MAINTAINS THE CHROMOSOME NUMBER

E   21. In mitosis, if a parent cell has 16 chromosomes, each daughter cell will have how many chromosomes?
         a. 64
         b. 32
    *   c. 16
         d. 8
         e. 4

E   22. If a parent cell has 16 chromosomes, how many sister chromatids will be present after duplication of the chromosomes?
         a. 64
    *   b. 32
         c. 16
         d. 8
         e. 4

E   23. Cells with two of each kind of chromosome are described by the term
         a. *polyploid.*
    *   b. *diploid.*
         c. *triploid.*
         d. *haploid.*
         e. *tetraploid.*

E   24. The spindle apparatus is made of
         a. Golgi bodies.
    *   b. microtubules.
         c. endoplasmic reticulum.
         d. nucleoprotein.
         e. chromatids.

D   25. What can be determined by examining a karyotype?
         a. the number of diploid chromosomes
         b. the sex of the person who contributed the chromosomes
         c. any abnormalities in chromosome length
         d. abnormalities in chromosome quantity
    *   e. all of these

E   26. The spindle apparatus begins to become visible during
    a. anaphase.
    b. metaphase.
    c. interphase.
  * d. prophase.
    e. telophase.

M   27. In eukaryotic cells, which can occur during the stages of mitosis?
    a. the duplication of chromatids
    b. the replication of DNA
    c. synapsis and crossing over
  * d. fragmentation and disappearance of nuclear envelope
    e. all of these

E   28. Chromosomes are aligned at the spindle equator during
    a. anaphase.
  * b. metaphase.
    c. interphase.
    d. prophase.
    e. telophase.

D   29. In which of the stages below does each chromosome consist of two DNA molecules?

    I. **metaphase**   III. **prophase**
    II. **telophase**   IV.   **anaphase**

    a. III and IV
    b. I, III, and IV
  * c. I and III
    d. I, II, and III
    e. I, II, III, and IV

M   30. The chromatids detach from one another and become visibly separate chromosomes during
  * a. anaphase.
    b. metaphase.
    c. interphase.
    d. prophase.
    e. telophase.

D   31. The entire process of producing two cells from one cell
    a. starts with prophase.
    b. ends with cytoplasmic division.
    c. results in the equal distribution of organelles between cells.
    d. occurs only in multicellular organisms.
  * e. starts with prophase and ends with cytoplasmic division.

E   32. The chromosomes are moving to opposite poles during
  * a. anaphase.
    b. metaphase.
    c. interphase.
    d. prophase.
    e. telophase.

E   33. What phase is marked by the arrival of the chromosomes at the poles?
    a. anaphase
    b. metaphase
    c. interphase
    d. prophase
  * e. telophase

E   34. The nuclear membrane re-forms during
    a. anaphase.
    b. metaphase.
    c. interphase.
    d. prophase.
  * e. telophase.

D   35. Which of the following statements is FALSE?
    a. One diploid parent cell produces two diploid daughter cells.
  * b. Genes and chromosomes are duplicated during prophase.
    c. There is a specific number of chromosomes for each species.
    d. New nuclei are formed during telophase.
    e. Cytoplasmic division is the final act in cell division.

D   36. Which of the following statements is TRUE?
    a. After separation, the chromatids are called chromosomes.
    b. Old patches of the old nuclear envelope are used to build the two daughter nuclei.
    c. During anaphase microtubules shorten.
    d. Telophase is essentially a reversal of the events of prophase.
  * e. all of these

D   37. Which of the following is the proper sequence for mitosis?

    I. **metaphase**   III. **prophase**
    II. **telophase**   IV.   **anaphase**

    a. I, III, IV, II
    b. I, II, III, IV
  * c. III, I, IV, II
    d. IV, I, III, II
    e. III, IV, I, II

DIVISION OF THE CYTOPLASM

M   38. Division of the cytoplasm (cytokinesis)
    a. in animal cells begins with various deposits of material associated with groups of microtubules at each pole of the nucleus.
    b. in animal cells occurs when the plasma membrane is pulled inward by a ring of microtubules that has become attached to the cell plate.
    c. usually precedes nuclear division.
    d. in plant cells begins with the deposition of a very rigid lipid bilayer, which is the major constituent of the cell wall.
  * e. is visible as a cleavage furrow caused by actin filaments in the cell's midsection.

M 39. The distribution of cytoplasm to daughter cells is
       accomplished during
       a. prokaryotic fission.
       b. mitosis.
       c. meiosis.
    * d. cytoplasmic division (cytokinesis).
       e. karyokinesis.

M 40. The cell plate is composed of
       a. the nuclear membrane.
       b. the cytoplasmic membrane.
    * c. vesicles of wall-building materials.
       d. cellular organelles.
       e. chitin and centrioles.

MEIOSIS AND SEXUAL REPRODUCTION

D 41. Asexual reproduction
       a. precedes the events of meiosis.
    * b. produces clones.
       c. is more like meiosis than mitosis.
       d. leads to increased variation in offspring.
       e. involves episodes of crossing over.

D 42. If meiosis did NOT occur in sexually reproducing
       organisms,
       a. growth of the zygote would be halted.
       b. mitosis would be sufficient.
       c. gametes would be haploid.
    * d. the chromosome number would double in each
          generation.
       e. eggs would be haploid, but sperm would be
          diploid.

M 43. Asexually produced daughter cells are
       a. identical to each other.
       b. identical to the parental cell.
       c. different from the parental cell.
       d. different from each other.
    * e. identical to each other and to the parental cell.

M 44. Sexual reproduction
       a. leads to uniform characteristics in a population.
    * b. results in new combinations of genetic traits.
       c. produces genetic clones.
       d. requires less tissue differentiation than asexual
          reproduction.
       e. produces genetic clones and requires less tissue
          differentiation than asexual reproduction.

D 45. Which of the following statements is NOT true?
       a. In asexual reproduction, the parent passes a
          complete set of genes to its offspring.
       b. In sexual reproduction, both meiosis and
          fertilization are usual events in the life cycle.
       c. In sexual reproduction, a human offspring
          receives two genes for every trait.
       d. Sexual reproduction puts together new
          combinations of genes.
    * e. Sexual reproduction produces clones.

D 46. Through meiosis,
       a. alternate forms of genes are shuffled.
       b. parental DNA is divided and distributed to
          forming gametes.
       c. the diploid chromosome number is reduced to
          haploid.
       d. offspring are provided with new gene
          combinations.
    * e. all of these

M 47. Different, or alternative, forms of the same gene are
       called
       a. genetomorphs.
    * b. alleles.
       c. mutants.
       d. chromatids.
       e. homologous.

M 48. The essence of meiosis is that
       a. gametes receive two copies of *each* member of
          each pair of homologous chromosomes.
       b. gametes are formed that are diploid.
       c. each gamete receives one member of *each* pair of
          homologous chromosomes.
       d. gametes are formed that are haploid.
    * e. each gamete receives one member of *each* pair of
          homologous chromosomes and gametes are
          formed that are haploid.

M 49. Homologous chromosomes
       a. may exchange parts during meiosis.
       b. have alleles for the same characteristics even
          though the gene expression may not be the same.
       c. are in pairs, one chromosome of each pair from
          the father and one from the mother.
       d. pair up during meiosis.
    * e. all of these

M 50. Chromosomes of a pair of homologous chromosomes
       may differ from other pairs of chromosomes in terms
       of
       a. size.
       b. shape.
       c. alleles they carry.
       d. position of the centromere.
    * e. all of these

E 51. Copies of chromosomes linked together at their
       centromeres at the beginning of meiosis are
       appropriately called what kind of chromatids?
       a. mother
       b. daughter
    * c. sister
       d. homologous
       e. look-alike

M 52. Chromatids are
a. attached at the centriole.
b. a pair of chromosomes, one from the mother and one from the father.
c. attached at their centromeres.
d. identical until crossing over occurs.
* e. attached at their centromeres and are identical until crossing over occurs.

M 53. Sister chromatids are separated from each other during _?_ of meiosis.
a. metaphase I
b. anaphase I
c. telophase II
* d. anaphase II
e. metaphase II

D 54. Anaphase II
a. involves the lining up of the chromosomes across the equatorial plate.
b. is the same in mitosis and meiosis I and II.
* c. is initiated when the newly divided centromeres begin to move apart.
d. results in an unequal distribution of chromosomes to the resulting cells.
e. results in the separation of homologous chromosomes.

M 55. Which of the following occur in prophase I, but do NOT occur in prophase II?
a. crossing over
b. synapsis (pairing of homologous chromosomes)
c. disappearance of nuclear membrane
d. crossing over and synapsis only
* e. crossing over, pairing of chromosomes, and disappearance of the nuclear membrane

M 56. During meiosis II,
a. cytokinesis results in the formation of a total of two cells.
* b. sister chromatids of each chromosome are separated from each other.
c. homologous chromosomes pair up.
d. homologous chromosomes separate.
e. sister chromatids exchange parts.

M 57. Meiosis typically results in the production of
a. two diploid cells.
b. four diploid cells.
* c. four haploid cells.
d. two haploid cells.
e. one triploid cell.

D 58. Which of the following is NOT true of human chromosomes?
a. The haploid number is 23.
b. The diploid number is 46.
c. There are 23 pairs of chromosomes.
* d. Human gametes end up with two of each type of 23 chromosomes.
e. Human gametes end up with one of each type of 23 chromosomes.

D 59. In comparing mitosis and meiosis, which of the following statements is TRUE?
a. Meiosis I is more like mitosis than is meiosis II.
b. Both processes result in four cells.
c. Chromosome pairing occurs in both.
d. Chromatids are present only in mitosis.
* e. Meiosis II resembles mitosis.

HOW MEIOSIS PUTS VARIATION IN TRAITS

E 60. The pairing of chromosomes and crossing over occur during
a. anaphase I.
b. metaphase II.
* c. prophase I.
d. prophase II.
e. telophase II.

D 61. Crossing over
a. generally results in pairing up and binary fission.
b. involves nucleoli.
c. involves breakages and exchanges between *sister* chromatids.
* d. alters the composition of chromosomes and results in new combinations of alleles being channeled into the daughter cells.
e. all of these

D 62. Under favorable conditions, during which phase of meiosis will the chromosomes appear as packets of four chromatids?
a. anaphase I
b. telophase II
c. anaphase II
* d. prophase I
e. metaphase II

D 63. Paired homologous chromosomes are found at the spindle equator during
* a. metaphase I.
b. telophase I.
c. prophase II.
d. metaphase II.
e. anaphase II.

D 64. Crossing over is one of the most important events in meiosis because
* a. it produces new arrays of alleles on chromosomes.
b. homologous chromosomes must be separated into different daughter cells.
c. the number of chromosomes allotted to each daughter cell must be halved.
d. homologous chromatids must be separated into different daughter cells.
e. all of these

M   65. Which of the following does NOT occur in prophase I
         of meiosis?
     *   a. cytoplasmic division
         b. tetrad formation (four chromatids)
         c. synapsis (pairing of homologous chromosomes)
         d. crossing over
         e. condensation of chromatin

D   66. At the beginning of prophase I, there are _?_
         molecules of DNA in a developing human sperm cell.
     *   a. 92
         b. 23
         c. 46
         d. half as many (as compared to somatic cells)
         e. twice as many (as compared to mature sperm)

D   67. Relocation of genes on chromosomes takes place in
     *   a   prophase I.
         b. metaphase I.
         c. anaphase I.
         d. metaphase II.
         e. anaphase II.

D   68. Crossing over
     *   a. increases variability in gametes.
         b. results in only one exchange per homologue.
         c. occurs between sister chromatids.
         d. prevents genetic recombination.
         e. is followed immediately by separation of each of
             the chromatids.

D   69. If a child more strongly resembles one parent's
         physical traits than the other parent's, the explanation
         could be due to random chromosome movements
         during
         a. anaphase II.
         b. metaphase II.
         c. prophase II.
     *   d. anaphase I.
         e. telophase I.

D   70. At the end of telophase I in corn (20 chromosomes),
         which of the following is TRUE?
         a. Each cell has 10 chromosomes.
         b. Each chromosome is duplicated.
         c. Centromeres are undivided.
         d. Each cell has 10 chromosomes, and each
             chromosome is duplicated.
     *   e. Each cell has 10 chromosomes, each chromosome
             is duplicated, and centromeres are undivided.

D   71. If a diploid organism has a genome consisting of 4
         chromosomes, it can produce _?_ different
         combinations of maternal and paternal chromosomes
         (disregarding crossing over).
         a. 4
         b. 8
         c. 12
     *   d. 16
         e   32

FROM GAMETES TO OFFSPRING

M   72. Gamete formation is
         a. always the result of the process of meiosis.
         b. the pairing of homologous chromosomes.
     *   c. the formation of sex cells.
         d. the fusion of gametes.
         e. a process that occurs only in asexually
             reproducing forms.

M   73. Which of the following cells is NOT haploid?
         a. secondary spermatocyte
         b. sperm
     *   c. oocyte
         d. spermatids
         e. polar bodies

E   74. Which of the following will NOT develop into a
         gamete?
         a. spermatogonium
     *   b. polar bodies
         c. oocyte
         d. spermatid
         e. secondary spermatocyte

D   75. Polar bodies
         a. are dumping places for excess genetic material.
         b. have no known biological function.
         c. are produced by meiosis.
         d. will serve as the gametes if something happens to
             the egg.
     *   e. Answers a, b, and c are all true.

E   76. Sperm are formed from the direct maturation of
         a. sperm mother cells.
     *   b. spermatids.
         c. spermatogonial cells.
         d. primary spermatocytes.
         e. secondary spermatocytes.

M   77. The mature ovum is produced by maturation of the
         a. oogonium.
         b. primary oocyte.
         c. secondary polar body.
         d. polar body I.
     *   e. secondary oocyte.

D   78. In plants, which of the following cells is (are) diploid?
         a. egg
         b. sperm
         c. spore
     *   d. leaf cell
         e. spore and leaf cell

D   79. A pine tree is called a sporophyte because it
         a. develops from a germinated spore.
     *   b. produces spores by meiosis.
         c. is haploid.
         d. undergoes fertilization.
         e. reproduces by both sexual and asexual means.

M 80. Fertilization of plant gametes produces a
    *   a. zygote.
         b. gametophyte.
         c. spore.
         d. meiospore.
         e. multicellular haploid plant.

D 81. Which of the following does NOT produce variation?
         a. crossing over
         b. random alignment of chromosomes during meiosis
    *   c. asexual reproduction
         d. genetic recombination of alleles
         e. sexual reproduction

THE CELL CYCLE AND CANCER

M 82. The forward progress of the cell cycle is regulated by
         a. hormones.
    *   b. checkpoint proteins.
         c. ATP.
         d. neoplasms.
         e. adhesion substances.

M 83. Growth factors
         a. are adhesion substances.
         b. inhibit the cell cycle.
         c. can cause neoplasms.
    *   d. invite transcription of growth genes.
         e. are nucleic acids.

M 84. Cancer cells could be described by all of the following EXCEPT
         a. uninhibited.
         b. neoplasm.
    *   c. benign.
         d. malignant.
         e. metastizing.

M 85. A growing tissue mass of defective cellular descendants is known as
         a. metastasis.
         b. benign.
    *   c. a tumor.
         d. a carcinogen.
         e. a puff.

M 86. Unusual growth of cells that do not pose a threat to surrounding tissues are termed
         a. malignant.
    *   b. benign.
         c. metastatic.
         d. carcinogenic.
         e. repressed.

M 87. Which of the following statements concerning cancer cells is most accurate?
         a. Neoplasms are usually cancerous.
    *   b. Tumor cells have lost their inhibition to stop dividing.
         c. They have an increased capacity for adhesion.
         d. Benign tumors usually spread to other body parts.
         e. Metastasis is the spread of benign tumors.

D 88. Cancer cells
         a. have altered plasma membranes.
         b. are unable to attach to other cells.
         c. divide to produce high densities of cells.
         d. have a different metabolism, using glycolysis even when oxygen is available.
    *   e. all of these

E 89. The spread of a cancer from one site to others in the body is known as
         a. a benign tumor.
    *   b. metastasis.
         c. a malignant tumor.
         d. remission.
         e. both a benign tumor and a malignant tumor.

Matching Questions

E 90. Matching. Choose the one most appropriate answer for each.
         1. ___ centriole
         2. ___ centromere
         3. ___ chromatid
         4. ___ cytoplasmic division
         5. ___ metaphase
         6. ___ microtubules
         7. ___ prophase
         8. ___ telophase
         9. ___ anaphase

         A. cytoplasm apportioned between the two daughter cells
         B. final phase of mitosis; daughter nuclei re-form
         C. two sister chromatids are joined here
         D. chromosomes condense and mitotic spindle begins to form
         E. chromosomes line up at spindle equator
         F. sister chromatids separate, move to opposite spindle poles now
         G. form the mitotic spindle
         H. half of a chromosome in prophase
         I. in pairs in some eukaryotic cells; move to poles during spindle formation

Answers: 1. I   2. C   3. H
             4. A   5. E   6. G
             7. D   8. B   9. F

Classification Questions

Answer questions 91–100 in reference to the eukaryotic cell cycle. Each question has only one BEST answer.

    a. G_2
    b. mitosis
    c. S
    d. G_1
    e. cytoplasmic division

E   **91.**   period when DNA is duplicated

E   **92.**   period when interphase ends in the parent cell

M   **93.**   event that forms two daughter cytoplasmic masses

D   **94.**   period of cell growth before DNA duplication

E   **95.**   period after DNA is duplicated

M   **96.**   period of nuclear division

E   **97.**   period when interphase begins in a daughter cell

M   **98.**   period commonly followed by cytoplasmic division

M   **99.**   period in which metaphase occurs

D   **100.**   period prior to mitosis

Answers: 91. c   92. a   93. e

           94. d   95. a   96. b

           97. d   98. b   99. b

           100. a

The stages of mitosis plus interphase are listed under a–e below. Answer questions 101–111 with reference to these phases.

    a. interphase
    b. prophase
    c. metaphase
    d. anaphase
    e. telophase

E   **101.**   During this stage, homologous pairs of chromosomes are lined up on the equatorial plate.

M   **102.**   Chromosomes replicate during this phase.

M   **103.**   Genes replicate during this phase.

E   **104.**   DNA replicates during this phase.

E   **105.**   Condensation and shortening of chromosomes occurs during this phase.

E   **106.**   Spindle fibers first appear during this stage.

M   **107.**   During this phase, the centromeres break apart as the separated sister chromatids begin to move to opposite poles.

E   **108.**   The microtubular spindle develops during this phase.

E   **109.**   Alignment of duplicated chromosomes is crucial to the next step.

M   **110.**   Cytoplasmic division occurs as this phase of mitosis proceeds.

E   **111.**   New daughter nuclear membranes form during this phase.

Answers: 101. c   102. a   103. a

           104. a   105. b   106. b   107. d

           108. b   109. c   110. e   111. e

With reference to the mammalian reproductive system, answer questions 112–114 by using the five items listed below.

    I. sperm
    II. mature ova
    III. secondary oocytes
    IV. primary spermatocytes
    V. zygotes

E   **112.**   During fertilization, which two items combine to form a fertilized egg?
   *   a. I and II
      b. I and III
      c. I and IV
      d. II and IV
      e. III and IV

E   **113.**   Which item or items are the same as a fertilized egg?
      a. II only
      b. III only
   *   c. V only
      d. II and III
      e. III and V

D   **114.**   Which is a normal sequence of development?
      a. I >>> II >>> III
      b. I >>> IV >>> V
      c. II >>> III >>> V
   *   d. III >>> II + I >>> V
      e. I >>> IV + II >>> V

Answer questions 115–118 by using the five numbers below.

    a. 10
    b. 20
    c. 40
    d. 60
    e. 80

M   **115.**   How many sperm would eventually be produced from 20 spermatids?

M   **116.**   How many sperm would eventually be produced from 20 primary spermatocytes?

M   **117.**   How many ova (eggs) would eventually result from 20 secondary oocytes?

M   **118.**   How many ova (eggs) would eventually result from 20 primary oocytes?

Answers: 115. b   116. e   117. b   118. b

Some of the stages of meiosis are listed under a–e below. Answer questions 119–126 with reference to these phases of meiosis.

    a. prophase I
    b. prophase II
    c. metaphase II
    d. anaphase I
    e. telophase I

E **119.** The formation of clusters of four chromatids by homologous pairing occurs during this stage.

E **120.** Recombination via crossing over occurs during this stage.

D **121.** By the end of this phase, the number of homologous chromosomes is reduced in half.

M **122.** During this stage, the sister chromatids begin to separate.

D **123.** Following this phase, each individual *cell* is haploid.

M **124.** Swapping of gene segments occurs during this stage.

D **125.** During this phase, duplicated chromosomes are midway between the spindle poles in two cells.

D **126.** New genetic combinations, upon which natural selection can act, is present after this stage.

Answers: 119. a   120. a   121. d

           122. c   123. e   124. a

           125. c   126. a

Selecting the Exception

E **127.** Four of the five answers listed below are stages of actual nuclear division. Select the exception.
    a. anaphase
    b. prophase
   * c. interphase
    d. telophase
    e. metaphase

D **128.** Four of the five answers listed below are related by a common phase of mitosis. Select the exception.
    a. beginning of microtubule assembly outside the nucleus
   * b. division of centromere
    c. disappearance of nucleolus
    d. disappearance of nuclear membrane
    e. shortening and condensation of chromosomes make them more visible

M **129.** Four of the five answers listed below are periods of the same cycle. Select the exception.
    a. G_1
    b. M
   * c. R
    d. S
    e. G_2

D **130.** Four of the five answers listed below are related by a common phase of mitosis. Select the exception.
    a. chromosomes decondense
    b. spindle microtubules disappear
    c. nucleolus reappears
   * d. chromosomes separate
    e. nuclear envelope re-forms

M **131.** Four of the five answers listed below are events occurring during mitosis. Select the exception.
   * a. chromosome replication
    b. division of centromere
    c. lining up of chromosomes at the cellular equator
    d. attachment of spindle microtubules to centromeres
    e. migration of chromosomes to opposite ends of the cell

M **132.** Four of the five answers listed below concern cells with two chromosome sets. Select the exception.
    a. zygote
    b. somatic cells
   * c. gamete
    d. diploid
    e. two full chromosome sets

D **133.** Four of the five answers listed below are related to the process of homologous pairing. Select the exception.
    a. genetic recombination
    b. increase in variability
    c. exchange of genes
   * d. identical daughter cells
    e. chiasmata

D **134.** Four of the five answers listed below are characteristic of meiosis. Select the exception.
    a. involves two divisions
    b. reduces the number of chromosomes
   * c. results in producing genetically identical cells
    d. produces haploid cells
    e. involves synapsis

M **135.** Four of the five answers listed below are terms describing haploid cells. Select the exception.
    a. ovum
   * b. primary spermatocyte
    c. spermatid
    d. polar body
    e. secondary spermatocyte

M **136.** Four of the five answers listed below are haploid. Select the exception.
   * a. zygote
    b. spore
    c. egg
    d. sperm
    e. gametophyte

Labeling

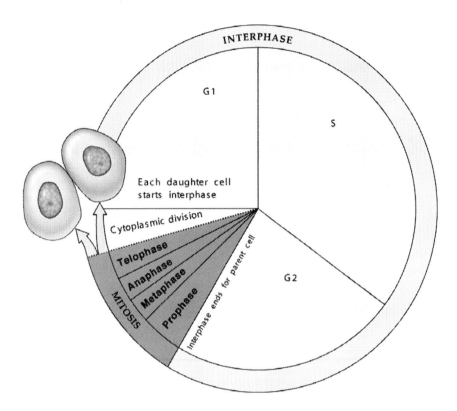

E   137.   The interval when DNA is duplicated is indicated by
             a. G₁.
        *   b. S.
             c. G₂.
             d. prophase.
             e. mitosis.

E   138.   Interphase would include all of the following
             EXCEPT
             a. G₁.
             b. daughter cells.
             c. S.
             d. G₂.
        *   e. mitosis.

E   139.   During what phase is the cell making proteins that will
             be used to drive mitosis?
             a. G₁.
             b. interphase.
             c. S.
        *   d. G₂.
             e. mitosis.

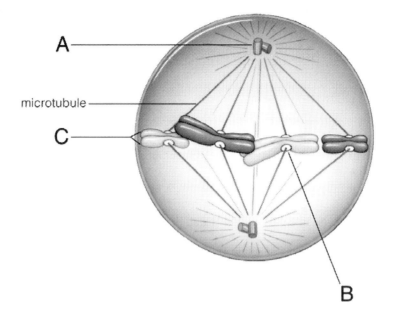

E **140.** The structures labeled at "A" represent
    a. centromeres.
    b. centrobodies.
    c. centrophils.
   * d. centrioles.
    e. centers.

E **141.** The attachment site of a spindle fiber to a duplicated chromosome is represented by letter _?_.

M **142.** The duplicated chromosome consists of two DNAs called
    a. heterologs.
    b. homologous chromosomes.
   * c. sister chromatids.
    d. helicases.
    e. centrioles.

M **143.** The microtubule labeled in this figure is actually a part of the
    a. nucleus.
   * b. spindle apparatus.
    c. plasma membrane.
    d. Golgi apparatus.
    e. ribosome.

E **144.** This drawing shows a cell in
    a. interphase.
    b. prophase.
   * c. metaphase.
    d. anaphase.
    e. telophase.

Answers: 141. B

CHAPTER 8
OBSERVING PATTERNS IN INHERITED TRAITS

Multiple-Choice Questions

TRACKING TRAITS WITH HYBRID CROSSES

M   1. The pea plant was an excellent choice for Mendel's experiments because
    a. true-breeding varieties were available.
    b. the plant can self-fertilize.
    c. it can be cross-fertilized.
    d. true-breeding varieties were available and it can be cross-fertilized.
   * e. some pea plants breed true for certain traits.

M   2. In his experiments with plants, Mendel removed which part of the plant to prevent unwanted fertilizations?
    a. flowers
    b. petals
    c. pistils
   * d. stamens
    e. stigmas

E   3. A locus is
    a. a recessive gene.
    b. an unmatched allele.
    c. a sex chromosome.
   * d. the location of an allele on a chromosome.
    e. a dominant gene.

E   4. Various forms of a gene at a given locus are called
    a. chiasmata.
   * b. alleles.
    c. autosomes.
    d. loci.
    e. chromatids.

M   5. Diploid organisms
    a. have corresponding alleles on homologous chromosomes.
    b. are usually the result of the fusion of two haploid gametes.
    c. have two sets of chromosomes.
    d. have pairs of homologous chromosomes.
   * e. all of these

E   6. Which of the following genotypes is homozygous?
    a. *AaBB*
    b. *aABB*
   * c. *aaBB*
    d. *aaBb*
    e. *AaBb*

M   7. The most accurate description of an organism with genotype *AaBb* is
    a. homozygous dominant.
   * b. heterozygous.
    c. heterozygous dominant.
    d. homozygous recessive.
    e. heterozygous recessive.

D   8. Gene *A* occurs on chromosome #5; gene *B* occurs on chromosome #21. Therefore, these two portions of the chromosomes CANNOT be
    a. genes.
    b. dominant.
    c. loci.
   * d. alleles.
    e. recessive.

E   9. Which organism did Mendel utilize to work out the laws of segregation and independent assortment?
    a. the fruit fly
    b. *Neurospora*
   * c. the garden pea
    d. the chicken
    e. *E. coli*

D   10. Mendel's study of genetics differed from his contemporaries' studies because he
    a. used only pure-breeding parents.
    b. examined several different traits at the same time.
   * c. kept careful records and analyzed the data statistically.
    d. worked on plants rather than animals.
    e. confirmed the blending theory of inheritance.

D   11. Mendel found that pea plants expressing a recessive trait
   * a. were pure-breeding.
    b. appeared only in the first generation of a cross between two pure-breeding plants expressing contrasting forms of a trait.
    c. disappeared after the second generation.
    d. could be produced only if one of the parents expressed the recessive trait.
    e. none of these

M   12. Hybrid organisms produced from a cross between two pure-breeding organisms belong to which generation?
    a. P_1
    b. H_1
    c. A_1
   * d. F_1
    e. F_2

M   13.   If *R* is dominant to *r,* the offspring of the cross of *RR* with *rr* will
            a. be homozygous.
        *   b. display the same phenotype as the *RR* parent.
            c. display the same phenotype as the *rr* parent.
            d. have the same genotype as the *RR* parent.
            e. have the same genotype as the *rr* parent.

E   14.   If short hair (*L*) is dominant to long hair (*l*), animals *LL* and *Ll* have the same
            a. parents.
            b. genotypes.
        *   c. phenotypes.
            d. alleles.
            e. genes.

M   15.   According to Mendel, what kind of genes "disappear" in F_1 pea plants?
            a. sex-linked
            b. dominant
        *   c. recessive
            d. codominant
            e. lethal

M   16.   If tall (*D*) is dominant to dwarf (*d*), and two homozygous varieties *DD* and *dd* are crossed, then what kind of progeny will be produced?
            a. all intermediate forms
        *   b. all tall
            c. all dwarf
            d. 1/2 tall, 1/2 dwarf
            e. 3/4 tall, 1/4 dwarf

M   17.   If all offspring of a cross have the genotype *Aa,* the parents of the cross would most likely be
        *   a. *AA* x *aa.*
            b. *Aa* x *Aa.*
            c. *Aa* x *aa.*
            d. *AA* x *Aa.*
            e. none of these

D   18.   Short hair (*L*) is dominant to long hair (*l*). If a short-haired animal of unknown origin is crossed with a long-haired animal and they produce one long-haired and one short-haired offspring, this would indicate that
            a. the short-haired animal was pure-breeding.
        *   b. the short-haired animal was not pure-breeding.
            c. the long-haired animal was not pure-breeding.
            d. the long-haired animal was pure-breeding.
            e. none of these can be determined with two offspring.

D   19.   For Mendel's explanation of inheritance to be correct,
            a. the genes for the traits he studied had to be located on the same chromosome.
        *   b. which gametes combine at fertilization had to be due to chance.
            c. genes could not be transmitted independently of each other.
            d. only diploid organisms would demonstrate inheritance patterns.
            e. none of these

M   20.   In a Punnett square, the letters within the little boxes represent
        *   a. offspring genotypes.
            b. parental genotypes.
            c. gametes.
            d. offspring phenotypes.
            e. parental phenotypes.

D   21.   The theory of segregation applies most specifically to events occurring in preparation of
            a. offspring.
            b. zygotes.
            c. homologous chromosomes.
        *   d. gametes.
            e. loci.

E   22.   If short hair (*L*) is dominant to long hair (*l*), then what fraction of the offspring produced by a cross of *Ll* x *ll* will be homozygous dominant?
            a. 1/2
            b. 1/4
            c. 1/3
        *   d. none (no chance of this offspring)
            e. none of these is correct

M   23.   Short hair (*L*) is dominant to long hair (*l*); to determine the genotype of a short-haired animal, it should be crossed with
            a. *LL.*
            b. *Ll.*
        *   c. *ll.*
            d. all of these
            e. none of these

D   24.   If Mendel had not examined the _?_ generation, he would not have discovered his theory of segregation.
            a. P_1
            b. H_1
            c. A_1
            d. F_1
        *   e. F_2

D   25.   The F_2 phenotypic ratio of a monohybrid cross is
            a. 1:1.
            b. 2:1.
            c. 9:3:3:1.
            d. 1:2:1.
        *   e. 3:1.

D   26.   In a cross involving plants with round/wrinkled seeds, yellow/green pods, and tall/dwarf stems, the researcher is actually observing _?_ traits.
            a. 4
        *   b. 3
            c. 6
            d. 12
            e. none of these

D 27. Solid color allele is dominant to striped, and long hair allele is dominant to short hair in a laboratory animal. If the mating of a long, solid animal with a short, striped animal produced the maximum number of phenotypes, how many would be produced?
    a. 1
    b. 2
*   c. 4
    d. 8
    e. 12

D 28. Some dogs have erect ears; others have drooping ears. Some dogs bark when following a scent; others are silent. Erect ears and barking are due to dominant alleles located on different chromosomes. A dog homozygous for both dominant traits is mated to a droopy-eared, silent follower. The phenotypic ratio expected in the F_1 generation is
    a. 9:3:3:1.
*   b. 100 percent of one phenotype.
    c. 1:1.
    d. 1:2:1.
    e. none of these

M 29. Some dogs have erect ears; others have drooping ears. Some dogs bark when following a scent; others are silent. Erect ears and barking are due to dominant alleles located on different chromosomes. If two dihybrids are crossed,
    a. the most common phenotype is drooping ears and barking.
*   b. all droopy-eared, silent dogs are pure-breeding.
    c. the least common phenotype is drooping ears and barking.
    d. there will be no phenotypes or genotypes that resemble the original parents.
    e. there will be no offspring that resemble the F_1 generation.

M 30. Mendel's theory of independent assortment states that
    a. one allele is always dominant to another.
    b. hereditary units from the male and female parents are blended in the offspring.
    c. the two hereditary units that influence a certain trait segregate during gamete formation.
*   d. each hereditary unit is inherited separately from other hereditary units.
    e. all of these

D 31. Which of the following statements about the F_2 generation produced in the dihybrid cross is NOT true?
*   a. All offspring with the same phenotype will have the same genotype.
    b. All offspring with the same genotype will possess the same phenotype.
    c. It will not be possible to determine the genotype of some individuals by their phenotype.
    d. It will be possible to tell the genotype of some offspring by looking at their phenotypes.
    e. Nine genotypes and four phenotypes will be produced.

D 32. Individuals with the genotype *Gg Hh Ii Jj* will produce how many different kinds of gametes?
    a. 2
    b. 4
    c. 6
    d. 8
*   e. 16

D 33. An individual with a genotype of *Aa Bb CC* is able to produce how many different kinds of gametes?
    a. 2
    b. 3
*   c. 4
    d. 7
    e. 8

D 34. An animal has the genotype *Aa Cc DD gg*. How many different gametes can it produce?
    a. 2
    b. 3
*   c. 4
    d. 8
    e. 12

D 35. In cocker spaniels, black coat color (*B*) is dominant over red (*b*), and solid color (*S*) is dominant over spotted (*s*). If a red male was crossed with a black female to produce a red, spotted puppy, the genotypes of the parents (with male genotype first) would be
    a. *Bb Ss* x *Bb Ss*.
*   b. *bb Ss* x *Bb Ss*.
    c. *bb ss* x *Bb Ss*.
    d. *bb Ss* x *Bb ss*.
    e. *Bb Ss* x *Bb ss*.

D 36. If one pair of alleles exhibits simple dominance while the other pair exhibits incomplete dominance, the F_2 phenotype produced from a cross of *AA BB* with *aa bb* will produce a _?_ ratio.
    a. 1:1:1:1
    b. 9:3:3:1
    c. 1:4:6:4:1
    d. 1:2:1
*   e. 3:6:3:1:2:1

D 37. In cocker spaniels, black coat color (*B*) is dominant over red (*b*), and solid color (*S*) is dominant over spotted (*s*). If a red, spotted male was crossed with a black, solid female and all the offspring from several crosses expressed only the dominant traits, the genotype of the female would be
*   a. *BB SS*.
    b. *Bb SS*.
    c. *Bb Ss*.
    d. *BB Ss*.
    e. none of these

D 38. In cocker spaniels, black coat color (*B*) is dominant over red (*b*), and solid color (*S*) is dominant over spotted (*s*). If two black, solid dogs were crossed several times and the total offspring were eighteen black, solid puppies and five black, spotted puppies, the genotypes of the parents would most likely be
   a. *Bb Ss* x *Bb Ss.*
   b. *Bb Ss* x *Bb SS.*
   c. *BB Ss* x *Bb ss.*
   * d. *BB Ss* x *Bb Ss.*
   e. *Bb ss* x *Bb SS.*

M 39. In cocker spaniels, black coat color (*B*) is dominant over red (*b*), and solid color (*S*) is dominant over spotted (*s*). If two dihybrids (*Bb Ss*) were crossed, the most common phenotype would be
   * a. black and solid.
   b. black and spotted.
   c. red and solid.
   d. red and spotted.
   e. none of these

M 40. In cocker spaniels, black coat color (*B*) is dominant over red (*b*), and solid color (*S*) is dominant over spotted (*s*). If two dihybrids (*Bb Ss*) were crossed, which would be produced?
   a. black and spotted pure-breeding forms
   b. black and solid pure-breeding forms
   c. red and solid pure-breeding forms
   d. red and spotted pure-breeding forms
   * e. all of these

D 41. In cocker spaniels, black coat color (*B*) is dominant over red (*b*), and solid color (*S*) is dominant over spotted (*s*). If two dihybrids (*Bb Ss*) were crossed, what fraction of the black, solid offspring would be homozygous?
   a. 4/16
   b. 9/16
   * c. 1/9
   d. 3/16
   e. 3/4

D 42. In cocker spaniels, black coat color (*B*) is dominant over red (*b*), and solid color (*S*) is dominant over spotted (*s*). In the F_2 generation of a cross between *BB ss* with *bb SS*, what fraction of the offspring would be expected to be black and spotted?
   a. 1/16
   b. 9/16
   c. 1/9
   * d. 3/16
   e. 3/4

D 43. In cocker spaniels, black coat color (*B*) is dominant over red (*b*), and solid color (*S*) is dominant over spotted (*s*). A cross of *Bb Ss* with *bb ss* would produce the phenotypic ratio
   a. 9:3:3:1.
   * b. 1:1:1:1.
   c. 1:2:1.
   d. 3:1.
   e. none of these

D 44. In cocker spaniels, black coat color (*B*) is dominant over red (*b*), and solid color (*S*) is dominant over spotted (*s*). If *Bb Ss* were crossed with *Bb ss,* the chance that a black, solid individual would be produced is
   a. 3/16.
   b. 1/3.
   c. 9/16.
   * d. 3/8.
   e. 1/16.

M 45. Assume that short hair (*L*) is dominant to long hair (*l*) and black hair (*B*) is dominant to brown (*b*). If you found a black, short-haired animal, you could determine its genotype by crossing it to an animal with a genotype of
   a. *LL BB.*
   b. *ll BB.*
   c. *ll Bb.*
   * d. *ll bb.*
   e. *LL bb.*

D 46. In the second generation of a cross of *DD RR* with *dd rr,* the most common genotype would be
   a. *DD RR.*
   b. *Dd RR.*
   * c. *Dd Rr.*
   d. *dd RR.*
   e. *dd Rr.*

E 47. The usual F_2 phenotypic ratio of a dihybrid cross is
   a. 1:1.
   b. 2:1.
   * c. 9:3:3:1.
   d. 1:2:1.
   e. 3:1.

M 48. The theory of independent assortment
   * a. cannot be demonstrated in a monohybrid cross.
   b. is illustrated by the behavior of linked genes.
   c. indicates that the expression of one gene is independent of the action of another gene.
   d. states that alleles for the same characteristic separate during meiosis.
   e. is negated by the phenomenon of epistasis.

M 49. If all the offspring of a cross had the genotype *Aa Bb,* the parents of the cross would most likely be
   a. *AA BB* x *aa bb.*
   b. *AA bb* x *aa BB.*
   c. *Aa Bb* x *Aa Bb.*
   d. *Aa bb* x *aa Bb.*
   * e. *AA BB* x *aa bb* or *AA bb* x *aa BB.*

D 50. What fraction of the time will the cross of *Aa Bb Cc* with *Aa Bb Cc* produce an offspring of genotype *aa bb cc?*
   * a. 1/64
   b. 1/32
   c. 3/64
   d. 1/16
   e. 9/64

D **51.** What fraction of the time will the cross of *Aa Bb Cc* with *Aa Bb Cc* produce an offspring of genotype *Aa bb CC*?
   a. 1/64
 * b. 1/32
   c. 3/64
   d. 1/16
   e. 9/64

M **52.** Mendel's dihybrid crosses, but not his monohybrid crosses, showed that
   a. some genes were linked together.
   b. the two alleles controlling a trait were divided equally among the gametes.
 * c. alleles for different traits were inherited independently.
   d. one of the pair of alleles is dominant to the other.
   e. the crossing of two different homozygous forms will not produce any offspring in the first generation that will look like either of the parents.

E **53.** An individual with a genetic makeup of *aa BB* is said to be
 * a. pure-breeding.
   b. recessive.
   c. hybrid.
   d. dihybrid.
   e. heterozygous.

M **54.** A dihybrid cross of two contrasting pure-breeding organisms
   a. produces homozygous offspring.
   b. must produce a phenotype different from either pure-breeding parent.
 * c. results in the disappearance of the recessive traits for the first generation.
   d. takes place only in the laboratory under precisely controlled conditions.
   e. will result in the immediate formation of another pure-breeding variety.

E **55.** Who proposed the law of independent assortment?
   a. Morgan
 * b. Mendel
   c. Sturtevant
   d. Weismann
   e. Fleming

NOT-SO-STRAIGHT FORWARD PHENOTYPES

D **56.** Coat color in one breed of mice is controlled by incompletely dominant alleles so that yellow and white are homozygous, while cream is heterozygous. The cross of two cream individuals will produce
   a. all cream offspring.
   b. equal numbers of white and yellow mice, but no cream offspring.
   c. equal numbers of white and cream mice.
   d. equal numbers of yellow and cream mice.
 * e. equal numbers of white and yellow mice, with twice as many creams as the other two colors.

D **57.** An incompletely dominant gene controls the color of chickens so that *BB* produces black, *Bb* produces a slate-gray color called blue, and *bb* produces splashed white. A second gene controls comb shape, with the dominant gene *R* producing a rose comb and *r* producing a single comb. If a pure-breeding black chicken with a rose comb is mated to a splashed white chicken with a single comb in the F_2 generation, what fraction of the offspring will be black with rose comb?
   a. 9/16
   b. 3/8
 * c. 3/16
   d. 1/8
   e. 1/16

D **58.** An incompletely dominant gene controls the color of chickens so that *BB* produces black, *Bb* produces a slate-gray color called blue, and *bb* produces splashed white. A second gene controls comb shape, with the dominant gene *R* producing a rose comb and *r* producing a single comb. If a pure-breeding black chicken with rose comb is mated to a splashed white chicken with a single comb in the F_2 generation, what fraction of the offspring will be black with single comb?
   a. 9/16
   b. 3/8
   c. 3/16
   d. 1/8
 * e. 1/16

D **59.** An incompletely dominant gene controls the color of chickens so that *BB* produces black, *Bb* produces a slate-gray color called blue, and *bb* produces splashed white. A second gene controls comb shape, with the dominant gene *R* producing a rose comb and *r* producing a single comb. If a pure-breeding black chicken with a rose comb is mated to a splashed white chicken with a single comb in the F_2 generation, what fraction of the offspring will be blue with single comb?
   a. 9/16
   b. 3/8
   c. 3/16
 * d. 1/8
   e. 1/16

D **60.** An incompletely dominant gene controls the color of chickens so that *BB* produces black, *Bb* produces a slate-gray color called blue, and *bb* produces splashed white. A second gene controls comb shape, with the dominant gene *R* producing a rose comb and *r* producing a single comb. If a pure-breeding black chicken with a rose comb is mated to a splashed white chicken with a single comb in the F_2 generation, what fraction of the offspring will be blue with rose comb?
   a. 9/16
 * b. 3/8
   c. 3/16
   d. 1/8
   e. 1/16

M   61.   If red (*RR*) is crossed with white (*rr*) and produces a pink flower (*Rr*), and tall (*D*) is dominant to dwarf (*d*), the F_2 phenotypic ratio from a cross of *RR dd* with *rr DD* would be
         a. 9:3:3:1.
         b. 1:1:1:1.
         c. 1:2:2:4:1:2:1:2:1.
    *   d. 3:6:3:1:2:1.
         e. none of these

M   62.   The F_2 phenotypic ratio of a monohybrid cross involving a gene with incompletely dominant alleles is
         a. 1:1.
         b. 2:1.
         c. 9:3:3:1.
    *   d. 1:2:1.
         e. 3:1.

D   63.   If shape and color of radishes are due to incompletely dominant genes, crossing two dihybrid heterozygotes will produce how many different phenotypes?
         a. 2
         b. 3
         c. 4
         d. 5
    *   e. 9

M   64.   In radishes, red and white are the pure-breeding colors and long and round are the pure-breeding shapes, while the hybrids are purple and oval. The cross of a red, long radish and a white, round radish will produce an F_1 generation of what phenotype?
         a. all long, red radishes
         b. all long, white radishes
         c. all long, purple radishes
         d. all round, purple radishes
    *   e. none of these

D   65.   The type of inheritance that would suggest the concept of blending is
         a. multiple alleles.
         b. autosomal dominance.
         c. codominance.
    *   d. incomplete dominance.
         e. codominance and incomplete dominance.

D   66.   Roan cattle are the heterozygous hybrids of a cross between a white bull and a red cow. If a roan bull were crossed with a red cow, their offspring would show which of the following ratios?
         a. all roan
         b. 1 red: 2 roan: 1 white
         c. 1 red: 1 white
    *   d. 1 red: 1 roan
         e. all roan

D   67.   In radishes, red and white are the pure-breeding colors and long and round are the pure-breeding shapes, while the hybrids are purple and oval. The cross of a red, long radish and a white, round radish will produce an F_2 generation in which
         a. the most common phenotype will be oval and purple.
         b. the purple color will occur with all three shapes of radish.
         c. the red color will occur with all three shapes of radish.
         d. all white, long forms produced will be pure-breeding.
    *   e. all of these

D   68.   In radishes, red and white are the pure-breeding colors and long and round are the pure-breeding shapes, while the hybrids are purple and oval. The cross of a red oval with a purple oval will produce all EXCEPT which of the following phenotypes?
    *   a. white and long
         b. purple and oval
         c. red and oval
         d. purple and long
         e. red and long

D   69.   In radishes, red and white are the pure-breeding colors and long and round are the pure-breeding shapes, while the hybrids are purple and oval. The cross of a white oval and a purple oval will produce more
         a. red long than white long.
         b. purple round than white long.
    *   c. purple oval than purple long.
         d. purple long than purple round.
         e. purple round than white oval.

D   70.   In radishes, red and white are the pure-breeding colors and long and round are the pure-breeding shapes, while the hybrids are purple and oval. The cross of a purple oval with a purple oval
         a. is a cross between two pure-breeding forms.
         b. is an example of a testcross.
         c. produces only homozygous pure-breeding forms.
         d. produces only heterozygous offspring.
    *   e. none of these

D   71.   In radishes, red and white are the pure-breeding colors and long and round are the pure-breeding shapes, while the hybrids are purple and oval. The F_2 generation of a cross between long and white and red and round will produce
         a. offspring that will all express dominant traits.
         b. offspring that will all be phenotypically identical.
         c. offspring that will all be genotypically identical.
    *   d. purple round, purple long, white oval, and red oval offspring in equal numbers, as well as other phenotypes.
         e. offspring that will all be phenotypically and genotypically identical.

E 72. In incomplete dominance,
   a. one allele is not dominant to another allele.
   b. the genotype can be determined by the phenotype.
   c. the heterozygote is somewhat intermediate to the two homozygotes.
   d. the intermediate phenotype may be the result of enzyme insufficiency.
   * e. all of these

D 73. If a pure-breeding long-tail cat (*LL*) is crossed with a pure-breeding cat with no tail (rumpy, *ll*), and a cat with a short tail (stumpy) is produced, the simplest explanation is
   a. a mutation.
   b. an X-linked gene.
   * c. an incompletely dominant gene.
   d. a lethal gene.
   e. chromosomal aberration.

D 74. Susan, a mother with type B blood, has a child with type O blood. She claims that Craig, who has type A blood, is the father. He claims that he cannot possibly be the father. Further blood tests ordered by the judge reveal that Craig is *AA*. The judge rules that
   a. Susan is right and Craig must pay child support.
   * b. Craig is right and doesn't have to pay child support.
   c. Susan cannot be the real mother of the child; there must have been an error made at the hospital.
   d. it is impossible to reach a decision based on the limited data available.
   e. none of these

M 75. If a child has an AB blood type, the parents
   a. must both have different blood types.
   b. must be A and B, but not AB.
   c. must both be AB.
   d. can be any blood type.
   * e. can have different blood types, but neither can be blood type O.

E 76. Blood types (A, B, and O) are controlled by
   a. sex-linked genes.
   b. linked genes.
   c. incompletely dominant genes.
   * d. multiple alleles.
   e. simple dominance.

M 77. The ABO blood types are examples of
   a. pleiotropy.
   b. multiple alleles.
   c. incomplete dominance.
   d. codominance.
   * e. multiple alleles and codominance.

D 78. The ABO blood types have _?_ different genotypes.
   a. 4
   * b. 6
   c. 8
   d. 12
   e. 16

M 79. If a child belonged to blood type O, he or she could NOT have been produced by which set of parents?
   a. Type A mother and type B father
   b. Type A mother and type O father
   * c. Type AB mother and type O father
   d. Type O mother and type O father
   e. none of these

D 80. The number of different alleles for ABO blood types in the total human population is
   a. 4.
   b. 6.
   c. 9.
   d. undetermined.
   * e. 3.

D 81. If a woman of blood type A has a child of blood type O, the father may belong to
   a. blood type A, AB, O, but not B.
   b. blood type O only.
   * c. blood type A, B, O, but not AB.
   d. any blood type other than type A.
   e. any blood type.

D 82. If one parent has type A blood and the other parent has type B, then which of the following is possible in the children?
   a. only AB
   b. A and AB
   c. B and AB
   * d. A, B, AB, O
   e. only O

E 83. A gene that produces multiple effects is called
   a. a multiple allele.
   b. an autosome.
   c. an epistatic gene.
   * d. a pleiotropic gene.
   e. an incompletely dominant gene.

E 84. Multiple effects of a single gene is known as
   a. expressivity.
   b. penetrance.
   c. codominance.
   * d. pleiotropy.
   e. multiple alleles.

E 85. Pleiotropic genes
   a. act on secondary sexual characteristics.
   * b. influence more than one aspect of phenotype.
   c. are additive.
   d. produce lethal effects when homozygous.
   e. none of these

M 86. Which of the following is NOT a known effect in the expression of Marfan syndrome?
   a. skeleton lacks elasticity
   b. weakened blood vessels
   c. a weakened aorta
   * d. excessive absorption of oxygen causing the blood cells to swell
   e. altered fibrillin

COMPLEX VARIATIONS IN TRAITS

E 87. A bell-shaped curve of phenotypic variation is indicative of
    a. incomplete dominance.
*   b. continuous variation.
    c. multiple alleles.
    d. epistasis.
    e. environmental variables on phenotypes.

E 88. The color of Siamese cats is controlled by
    a. multiple alleles.
    b. quantitative inheritance.
    c. incompletely dominant genes.
    d. nondisjunction.
*   e. variation in temperature, with cold temperature producing dark fur.

E 89. The variation of the color in Siamese cats is due to
    a. incomplete codominance.
    b. inactive X chromosomes.
*   c. environmental effects on phenotypes.
    d. quantitative inheritance.
    e. multiple alleles.

M 90. The reason for the darker fur on the tail, ears, nose, and legs of a Siamese cat is
    a. incomplete dominance.
*   b. the interaction of the environment with gene expression.
    c. quantitative inheritance.
    d. epistasis.
    e. none of these

THE CHROMOSOMAL BASIS OF INHERITANCE

M 91. Genes are
    a. located on chromosomes.
    b. distributed among a number of chromosomes in eukaryotic cells.
    c. units of DNA information.
    d. assorted independently during meiosis.
*   e. all of these

E 92. Chromosomes other than those involved in sex determination are known as
    a. nucleosomes.
    b. heterosomes.
    c. alleles.
*   d. autosomes.
    e. liposomes.

E 93. Sex chromosomes
    a. determine gender.
    b. vary from one sex to another.
    c. carry some genes that have nothing to do with sex.
    d. were unknown to Mendel.
*   e. all of these

M 94. All of the slightly different molecular forms of a gene are called
    a. homologues.
*   b. alleles.
    c. autosomes.
    d. loci.
    e. gametes.

E 95. The location of a gene on a chromosome is its
    a. centromere.
*   b. locus.
    c. autosome.
    d. allele.
    e. none of these

M 96. A karyotype
    a. compares one set of chromosomes to another.
*   b. is a visual display of chromosomes arranged according to size.
    c. is a photograph of cells undergoing mitosis during anaphase.
    d. of a normal human cell shows 48 chromosomes.
    e. cannot be used to identify individual chromosomes beyond the fact that two chromosomes are homologues.

M 97. In karyotyping, individual chromosomes may be distinguished from others by
    a. a comparison of chromosome lengths.
    b. shape.
    c. the position of centromeres.
*   d. all of these
    e. none of these

M 98. Which chemical is used to keep chromosomes from separating during metaphase?
    a. Giemsa stain
    b. acetone
*   c. colchicine
    d. alcohol
    e. formaldehyde

M 99. Colchicine interferes with the function of
*   a. microtubules of the spindle.
    b. ribosomes on the ER.
    c. centrioles.
    d. centromeres joining chromatids.
    e. chromosomes.

M 100. Karyotype analysis
    a. is a means of detecting and reducing mutagenic agents.
    b. is a surgical technique that separates chromosomes that have failed to segregate properly during meiosis II.
*   c. a diagnostic tool that helps us analyze an individual's diploid complement of chromosomes.
    d. substitutes defective alleles with normal ones.
    e. all of these

M 101. Karyotyping involves taking pictures of chromosomes during
    a. prophase.
    b. telophase.
  * c. metaphase.
    d. interphase.
    e. anaphase.

D 102. With respect to chromosomes, the difference between normal human males and females is defined by which of the following?
    a. In females, one X is deleted.
    b. Females possess one X and one Y.
  * c. In males, an X is replaced by a Y.
    d. Females have three Xs.
    e. Males have two Xs and a Y.

D 103. Which of the following statements is FALSE?
    a. The SRY gene is absent in all females.
    b. The SRY gene apparently is the gene that controls the development of testes.
  * c. The development of maleness is by default because males lack two X chromosomes.
    d. The SRY gene is on the human Y chromosome.
    e. There is no difference in external genitalia of males and females in the early human embryo.

D 104. Concerning the sex chromosomes, which of the following is CORRECT?
    a. The Y chromosome carries a greater number of nonsexual traits.
    b. X and Y are different in size but carry nearly equal numbers of genes.
  * c. The X chromosome carries more genes for nonsexual traits.
    d. The X chromosome carries only gender-related genes.
    e. The X chromosome carries the SRY gene.

IMPACT OF CROSSING OVER ON INHERITANCE

D 105. Mendel would not have seen four different phenotypes in the F_2 generation of his dihybrid crosses if
  * a. the genes had been on the same chromosomes.
    b. the P_1 generation had been homozygous.
    c. purple had been dominant to white.
    d. more than two traits were traced.
    e. all of these

D 106. Which of the following would be an exception to the theory of independent assortment?
    a. dominance
    b. recessiveness
    c. incomplete dominance
    d. pleiotropy
  * e. linkage

D 107. Mendel's dihybrid crosses provided indirect evidence for all EXCEPT which one of the following?
    a. independent assortment
    b. dominance
  * c. linkage
    d. presence of two factors in parents and offspring
    e. segregation of factors

M 108. All of the genes located on a given chromosome constitute a
    a. karyotype.
    b. bridging cross.
    c. wild-type allele.
  * d. linkage group.
    e. none of these

E 109. If two genes are on the same chromosome,
    a. crossing over occurs frequently.
    b. they assort independently.
  * c. they are in the same linkage group.
    d. they are segregated during meiosis.
    e. an inversion will usually occur.

D 110. In genetic analyses, researchers know that linkage of genes will introduce exceptions to the principle of
    a. dominance.
    b. segregation.
    c. recessiveness.
  * d. independent assortment.
    e. chromosomal inheritance.

M 111. Genes that are located on the same chromosome
    a. tend to be inherited together.
    b. will appear together in the gamete.
    c. are said to be linked.
    d. may be separated during chromosome pairing and crossing over.
  * e. all of these

D 112. If alleles L, M, and N are on the maternal chromosome and l, m, and n are on the paternal chromosome, the only way that a gamete from a heterozygote will produce a gamete with alleles l, m, and N is through
    a. nondisjunction.
    b. the laws of segregation.
    c. the law of independent assortment.
  * d. crossing over.
    e. chromosome aberration.

D 113. If the paternal chromosome has alleles L, M, and n and the maternal chromosomes have l, m, and N, then the chromosome that cannot be produced by crossing over is
    a. LMN
  * b. LMn
    c. LmN
    d. Lmn
    e. lmn

M 114. Genetic recombination as a result of crossing over occurs more readily in genes
  a. that are on the sex chromosomes.
  b. that are on the autosomes.
  c. that are located close together on the same chromosome.
  * d. that are located far apart on the same chromosome.
  e. that are located on different chromosomes.

D 115. Which of the following statements is FALSE?
  a. Crossing over tends to reduce the frequency that two linked genes are inherited together.
  b. Independent assortment of homologous chromosomes during meiosis increases variation.
  c. Crossing over leads to variation.
  d. Abnormal number or structure of chromosomes may influence the course of evolution.
  * e. The closer together genes are found on a chromosome the greater is the chance that crossing over will occur between them.

M 116. If two genes are almost always found in the same gamete,
  * a. they are located close together on the same chromosome.
  b. they are located on nonhomologous chromosomes.
  c. they are located far apart on the same chromosome.
  d. they are found on the sex chromosome.
  e. all except "they are located far apart on the same chromosome."

HUMAN GENETIC ANALYSIS

M 117. Which of the following would be the LEAST satisfactory organism for genetic research?
  * a. humans
  b. bacteria
  c. corn
  d. fruit flies
  e. peas

E 118. In a pedigree chart, a male showing the specific trait being studied is indicated by a
  * a. darkened square.
  b. clear square.
  c. darkened diamond.
  d. clear triangle.
  e. darkened circle.

E 119. In a pedigree chart, a female who does not demonstrate the trait being studied is represented by a
  a. darkened square.
  b. clear diamond.
  * c. clear circle.
  d. darkened triangle.
  e. darkened oval.

D 120. If a study of several pedigrees demonstrated that two parents express a characteristic and none of their children express it, then the trait is controlled by
  a. a codominant gene.
  * b. a simple dominant gene.
  c. a recessive gene.
  d. a sex-linked gene.
  e. none of these; no conclusion can be drawn

D 121. If a study of several pedigrees demonstrated that two parents are normal but their children express a trait, then the trait is controlled by a
  a. codominant gene.
  b. simple dominant gene.
  * c. recessive gene.
  d. sex-linked gene.
  e. none of these; no conclusion can be drawn

M 122. Six fingers on one hand would be classified as
  a. a genetic disorder.
  b. a disease.
  c. a syndrome.
  * d. a genetic abnormality.
  e. an illness.

E 123. Syndrome means
  a. a chromosome disorder.
  b. a simple genetic disease.
  * c. a set of symptoms that occur together.
  d. an incurable disease.
  e. a rare inborn defect.

EXAMPLES OF HUMAN INHERITANCE PATTERNS

D 124. An autosomal recessive disorder
  a. requires that only one parent be a carrier.
  b. displays its symptoms only in heterozygotes.
  c. is more frequent in males than females.
  * d. will appear only in children of parents who both carry the gene.
  e. is dominant in females.

M 125. The probability of producing a normal child by two parents who are carriers for an autosomal recessive disorder is
  a. 50 percent.
  b. 0 percent.
  c. 100 percent.
  d. 25 percent.
  * e. 75 percent.

M 126. Galactosemia
  a. is an X-linked recessive trait expressed more commonly in males.
  b. occurs more frequently in some ethnic groups than others.
  c. is an autosomal recessive inheritance.
  d. must be homozygous to be expressed.
  * e. is an autosomal recessive inheritance and must be homozygous to be expressed.

M 127. Like many genetic disorders, galactosemia is a disruption of a metabolic pathway due to a malfunctioning
  a. reactant.
  b. cofactor.
  * c. enzyme.
  d. energy source.
  e. product.

D 128. A woman is diagnosed to have the genetic disease known as Huntington's disorder. It is a rare defect caused by an autosomal dominant allele. The chance for any one of her children to inherit the disease is
  a. dependent on the sex of the child.
  b. 1/3.
  * c. 1/2.
  d. 3/4.
  e. 2/3.

D 129. In an autosomal dominant disorder such as Huntington's, two carrier parents have the probability of passing the gene on to _?_ percent of their children.
  a. 50
  b. 0
  c. 100
  d. 25
  * e. 75

M 130. An X-linked carrier is a
  a. homozygous dominant female.
  * b. heterozygous female.
  c. homozygous recessive female.
  d. homozygous male.
  e. heterozygous male.

D 131. A human X-linked gene is
  a. found only in males.
  b. more frequently expressed in females.
  c. found on the Y chromosome.
  d. transmitted from father to son.
  * e. found on the X chromosome.

M 132. Queen Victoria
  * a. was a carrier of hemophilia.
  b. had a hemophilic parent.
  c. had hemophilia.
  d. married a man with hemophilia.
  e. developed a mutation for hemophilia.

M 133. Hemophilia
  a. is rare in the human population.
  b. is more common among men.
  c. was common in English royalty.
  d. is an X-linked recessive trait.
  * e. all of these

D 134. Males tend to be affected in greater numbers by X-linked recessive genetic disorders than are females because
  a. females have two dominant genes for the disorder.
  * b. males have only one recessive gene for the disorder.
  c. males have a double dose of the gene.
  d. Y chromosomes are not as strong as X chromosomes.
  e. males have three copies of the X chromosome.

M 135. Which of the following would be considered a carrier of a sex-linked recessive defect?
  a. a man with the defect
  b. a woman with the defect
  c. a father of a son with the defect
  * d. the normal daughter whose father had the defect
  e. a son of two unaffected parents

M 136. A woman heterozygous for color blindness (an X-linked recessive allele) marries a man with normal color vision. What is the probability that their first child will be color blind?
  * a. 25 percent
  b. 50 percent
  c. 75 percent
  d. 100 percent
  e. none of these

D 137. A color-blind man and a woman with normal vision whose father was color blind have a son. Color blindness, in this case, is caused by an X-linked recessive gene. If only the male offspring are considered, the probability that their son is color blind is
  a. .25 (or 25 percent).
  * b. .50 (or 50 percent).
  c. .75 (or 75 percent).
  d. 1.00 (or 100 percent).
  e. none of these

M 138. Red-green color blindness is an X-linked recessive trait in humans. A color-blind woman and a man with normal vision have a son. What is the probability that the son is color blind?
  * a. 100 percent
  b. 75 percent
  c. 50 percent
  d. 25 percent
  e. 0 percent

M 139. Red-green color blindness is an X-linked recessive trait in humans. What is the probability that a color-blind woman and a man with normal vision will have a color-blind daughter?
  a. 100 percent
  b. 75 percent
  c. 50 percent
  d. 25 percent
  * e. 0 percent

M 140. What could the children of a color-blind woman and a man with normal vision be?
  a. All will be color blind.
  b. None will be color blind.
  c. Daughters will be color blind and sons will be normal.
* d. Sons will be color blind and daughters will be normal.
  e. About half will be color blind.

M 141. If a daughter expresses an X-linked recessive gene, she inherited the trait from
  a. her mother.
  b. her father.
* c. both parents.
  d. neither parent.
  e. her grandmother.

M 142. A human X-linked recessive gene may be
  a. found on the Y chromosome.
  b. passed to daughters from their fathers.
  c. passed to sons from their mothers.
  d. expressed more commonly among females.
* e. passed to daughters from their fathers and passed to sons from their mothers.

M 143. Color blindness is an X-linked trait in humans. If a color-blind woman marries a man with normal vision, the children will be
  a. all color-blind daughters, but normal sons.
* b. all color-blind sons, but carrier daughters.
  c. all normal sons, but carrier daughters.
  d. all color-blind children.
  e. all normal children.

STRUCTURAL CHANGES IN CHROMOSOMES

M 144. A chromosome's gene sequence that was ABCDEFG before modification and ABCDLMNOP afterward is an example of
  a. inversion.
  b. deletion.
  c. duplication.
* d. translocation.
  e. aneuploidy.

M 145. A chromosome's gene sequence that was ABCDEFG before modification and ABCDCDEFG afterward is an example of
  a. inversion.
  b. deletion.
* c. duplication.
  d. translocation.
  e. aneuploidy.

E 146. A chromosome that has been broken and rejoined in a reversal sequence has undergone
* a. inversion.
  b. deletion.
  c. duplication.
  d. translocation.
  e. aneuploidy.

E 147. A chromosome's gene sequence that was ABCDEFG before damage and ABCFG after is an example of
  a. inversion.
* b. deletion.
  c. duplication.
  d. translocation.
  e. aneuploidy.

E 148. A chromosome's gene sequence that was ABCDEFG before damage and ABFEDCG after is an example of
* a. inversion.
  b. deletion.
  c. duplication.
  d. translocation.
  e. aneuploidy.

M 149. Which of the following is a transfer of genes between nonhomologous chromosomes?
  a. crossing over
  b. aneuploidy
  c. trisomy
* d. translocation
  e. duplication

CHANGE IN THE NUMBER OF CHROMOSOMES

D 150. Which of the following does NOT belong with the other four?
  a. inversion
* b. polyploidy
  c. deletion
  d. duplication
  e. translocation

D 151. The condition occurring when an organism has a $2n + 1$ chromosome composition is known as
  a. monosomy.
  b. deletion.
  c. diploid.
* d. aneuploidy.
  e. both deletion and aneuploidy.

E 152. If a gamete is missing one chromosome,
  a. the chromosome number is expressed as $2n - 1$.
  b. then one chromosome is without its homologue.
  c. the condition is called monosomy.
  d. only the chromosome number is expressed as $2n - 1$, and the condition is called monosomy.
* e. the chromosome number is expressed as $2n - 1$, one chromosome is without its homologue, and the condition is called monosomy.

D 153. If nondisjunction occurs during anaphase I of meiosis,
  a. the resulting sex cells will be heterogametes.
* b. one-half of the resulting gametes will be diploid for one pair of chromosomes.
  c. diploid cells will be produced.
  d. all gametes would lack a chromosome and these gametes would be infertile.
  e. the gamete is incapable of being fertilized.

E 154. The failure of chromosomes to separate during mitosis or meiosis is called
   a. genetic displacement.
   b. trisomy.
   c. crossing over.
 * d. nondisjunction.
   e. disjunction.

D 155. Which of the following is different from the other four?
 * a. nondisjunction
   b. duplication
   c. inversion
   d. deletion
   e. translocation

E 156. Down syndrome involves trisomy
   a. 3.
   b. 5.
   c. 15.
   d. 19.
 * e. 21.

M 157. In Down syndrome,
 * a. as the age of the mother increases, the chance of the defect occurring in the unborn children increases.
   b. the father seems to have very little influence on the defect.
   c. most embryos abort before complete term.
   d. a person with the defect cannot have a normal child.
   e. none of these

E 158. Which of the following designates a normal human female?
   a. XXY
   b. XY
 * c. XX
   d. XYY
   e. XO

D 159. Which of the following conditions is characterized by a karyotype with 45 chromosomes?
 * a. Turner syndrome
   b. Down syndrome
   c. testicular feminization syndrome
   d. Klinefelter syndrome
   e. cri-du-chat

D 160. Suppose that a hemophilic male (X-linked recessive allele) and a female carrier for the hemophilic trait have a nonhemophilic daughter with Turner syndrome. Nondisjunction could have occurred in
   a. both parents.
   b. neither parent.
 * c. the father only.
   d. the mother only.
   e. none of these

M 161. The sex chromosome composition of a person with Turner syndrome is
   a. XXX.
 * b. XO.
   c. XXY.
   d. XYY.
   e. none of these

D 162. Nondisjunction involving the X chromosomes may occur during oogenesis and produce two kinds of eggs. If normal sperm fertilize these two types, which of the following pairs of genotypes are possible?
   a. XX and XY
 * b. XXY and XO
   c. XYY and XO
   d. XYY and YO
   e. none of these

D 163. The chromosome composition of a slightly taller female with learning difficulty but generally normal appearance is most probably
   a. XO.
   b. XX.
 * c. XXX.
   d. XXY.
   e. XYY.

E 164. Which of the following designates a normal human male?
   a. YY
   b. XX
 * c. XY
   d. XO
   e. XYY

E 165. The sex chromosome composition of a person with Klinefelter syndrome is
   a. XXX.
   b. XO.
 * c. XXY.
   d. XYY.
   e. none of these

M 166. A genetic abnormality that may result in sterile males with mental retardation or breast enlargement is
 * a. XXY.
   b. XYY.
   c. Turner syndrome.
   d. Down syndrome.
   e. none of these

D 167. Aneuploidy would describe all of the following except
   a. Turner syndrome.
   b. Klinefelter syndrome.
 * c. translocation.
   d. XYY.
   e. Down syndrome.

M 168. Which is NOT a chromosomal abnormality?
   a. deletion
   b. extra chromosomes
   c. translocation (exchange of parts between nonhomologs)
 * d. crossing over
   e. inversion

SOME PROSPECTS IN HUMAN GENETICS

M 169. Treatments for genetic disorders currently include
   a. substituting normal for defective parents.
   b. substituting normal for defective genes.
   c. supplying a missing gene.
 * d. supplying missing enzymes.
   e. all of these

D 170. Phenotypic treatments for genetic disorders include
   a. preventing the disorders in the carriers.
   b. eliminating the defective gene.
   c. preventing a disorder from being passed on.
 * d. preventing a disorder from being expressed.
   e. all of these

D 171. Phenotypic treatments
 * a. may increase the number of defective genes in a population.
   b. do not affect the number of defective genes in a population.
   c. decrease the number of defective genes in a population.
   d. are the ultimate cures for genetic disorders.
   e. have no biological value for either the individual or the population.

E 172. Symptoms of phenylketonuria (PKU) may be minimized or suppressed by a diet low in
   a. serine.
   b. glycine.
 * c. phenylalanine.
   d. proline.
   e. glutamic acid.

M 173. Amniocentesis involves sampling
   a. the fetus directly.
 * b. the fetal cells floating in the amniotic fluid.
   c. sperm.
   d. blood cells.
   e. placental cells.

M 174. Amniocentesis is
   a. a surgical means of repairing deformities.
   b. a form of chemotherapy that modifies or inhibits gene expression or the function of gene products.
 * c. used in prenatal diagnosis to detect chromosomal mutations and genetic disorders in embryos.
   d. a form of gene replacement therapy.
   e. all of these

D 175. In prenatal diagnosis, the newest procedure that can be performed early in pregnancy involves sampling the
   a. tissue enclosed by the chorion.
   b. allantois.
 * c. tissue enclosed by the amnion.
   d. yolk sac.
   e. umbilical cord.

M 176. The most recent technique for analyzing the genetics of the unborn child involves the sampling of
   a. the fetus directly.
   b. cells in the amniotic fluid.
   c. material from the allantois.
 * d. the chorionic villi.
   e. yolk sac material.

Matching Questions

M 177. Matching I. Choose the most appropriate answer for each.
   1. ___ colchicine
   2. ___ deletion
   3. ___ duplication
   4. ___ inversion
   5. ___ monosomy
   6. ___ translocation
   7. ___ triploidy
   8. ___ trisomy

   A. $3n$; generally sterile
   B. a chromosome segment is permanently transferred to a nonhomologous chromosome
   C. $(2n - 1)$; a gamete deprived of a chromosome
   D. a repeat of a particular DNA sequence in the same chromosome or in nonhomologous ones
   E. $(2n + 1)$; three chromosomes of the same kind are present in a set of chromosomes
   F. a piece of the chromosome is inadvertently left out during the repair process
   G. inhibits microtubule assembly and induces polyploidy
   H. a chromosome segment that has been cut out and rejoined at the same place, but backward

Answers: 1. G   2. F   3. D   4. H
            5. C   6. B   7. A   8. E

178. Matching II. Match the cause with the disorder.
1. ___ Down syndrome
2. ___ galactosemia
3. ___ color blindness
4. ___ hemophilia
5. ___ Turner syndrome

    A. autosomal recessive inheritance; lactose metabolism is blocked

    B. nondisjunction of the twenty-first chromosomal pair

    C. X-linked recessive inheritance

    D. nondisjunction of the sex chromosomes

Answers: 1. B   2. A   3. C

           4. C   5. D

Problem Set 1

D **179.** In a certain plant, when individuals with blue flowers are crossed with individuals with blue flowers, only blue flowers are produced. Plants with red flowers crossed with plants with red flowers sometimes produce only red flowers; although other times they produce either red or blue flowers. When plants with red flowers are crossed with plants with blue flowers, sometimes only red flowers are produced; other times either red or blue flowers are produced. Which gene is dominant?

D **180.** Which is easier to establish in a pure-breeding population, a dominant or a recessive gene?

M **181.** Tall (D) is dominant to dwarf (d). Give the F_2 genotypic and phenotypic ratios of a cross between a pure-breeding tall plant and a pure-breeding dwarf plant.

D **182.** If wire hair (W) is dominant to smooth hair (w), and you find a wire-haired puppy, how would you determine its genotype by a genetic breeding experiment? Give both the genotype and phenotype involved with the cross with the unknown.

M **183.** In poultry, rose comb is controlled by a dominant allele and its recessive allele controls single comb.
(a) Give the genotype and phenotype produced from crossing a pure-breeding rose comb chicken with a pure-breeding single comb chicken.
(b) Give the results of the backcross of the F_1 hybrid with both pure-breeding parents.

M **184.** If black fur color is controlled by a dominant allele (B) and brown by its recessive allele (b), give the genotypes of the parents and offspring of a cross of a black male with a brown female that produces 1/2 black offspring and 1/2 brown offspring.

D **185.** If 2 spot (S) is dominant to 4 spot (s), give the genotypes for the parents in the following crosses:
(a) 2 spot x 2 spot yields 2 spot and 4 spot
(b) 2 spot x 4 spot yields only 2 spot
(c) 2 spot x 4 spot yields 2 spot and 4 spot
(d) 2 spot x 2 spot yields only 2 spot
(e) 4 spot x 4 spot yields only 4 spot

D **186.** In humans, normal skin pigmentation is influenced by a dominant gene (C), which allows pigmentation to develop. All individuals who are homozygous for the recessive allele (c) are unable to produce an enzyme needed for melanin formation and are therefore referred to as albino. Two normal parents produce an albino child. What are the chances that the next child will be an albino?

D **187.** The allele for albinism (c) is recessive to the allele for normal pigmentation (C). A normally pigmented woman whose father is an albino marries an albino man whose parents are normal. They have three children, two normal and one albino. Give the genotypes for each person listed.

D **188.** In garden peas, one pair of alleles controls the height of the plant and a second pair of alleles controls flower color. The allele for tall (D) is dominant to the allele for dwarf (d), and the allele for purple (P) is dominant to the allele for white (p). A tall plant with purple flowers crossed with a dwarf plant with white flowers produces 1/2 tall with purple flowers and 1/2 tall with white flowers. What is the genotype of the parents?

D **189.** In garden peas, one pair of alleles controls the height of the plant and a second pair of alleles controls flower color. The allele for tall (D) is dominant to the allele for dwarf (d), and the allele for purple (P) is dominant to the allele for white (p). A tall plant with white flowers crossed with a dwarf plant with purple flowers produces all tall offspring with purple flowers. What is the genotype of the parents?

D **190.** In garden peas, one pair of alleles controls the height of the plant and a second pair of alleles controls flower color. The allele for tall (D) is dominant to the allele for dwarf (d), and the allele for purple (P) is dominant to the allele for white (p). A tall plant with purple flowers crossed with a dwarf plant with white flowers produces 1/4 tall purple, 1/4 tall white, 1/4 dwarf purple, and 1/4 dwarf white. What is the genotype of the parents?

D **191.** In garden peas, one pair of alleles controls the height of the plant and a second pair of alleles controls flower color. The allele for tall (D) is dominant to the allele for dwarf (d), and the allele for purple (P) is dominant to the allele for white (p). A tall plant with white flowers crossed with a dwarf plant with purple flowers produces 1/4 tall purple, 1/4 tall white, 1/4 dwarf purple, and 1/4 dwarf white. What is the genotype of the parents?

D 192. In garden peas, one pair of alleles controls the height of the plant and a second pair of alleles controls flower color. The allele for tall (D) is dominant to the allele for dwarf (d), and the allele for purple (P) is dominant to the allele for white (p). A tall plant with purple flowers crossed with a tall plant with white flowers produces 3/8 tall purple, 1/8 tall white, 3/8 dwarf purple, and 1/8 dwarf white. What is the genotype of the parents?

D 193. In garden peas, one pair of alleles controls the height of the plant and a second pair of alleles controls flower color. The allele for tall (D) is dominant to the allele for dwarf (d), and the allele for purple (P) is dominant to the allele for white (p). A tall purple crossed with a tall purple produces 3/4 tall purple and 1/4 tall white. What is the genotype of the parents?

D 194. In horses, black coat color is influenced by the dominant allele (B) and chestnut coat color is influenced by the recessive allele (b). Trotting gait is due to a dominant gene (T), pacing gait to the recessive allele (t). If a homozygous black trotter is crossed to a chestnut pacer,
  (a) what will be the appearance of the F_1 and F_2 generations?
  (b) which phenotype will be the most common?
  (c) which genotype will be the most common?
  (d) which of the potential offspring will be certain to breed true?

D 195. In horses, black coat color is influenced by the dominant allele (B) and chestnut coat color by the recessive allele (b). Trotting gait is due to a dominant gene (T), pacing gait to the recessive allele (t). What color horse would you use to find out the genotype of a black trotter? Give the genotype and phenotype.

D 196. Crosses between a yellow rat with a yellow rat always produce yellow. Crosses between a white rat with a white rat always produce white. The alleles affect the same aspect of coat color. The crosses of a white with a yellow produce a cream. What happens if you cross two creams?

D 197. Assume that red plants crossed with white plants give rise to pink plants. Explain how to eliminate red plants if you start with two pinks.

D 198. If long or round are homozygous forms of an incompletely dominant gene and oval is the phenotype of the heterozygote, give the F_2 ratio of the cross between long and round (both genotype and phenotype).

D 199. A breeder of cattle has a herd of white cows and a roan bull. Hair color in this breed is controlled by an incompletely dominant gene. The two homozygous forms are either red or white, and the heterozygous is roan.
  (a) What colors of calves are expected and in what proportions?
  (b) Outline a procedure to develop an all-red herd.

D 200. In radishes, two incompletely dominant genes control color and shape. Red and white radishes are homozygous, whereas the hybrid is purple. Long and round are homozygous and, if crossed, will produce an oval hybrid. Give the F_2 genotypic and phenotypic ratio produced by crossing pure-breed red, long radishes with white, round varieties.

D 201. In a certain breed of chicken, an incompletely dominant gene controls color. The homozygous black, when crossed with the homozygous splashed-white, produces an intermediate gray color pattern referred to as blue. A second gene controls the shape of the comb. The dominant allele (R) produces rose, whereas the recessive allele (r) produces single. Give the F_1 and F_2 genotypic and phenotypic ratios of a cross between a pure-breeding black single and a pure-breeding splashed-white rose.

D 202. There are three alleles controlling the ABO blood types. I^A and I^B are codominant genes so that the combination $I^A I^B$ produces the AB blood type. The third allele, I^O, is recessive to the other two alleles. Indicate which of these parents could produce the given child:

Parents	Child	Yes or No
(a) A x AB	B	
(b) A x O	A	
(c) A x B	O	
(d) A x AB	O	
(e) A x AB	B	
(f) B x B	O	
(g) AB x AB	A	

D 203. In horses there are four alleles at the A locus. Arranged in dominance sequence they are:

A (wild), a^b (bay), a^c (brown), a^d (black)

If you bred several bay mares whose sires were brown to a brown stallion whose sire was black, what type of offspring would be produced, and in what proportion?

D 204. In rabbits there are four alleles at the c locus. Arranged in dominance sequence they are:

C (agouti), c^{ch} (chinchilla), c^h (Himalayan), and c (albino)
  (a) Is it possible to cross two agouti rabbits and produce both chinchilla and Himalayan offspring?
  (b) Is it possible to cross two chinchillas and produce 1/2 chinchilla and 1/2 Himalayan?

D 205. Gray is homozygous while blue is a heterozygous form of a semilethal gene. Give the ratio of the offspring produced in the cross of two blues.

D 206. A cross of two Kerry horses always produces Kerry. A cross of a Kerry with a Dexter produces 1/2 and 1/2. Crosses of two Dexters produce two Dexters for every Kerry. Explain.

D **207.** In the late 1920s, a mutation occurred in many silver fox farms around the world. The fox farms that sold expensive furs were proud of the quality of their furs, and each advertised that it had the best, purest breed of all the fox farms. The new mutations produced a "platinum" coat pattern that was commercially desirable, so the farms crossed them to get more. The results of their breeding experiments were as follows: (1) silver x silver >>> all silver offspring; (2) silver x platinum >>> equal numbers of silver and platinum; (3) platinum x platinum >>> 2 platinum for each silver offspring. Explain.

D **208.** There is a color pattern inherited in certain mice in which agouti (gray) is homozygous and yellow is heterozygous. A cross of two yellows produces two yellows for each agouti. A second gene, C/c, controls the expression of the color genes: C is the dominant allele that allows color to be expressed, and the recessive gene in the homozygous condition (cc) prevents any color from being expressed.
(a) Give the genotypes of a white parent crossed with a yellow parent that produces 1/2 white, 1/3 yellow, 1/6 agouti offspring.
(b) Give the results of the cross of two forms heterozygous for each gene.
(c) Can you develop a pure-breed population for any of the colors?

D **209.** In poultry, the genes for rose comb (R) and pea comb (P) produce walnut whenever they occur together ($R\_\_ P\_\_$); single-combed individuals have the homozygous condition for both genes ($rr\ pp$).
(a) Give the F_1 and F_2 phenotypic results of a cross of a pure-breeding rose comb ($RR\ pp$) with a pure-breeding pea comb ($rr\ PP$).
(b) Give the phenotypic results of a cross of $Rr\ Pp$ x $rr\ Pp$.
(c) Give the phenotypic results of a cross of $RR\ Pp$ x $rr\ Pp$.
(d) Give the phenotypic results of a cross of $Rr\ pp$ x $rr\ Pp$.
(e) Give the phenotypic results of a cross of $Rr\ Pp$ x $rr\ pp$.

D **210.** Congenital deafness in humans is due to the homozygous condition of either of the recessive genes d or e, or both of these genes. Both dominant D and E are necessary for normal hearing. Gene D/d affects the middle ear, while gene E/e affects the inner ear. It does not matter how good the normal inner ear (as indicated by $E\_\_$) is; if there is something wrong in the middle ear, the individual is unable to hear. The same applies for the other gene. Give the phenotypic results of the following crosses:
(a) $Dd\ EE$ x $Dd\ EE$
(b) $Dd\ Ee$ x $Dd\ Ee$
(c) $dd\ EE$ x $DD\ ee$
(d) $Dd\ EE$ x $Dd\ ee$
(e) $Dd\ EE$ x $DD\ Ee$

D **211.** White fruit color in summer squash is influenced by a dominant allele W, whereas colored fruit must be ww. In the presence of ww, a dominant gene G results in yellow fruit, and if the individual had both recessive genes in the homozygous condition, it would be green. Give the F_2 phenotypic ratios resulting from a cross of a pure-breeding white of genotype $WW\ GG$ with a green.

D **212.** In cultivated stocks, the cross of a variety of white flower plants produced all red flowers in the F_1 generation, but the F_2 generation produced 87 red, 31 cream, and 39 white. Explain these results by giving the genotypes possible for each phenotype.

D **213.** In summer squash, spherical-shaped fruit has been shown to be dominant to elongated fruit. On one occasion, two different spherical varieties were crossed and produced all disk-shaped fruits. When these hybrid disk-shaped fruits were crossed they produced 75 disk-shaped fruits, 48 spherical fruits, and 9 elongated fruits. Explain these results.

D **214.** In sweet peas, genes C and P are necessary for colored flowers. In the absence of either ($\_\_ pp$ or $cc\ \_\_$) or both ($cc\ pp$), the flowers are white. What will be the color of the offspring of the crosses in what proportions for the following?
(a) $Cc\ Pp$ x $cc\ pp$
(b) $Cc\ Pp$ x $Cc\ Pp$
(c) $Cc\ PP$ x $Cc\ pp$
(d) $Cc\ pp$ x $cc\ Pp$

D **215.** In sweet peas, genes C and P are necessary for colored flowers. In the absence of either ($\_\_ pp$ or $cc\ \_\_$) or both ($cc\ pp$), the flowers are white. Give the probable genotype of a plant with colored flowers and a plant with white flowers that produced 38 plants with colored flowers and 42 plants with white flowers.

D **216.** In a certain variety of plants, a cross between a red-flowered plant and a white-flowered plant produced an all-red flower F_1. In the F_2 there were 140 red, 50 cream, and 65 white.
(a) Offer an explanation for this F_2 ratio.
(b) What ratio would be produced in a testcross of the F_1 hybrid?
(c) What ratio would be produced if all the white F_2 plants were crossed among themselves?

D **217.** In a certain breed of chicken, two genes control color. A dominant allele (I) inhibits the expression of any color gene (C). A second recessive gene (c) results in albinism when homozygous (cc). Give the F_2 phenotypic ratio of a colored chicken $ii\ CC$ with a white $II\ cc$.

D **218.** In mice the allele for colored fur (*C*) is dominant to the allele for albinism (*c*). The allele for normal behavior (*W*) is dominant to that for waltzing movement (*w*). Give the probable genotypes of the parents if they produced the offspring listed after the following crosses:

   (a) Colored normal x white waltzer produced 10 colored normal, 8 colored waltzers, 2 white waltzers, 11 white normal.

   (b) Colored normal x white normal produced 35 colored normal, 13 colored waltzers.

   (c) Colored normal x colored normal produced 37 colored normal, 14 colored waltzers, 9 white normal, and 5 white waltzers.

D **219.** Pure-breeding yellow guinea pigs crossed with pure-breeding white ones produce only cream-colored offspring. This pattern indicates incomplete dominance. Rough hair is found to be dominant to smooth hair. Give the F_1 and F_2 genotypic and phenotypic ratios of a cross of a smooth, white guinea pig with a homozygous, rough, yellow guinea pig.

D **220.** In tomatoes, red (*R*) is dominant to yellow (*r*), tall (*D*) is dominant to dwarf (*d*), and smooth (*H*) is dominant to peach or hairy (*h*).

   (a) How many different genotypes are there in relationship to these three characteristics?

   (b) How many different phenotypes are there in relationship to these three characteristics?

   (c) How many different homozygous pure-breeding forms can be produced?

Answers to Problem Set 1

179. Red

180. Recessive

181. 1 *DD*, 2 *Dd*, 1 *dd*; 3 tall, 1 dwarf

182. Smooth hair, *ww*

183. (a) *Rr*, rose
   (b) *Rr* x *RR* >>> all rose, *Rr* x *rr* >>> 1/2 rose, 1/2 single

184. Black male (*Bb*) x brown female (*bb*) offspring: black (*Bb*) brown (*bb*)

185. (a) *Ss* x *Ss* >>> *S__* + *ss*
   (b) *Ss* x *ss* >>> *Ss*
   (c) *Ss* x *ss* >>> *Ss* + *ss*
   (d) *SS* x *S__* >>> *S__*
   (e) *ss* x *ss* >>> *ss*

186. 1/4 chance

187. Normally pigmented woman, *Cc;* albino father, *cc;* albino man, *cc;* normal parents, *Cc* + *Cc;* 3 children, 2 normal *Cc,* 1 albino *cc*

188. *DD Pp* x *dd pp*

189. *DD pp* x *dd PP*

190. *Dd Pp* x *dd pp*

191. *Dd pp* x *dd Pp*

192. *Dd Pp* x *Dd pp*

193. *Dd Pp* x *DD Pp*

194. (a) F_1: black trotters; F_2: 9 black trotters, 3 black pacers, 3 chestnut trotters, 1 chestnut pacer
   (b) Black pacer
   (c) *Bb Tt*
   (d) *bb tt*, chestnut pacers

195. *bb tt,* chestnut pacer

196. 1 yellow, 2 cream, 2 white

197. Cross until you get white, and use white in crosses until you cross two whites, then all subsequent plants will be white.

198. 1 *LL,* 2 *Ll,* 1 *ll;* 1 long, 2 oval, 1 round

199. (a) 1/2 white, 1/2 roan
   (b) Roan with white >>> roan, roan x roan >>> red, roan x red >>> red, red x red >>> red

200. 1 *LL RR* long red, 2 *LL Rr* long purple, 2 *Ll RR* oval red, 4 *Ll RR* oval purple, 1 *ll RR* round red, 1 *ll Rr* round oval, 1 *Ll rr* long white, 2 *Ll rr* oval white, 1 *ll rr* round white

201. F_1: *Bb Rr* blue rose; F_2: 3 *BB R__* black rose, 6 *Bb R__* blue rose, 3 *bb R__* splashed-white rose, 1 *BB rr* black single, 2 *Bb rr* blue single, 1 *bb rr* splashed-white single

202. (a) yes; (b) yes; (c) yes; (d) no; (e) yes; (f) yes; (g) yes

203. $a^b a^c$ x $a^c a^d$; 1/2 bay, 1/2 brown

204. (a) no; (b) Not likely but possible—would expect a 3:1

205. 1 gray, 2 blues (1 lethal)

206. Kerry is homozygous (*DD*), Dexter is heterozygous (*Dd*), *dd* is lethal.

207. *PP* (silver), *Pp* (platinum), *pp* (lethal)

208. (a) *Yy Cc* x *Yy cc*
   (b) *Yy Cc* x *Yy Cc* >>> 3/12 *YY C__* agouti, 6/12 *Yy C__* yellow, 3/12 *__cc* albino
   (c) White and agouti

209. (a) F_1: *Rr Pp* walnut; F_2: 9 *R__P__* walnut, 3 *R__pp* rose, 3 *rr P__* pea, 1 *rr pp* single
   (b) 3/8 walnut, 3/8 pea, 1/8 rose, 1/8 single
   (c) 3/4 walnut, 1/4 rose
   (d) 1/4 walnut, 1/4 rose, 1/4 pea, 1/4 single
   (e) 1/4 walnut, 1/4 rose, 1/4 pea, 1/4 single

210. (a) 3/4 normal, 1/4 deaf
   (b) 9/16 normal, 7/16 deaf
   (c) All normal
   (d) 3/4 normal, 1/4 deaf
   (e) All normal

211. 12/16 *W__ __ __* white, 3/16 *ww G__* yellow, 1/16 *ww gg* green

212. *R*-red, *r*-cream, *A*-pigment, *a*-albino 9 *R__ A__* red, 3 *rr A__* cream, 4 *__aa* white

213. 9 *D__ S__* disk, 3 *D__ ss* spherical, 3 *dd S__* spherical, 1 *dd ss* elongated; presence of both dominant genes produces disk, whereas the presence of either one of the genes as homozygous recessive produces spherical, and both recessive produces elongated fruit.

214. (a) 1/4 color, 3/4 white

   (b) 9/16 color, 7/16 white

   (c) 3/4 color, 1/4 white

   (d) 1/4 color, 3/4 white

215. *Cc Pp* x *CC pp*

216. (a) *R*-red, *r*-cream, *A*-color, *a*-albino; 9 *R__ A__* red, 3 *rr A__* cream, 4 __ *aa* white

   (b) 1/4 red, 1/4 cream, 1/2 white

   (c) All offspring would be white because all would be __ *aa*

217. 9 *I__ C__* + 3 *I__ cc* + 1 *ii cc* = 13 white + 3 *ii C__* = 3 color

218. (a) *Cc Ww* x *cc ww*

   (b) *CC Ww* x *cc Ww*

   (c) *Cc Ww* x *Cc Ww*

219. *F₁*: rough cream *Yy Rr*; *F₂*: 3 *YY R__* yellow rough, 6 *Yy R__* cream rough, 3 *yy R__* white rough, 1 *YY rr* yellow smooth, 2 *Yy rr* cream smooth, 1 *yy rr* white smooth

220. (a) 27   (b) 8   (c) 8

Problem Set 2

D 221. In cats the allele *B* produces black, whereas *b* produces yellow. Neither gene is dominant, and in the heterozygous state the phenotype is a combination of yellow and black spots called tortoise-shell. The alleles *B* and *b* are X-linked. If a tortoise-shell cat has three tortoise-shell kittens and two black kittens, give the genotype and phenotype of the tomcat that produced them, and give the sex of the kittens.

D 222. An X-linked recessive gene (*c*) produces red-green color blindness. A normal woman whose father was color blind marries a color-blind man.

   a. What are the possible genotypes for the mother of the color-blind man?

   b. What are the possible genotypes for the father of the color-blind man?

   c. What are the chances that the first son will be color blind?

   d. What are the chances that the first daughter will be color blind?

D 223. In cats, an X-linked pair of alleles, *B* and *b,* control color of fur. The alleles are incompletely dominant: *B* produces black, *b* produces yellow, and *Bb* produces tortoise-shell.

   a. A yellow cat had a litter of two tortoise-shell and one yellow kittens. What is the sex of the yellow kitten?

   b. A tortoise-shell cat brings home a litter of black, yellow, and tortoise-shell kittens. The color of which sex would tell you the color of the tomcat that produced them?

   c. A yellow male is crossed with a tortoise-shell female. If the female has all male kittens in her litter of four, what color(s) would they be?

   d. A tortoise-shell cat brings home her litter of black, yellow, and tortoise-shell kittens. By what method could you possibly decide whether the male parent was the black tomcat next door?

D 224. If a father and a son are both color blind and the mother is normal, is it likely that the son inherited color blindness from his father?

D 225. In humans, an X-linked disorder called coloboma iridis (a fissure in the iris) is a recessive trait. A normal couple has an afflicted daughter. The husband sues the wife for divorce on the grounds of infidelity. Would you find in his favor?

D 226. In *Drosophila,* a narrow reduced eye is called a bar-eye. It is due to a dominant X-linked allele (*B*), whereas the full wild-type is due to the recessive gene (*B*+). Give the *F₁* and *F₂* genotypic and phenotypic expectations of a cross of a homozygous wild-type female with a bar-eyed male.

D 227. If the gene for yellow body color (*y*) is an X-linked recessive and its dominant counterpart (*y*+) produces wild body colors, give the phenotypes expected and their frequencies for the following four crosses:

   a. yellow female x wild male

   b. wild carrier female x wild male

   c. wild carrier female x yellow male

   d. homozygous wild female x yellow male

D 228. White eyes in *Drosophila* is a mutation that turned out to be an X-linked recessive. Would you expect that the first time the white eye was discovered it was in a male or female?

D 229. Hemophilia is an X-linked recessive gene. A normal woman whose father had hemophilia marries a normal man. What are the chances of hemophilia in their children?

D 230. Color blindness is an X-linked recessive gene. Two normal-visioned parents produce a color-blind child.

   a. Is this child male or female?

   b. What are the genotypes of the parents?

   c. What are the chances that their next child will be a color-blind daughter?

D 231. Red-green color blindness is an X-linked recessive trait. Two normal-visioned parents have a color-blind son. Indicate the genotype and phenotype of each parent and the son.

D **232.** Short index fingers (shorter than ring finger) are dominant in males and recessive in females, whereas long index fingers (as long as or longer than ring fingers) are dominant in females and recessive in males. Give the F_2 genotype and phenotype resulting from the cross of a male with long index fingers with a female with short index fingers.

Answers to Problem Set 2

221.   *BY* black, tortoise-shell female, black males

222.   a.   *Cc* or *cc*

     b.   *CY* or *cY*

     c.   ½

     d.   1/2

223.   a.   Male

     b.   Female

     c.   1/2 yellow, 1/2 black

     d.   Black female kitten

224.   No, males inherit all sex-linked traits from the mother.

225.   Yes, the daughter would have to inherit the recessive trait from both parents.

226.   *B+B+* x *BY* >>> F_1: *B+B* wild female, *B+Y* wild male; F_2: 1/4 *BY* bar male

     1/4 *B + Y* wild male, 1/4 *B+B+* wild female, 1/4 *B+B* wild female

227.   a.   Yellow male, wild female

     b.   1/4 wild male, 1/4 yellow male, 1/4 wild female, 1/4 wild carrier female

     c.   1/4 wild male, 1/4 yellow male, 1/4 yellow female, 1/4 wild carrier female

     d.   1/2 wild carrier female, 1/2 wild male

228.   Male

229.   All females normal but 1/2 of them would be carriers; 1/2 of the males would have hemophilia, the other 1/2 normal.

230.   a.   Male

     b.   *Cc* x *CY*

     c.   No chance to produce a color-blind daughter

231.   Father *CY*, mother *Cc*, son *cY*

232. F_2: 3/4 males with short fingers, 1/4 males with long fingers; F_2: 3/4 females with long fingers, 1/4 females with short fingers

Classification Questions

Answer questions 233–237 using the group of answers below.

     a.   4

     b.   6

     c.   8

     d.   12

     e.   24

D **233.** In a dihybrid cross between a parent that is a double heterozygote (*Aa Bb*) and a parent that is homozygous dominant for one gene and heterozygous for the other (*AA Bb*), how many unique genotypes potentially will be present in their offspring?

D **234.** In a dihybrid cross between a parent that is a double heterozygote (*Aa Bb*) and a parent that is homozygous recessive for one gene and heterozygous for the other (*aa Bb*), how many unique phenotypes potentially will be present in their offspring?

D **235.** In a dihybrid cross between a parent that is a double heterozygote (*Aa Bb*) and a parent that is a double homozygous recessive (*aa bb*), how many unique phenotypes potentially will be present in their offspring?

D **236.** Plant species X is diploid (2n = 24) and has a quantitative trait, the expression of which is controlled by gene loci on each of its chromosomes. What is the maximum number of alleles for this trait that any one individual of species X could have?

D **237.** Animal species X is tetraploid (4n = 12). Following gene duplication and translocation, a given gene is found on each chromosome. How many alleles for this gene can be present in an individual of this species?

Answers: 233. b   234. a   235. a

           236. e   237. d

Answer questions 238–240 in reference to the five items listed below.

     a.   12

     b.   23

     c.   24

     d.   46

     e.   47

D **238.** How many chromosomes does each somatic cell have in a human male who has two X chromosomes?

D **239.** How many chromosomes are present in the somatic cells of a child with Down syndrome (trisomy 21)?

D **240.** The normal sperm cell of species X carries 11 chromosomes. Following nondisjunction in the formation of secondary spermatocytes and their subsequent fertilization of normal ova, some of the zygotes will have 21 chromosomes, others will have 22, and the remainder will have how many chromosomes?

Answers: 238. e   239. e   240. b

Answer questions 241–245 in reference to the five disorders listed below.

    a. galactosemia
    b. Turner syndrome
    c. AIDS
    d. hemophilia
    e. Down syndrome

D   **241.** For this disorder, both a phenotypic cure and a genotypic cure are *potentially* possible.

D   **242.** This disorder is an autosomal recessive disorder.

M   **243.** This disorder is an X-linked recessive trait.

E   **244.** This disorder is also known as trisomy 21.

D   **245.** This disorder is due to a sex chromosome abnormality probably caused by nondisjunction of sex chromosomes at meiosis.

Answers: 241. a   242. a   243. d

            244. e   245. b

Answer questions 246–250 in reference to the five items listed below.

    a. genetic counseling
    b. prenatal diagnosis
    c. preimplantation diagnosis
    d. phenotypic treatments
    e. abortion

M   **246.** In-vitro fertilization.

M   **247.** CVS and amniocentesis.

M   **248.** An option with extremely severe birth problems.

M   **249.** Surgery and diet control.

M   **250.** Starts with the diagnosis of parental genotypes, pedigrees, and genetic testing for metabolic disorders.

Answers: 246. c   247. b   248. e

            249. d   250. a

Selecting the Exception

E   **251.** Four of the five answers listed below describe the heterozygous condition. Select the exception.
     *   a. homozygous
         b. carrier
         c. heterozygotes
         d. hybrid
         e. *Aa*

M   **252.** Four of the five answers listed below describe the gene makeup. Select the exception.
         a. pure-breeding
         b. homozygous
         c. heterozygous
         d. carrier
     *   e. phenotype

M   **253.** Four of the five answers listed below are accepted as valid explanations of genetic behavior. Select the exception.
     *   a. blending
         b. dominance
         c. segregation
         d. independent assortment
         e. probability

E   **254.** Four of the five answers listed below are pure-breeding. Select the exception.
         a. *AA BB*
     *   b. *Aa BB*
         c. *AA bb*
         d. *aa BB*
         e. *aa bb*

D   **255.** Four of the five answers listed below provide evidence that genes are located on chromosomes. Select the exception.
         a. The chromosome number is cut in half by meiosis.
         b. Original chromosome number is restored by fertilization.
         c. Some genes tend to be inherited together.
     *   d. Environmental factors may influence gene expression.
         e. There are two sets of chromosomes, one maternal, one paternal, in diploid forms.

D   **256.** Four of the five answers listed below are related conditions in which abnormal numbers of chromosomes are present. Select the exception.
         a. monosomy
         b. aneuploidy
         c. nondisjunction
     *   d. complete chromosome set
         e. trisomy

D 257. Four of the five answers listed below are terms related to a normal set of chromosomes by quantity. Select the exception.
*   a. aneuploid
    b. haploid
    c. tetraploid
    d. polyploid
    e. diploid

D 258. Four of the five answers listed below describe sets of chromosomes with extra numbers. Select the exception.
    a. polyploid
    b. tetraploid
*   c. diploid
    d. triploid
    e. allopolyploid

D 259. Four of the five answers listed below are conditions caused by chromosomal nondisjunction. Select the exception.
    a. Down syndrome
*   b. Huntington's disease
    c. Turner syndrome
    d. Klinefelter syndrome
    e. trisomy 21

M 260. Four of the five answers listed below are therapeutic measures applied to affected individuals. Select the exception.
*   a. prenatal diagnosis
    b. chemotherapy
    c. surgical correction
    d. diet modification
    e. environmental adjustment

D 261. Four of the five answers listed below are caused by recessive genes. Select the exception.
*   a. Huntington's disorder
    b. phenylketonuria
    c. color blindness
    d. hemophilia
    e. albinism

Labeling

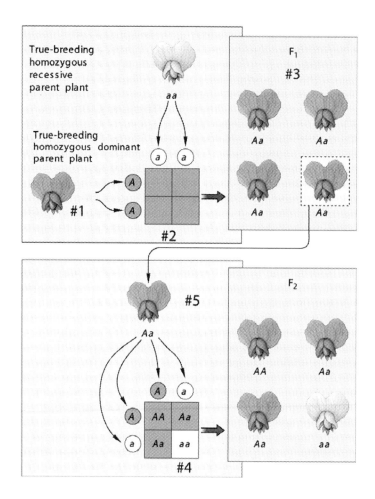

E   **262.** The genotype of the plant labeled as #1 is
   a. *Aa*.
   b. *aa*.
   c. heterozygous.
 * d. *AA*.
   e. hemizygous.

E   **263.** The squares at #2 represent the _?_ of the _?_.
   a. genotypes; parents
   b. phenotypes; parents
 * c. genotypes; offspring
   d. phenotypes; offspring
   e. none of these is accurate

E   **264.** The color of the flowers at #3 is called the
   a. dominant allele.
   b. genotype.
   c. offspring.
   d. recessive gene.
 * e. phenotype.

E   **265.** The probability of producing a plant with *aa* at #4 is
   a. 1/4.
   b. 25%.
   c. 1 out of 4.
   d. 0.25.
 * e. all of these

E   **266.** To get the results in the boxes located below the flower labeled #5, the flowers on that plant would have to
   a. be cross-pollinated.
 * b. self-fertilize.
   c. be crossed with a known recessive.
   d. be sex-linked.
   e. produce no seeds.

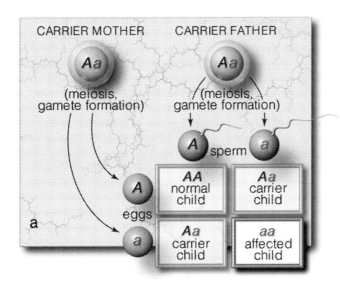

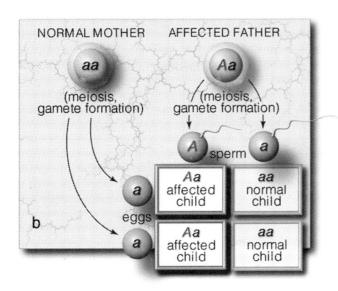

E **267.** The pattern illustrating autosomal dominant inheritance is labeled with the letter _?_.

E **268.** The pattern illustrating autosomal recessive inheritance is labeled with the letter _?_.

Answers: 267. b 268. a

CHAPTER 9

DNA STRUCTURE AND FUNCTION

Multiple-Choice Questions

THE HUNT FOR FAME, FORTUNE, AND DNA

M   1. Johann Miescher is credited with
      a. proposing DNA as the hereditary material.
      b. finding a cure for pneumonia.
      c. telling us that A=T and G=C.
  *   d. discovering nucleic acids.
      e. using bacteriophages to confirm the structure of DNA.

D   2. When Fred Griffith injected mice with a mixture of dead, pathogenic, encapsulated S cells and living unencapsulated R cells of *Streptococcus pneumoniae*, he discovered that
  *   a. the previously harmless strain (S) had inherited the ability to kill mice.
      b. the dead mice teemed with living pathogenic (R) cells.
      c. the killer strain (R) was encased in a protective capsule.
      d. the dead mice teemed with living pathogenic (R) cells and the killer strain (R) was encased in a protective capsule.
      e. all of these

D   3. Fred Griffith's experiments
      a. produced a vaccine against bacterial pneumonia.
      b. demonstrated that rough (R) bacteria cause pneumonia.
  *   c. provided evidence that genetic material from one bacterial culture could be transferred to another culture.
      d. showed that rough bacteria injected into mice will be changed by the mice to smooth (S) bacteria.
      e. converted harmless smooth bacteria into lethal rough bacteria.

D   4. The significance of Fred Griffith's experiment in which he used two strains of *Streptococcus pneumoniae* is that
      a. the semiconservative nature of DNA replication was finally demonstrated.
  *   b. it demonstrated that harmless cells had become permanently transformed through a change in the bacterial hereditary system.
      c. it established that pure DNA extracted from disease-causing bacteria transformed harmless strains into killer strains.
      d. it demonstrated that radioactively labeled bacteriophages transfer their DNA but not their protein coats to their host bacteria.
      e. all of these

D   5. Which of the following statements is NOT true about Fred Griffith's experiments?
      a. Mice injected with smooth (S) bacteria die.
  *   b. Mice injected with heat-killed smooth bacteria die.
      c. Mice injected with heat-killed smooth bacteria and live rough (R) bacteria die.
      d. Mice injected with rough bacteria live.
      e. Smooth bacteria are transformed into harmless rough bacteria.

M   6. Which scientist(s) identified the transforming substance involved in changing rough (R) bacteria to smooth (S) as DNA?
  *   a. Avery
      b. Griffith
      c. Chargaff
      d. Hershey and Chase
      e. Pauling

E   7. Bacteriophages are
      a. large bacteria.
      b. pathogens (disease-producing bacteria).
  *   c. viruses.
      d. cellular components.
      e. protistans.

D   8. The significance of the experiments in which ^{32}P and ^{35}S were used is that
      a. the semiconservative nature of DNA replication was finally demonstrated.
      b. they demonstrated that harmless bacterial cells had become permanently transformed through a change in the bacterial hereditary system.
      c. they established that pure DNA extracted from disease-causing bacteria transformed harmless strains into killer strains.
  *   d. they demonstrated that radioactively labeled bacteriophages transfer their DNA but not their protein coats to their host bacteria.
      e. none of these

D   9. If a mixture of viruses labeled with radioactive sulfur and phosphorus is placed in a bacterial culture,
      a. the bacteria will absorb radioactive sulfur.
  *   b. the bacteria will absorb radioactive phosphorus.
      c. the bacteria will absorb both radioactive sulfur and phosphorus.
      d. the bacteria will not absorb either sulfur or phosphorus.
      e. the viruses will not attach to the bacteria.

M   10. Nucleic acid contains
          a. sulfur.
     *   b. phosphorus.
          c. potassium.
          d. iron.
          e. manganese.

D   11. Which of the following statements is FALSE?
          a. Protein molecules contain no phosphorus.
     *   b. Hershey and Chase discovered that ^{35}S and not ^{32}P had been incorporated into the hereditary system of the bacteria.
          c. Bacteriophages are viruses that inject their nucleic-acid genetic code into bacteria and use the bacterial genetic apparatus to make viral proteins.
          d. Each nucleotide is composed of a five-carbon sugar, a phosphate group, and either a purine or pyrimidine.
          e. Viruses are particles of nucleic acid encased in protein.

M   12. The experiments of which of the following researchers clearly distinguised DNA as the hereditary material (as opposed to protein)?
          a. Pauling
     *   b. Hershey and Chase
          c. Griffith
          d. Watson and Crick
          e. Avery

M   13. Sulfur is
     *   a. found in proteins, but not nucleic acids.
          b. a vital component of nucleic acids.
          c. found in nucleic acids, but not proteins.
          d. needed for bacteriophages to attach to bacteria.
          e. needed for the enzyme that splits the wall of bacteria.

DNA STRUCTURE AND FUNCTION

E   14. The building blocks of nucleic acids are
          a. amino acids.
     *   b. nucleotides.
          c. pentose sugars.
          d. phosphate groups.
          e. nitrogenous bases.

D   15. Which of the following terms is NOT related to the other four?
     *   a. amino acids
          b. nucleotides
          c. five-carbon sugars
          d. phosphate groups
          e. nitrogenous bases

M   16. A nucleotide may contain
          a. a purine.
          b. five-carbon sugar.
          c. a phosphate group.
          d. a pyrimidine.
     *   e. all of these

M   17. Which scientist(s) discovered the basis for the base-pair rule, which states that the amounts of adenine and thymine match, as do the amounts of cytosine and guanine?
          a. Avery
          b. Griffith
     *   c. Chargaff
          d. Hershey and Chase
          e. Pauling

M   18. DNA varies from species to species in its
          a. base-pair bonding only.
          b. relative amounts of nucleotide bases only.
          c. sequence of base pairs only.
          d. base-pair bonding and sequence of base pairs.
     *   e. relative amounts of nucleotide bases and sequence of base pairs.

E   19. From X-ray diffraction data, which of the following was determined about DNA?
          a. The molecule had two chains.
          b. Phosphate groups formed the backbone of the helix.
          c. Each turn of the helix contains 10 bases.
          d. The shape of the molecule could be a double helix.
     *   e. all of these

M   20. Rosalind Franklin's research contribution was essential in
          a. establishing the single-stranded nature of DNA.
          b. establishing the principle of base pairing.
     *   c. establishing most of the principal structural features of DNA.
          d. sequencing DNA molecules.
          e. determining the bonding energy of DNA molecules.

M   21. Rosalind Franklin used which technique to determine many of the physical characteristics of DNA?
          a. transformation
          b. transmission electron microscopy
          c. density-gradient centrifugation
     *   d. X-ray crystallography
          e. all of these

E   22. In the bonding of nitrogenous bases,
          a. adenine is paired with cytosine.
          b. adenine is paired with guanine.
          c. cytosine is paired with thymine.
     *   d. guanine is paired with cytosine.
          e. none of these is correct

M   23. In the bonding of two nucleotides,
          a. hydrogen bonds are used.
          b. adenine and thymine bind together.
          c. purines bind with pyrimidines.
          d. double-ring nitrogenous bases connect to single-ring bases.
     *   e. all of these

E 24. The DNA molecule could be compared to a
       a. hair pin.
     * b. ladder.
       c. key.
       d. globular mass.
       e. flat plate.

M 25. In DNA, complementary base pairing occurs between
       a. cytosine and uracil.
       b. adenine and guanine.
       c. adenine and uracil.
     * d. adenine and thymine.
       e. all of these

E 26. Adenine and guanine are
     * a. double-ringed purines.
       b. single-ringed purines.
       c. double-ringed pyrimidines.
       d. single-ringed pyrimidines.
       e. amino acids.

M 27. In the comparison between a spiral staircase and a DNA molecule, the steps would correspond to
       a. sugars.
       b. hydrogen bonds.
     * c. base pairs.
       d. nucleotides.
       e. phosphates.

E 28. In DNA molecules,
     * a. the nucleotides are arranged in a linear, unbranched pattern.
       b. the nitrogenous bases are found on the outside of the molecule.
       c. the sugar-phosphate pattern runs the same way on each DNA strand.
       d. all of these
       e. none of these

M 29. Which of the following statements is TRUE?
     * a. The hydrogen bonding of cytosine to guanine is an example of complementary base pairing.
       b. Adenine always pairs up with guanine in DNA, and cytosine always teams up with thymine.
       c. Each of the four nucleotides in a DNA molecule has the same nitrogen-containing base.
       d. When adenine base pairs with thymine, they are linked by three hydrogen bonds.
       e. In the DNA of all species, the amount of purines never equals the amount of pyrimidines.

E 30. Each DNA strand has a backbone that consists of alternating
       a. purines and pyrimidines.
       b. nitrogen-containing bases.
       c. hydrogen bonds.
     * d. sugar and phosphate molecules.
       e. amines and purines.

M 31. Who among the following was NOT involved in working out the structure of DNA?
     * a. Avery
       b. Watson
       c. Wilkins
       d. Franklin
       e. Chargaff

DNA REPLICATION AND REPAIR

M 32. The appropriate adjective to describe DNA replication is
       a. nondisruptive.
     * b. semiconservative.
       c. progressive.
       d. natural.
       e. lytic.

E 33. Replication of DNA
       a. produces RNA molecules.
       b. produces only new DNA.
     * c. produces two molecules, each of which is half-new and half-old DNA joined lengthwise to each other.
       d. generates excessive DNA, which eventually causes the nucleus to divide.
       e. is too complex to characterize.

M 34. Each DNA strand serves as which of the following during DNA synthesis?
       a. replicate
       b. substitute
     * c. template
       d. source of nucleotides
       e. all of these

D 35. The primary function of DNA ligase is to
       a. cut the two strands of the DNA molecule prior to replication.
       b. attach free nucleotides to the growing chain.
       c. remove bases that might have been inserted incorrectly.
     * d. seal any tiny gaps in the new DNA.
       e. fragment old DNA that is no longer of use to the cell.

M 36. DNA polymerase
       a. is an enzyme.
       b. adds new nucleotides to a strand.
       c. proofreads DNA strands to see that they are correct.
       d. derives energy from free nucleotides for strand assembly.
     * e. all of these

M 37. In the technique of artificial twinning,
    a. two zygotes are used.
   * b. two parts of a tiny ball of cells splits.
    c. zygotes produced by in vitro fertilization are placed into a surrogate to begin division.
    d. no sperm is needed.
    e. all of these

M 38. Cloning includes
    a. producing artificial twins.
    b. producing many DNA copies in the laboratory.
    c. nuclear transfer.
    d. producing identical copies of cats and sheep.
   * e. all of these

Matching Questions

D 39. Matching. Choose the one most appropriate answer for each.
    1. ___ Avery and colleagues
    2. ___ Chargaff
    3. ___ Franklin
    4. ___ Griffith
    5. ___ Hershey and Chase
    6. ___ Pauling
    7. ___ Miescher
    8. ___ Watson and Crick
    A. discovered that the hereditary system of one strain of bacteria could be transformed by materials from another strain of bacteria
    B. first to discover a nucleic acid and isolate it from fish sperm
    C. reported evidence that DNA was the hereditary material
    D. the first to build a scale model of DNA and to describe it explicitly in a publication
    E. the first to demonstrate, through the use of radioactive isotopes, that DNA, not protein, was the substance transmitted through generations of cells
    F. provided two important clues to the structure of DNA; one clue was A = T and C = G
    G. discovered part of the secondary structure of proteins
    H. obtained excellent X-ray diffraction photographs that suggested that DNA had phosphate groups forming the backbone on the outside of two chains; also said that DNA was a double helix

Answers: 1. C   2. F   3. H
             4. A   5. E   6. G
             7. B   8. D

Classification Questions

Answer questions 40–44 in reference to the five nucleotides listed below.
    a. guanine
    b. cytosine
    c. pyrimidine
    d. thymine
    e. uracil

M 40. The data of Erwin Chargaff indicated that within a species the amount of adenine was always equal to the amount of this.

E 41. This nucleotide is not incorporated into the structure of the DNA helix.

D 42. This nucleotide is a double-ringed molecule.

M 43. If one chain of a DNA molecule had a purine at a given position, this would be its complement on the other chain.

D 44. Two hydrogen bonds connect adenine to _?_ in the DNA molecule.

Answers: 40. d   41. e   42. a
             43. c   44. d

Selecting the Exception

M 45. Four of the five answers listed below are bases used to construct nucleic acids. Select the exception.
    a. cytosine
    b. adenine
    c. thymine
    d. guanine
   * e. phenylalanine

D 46. Four of the five answers listed below are people who helped develop the double helix explanation of DNA. Select the exception.
    a. Wilkins
   * b. Griffith
    c. Watson
    d. Franklin
    e. Crick

D 47. Four of the five answers listed below are correctly paired. Select the exception.
   * a. A—C
    b. C—G
    c. A—T
    d. T—A
    e. purine—pyrimidine

D   **48.** Four of the five answers listed below are pairs of people who worked in fields related to genetics. Select the exception.

   *   a. Wallace and Darwin
       b. Avery and Griffith
       c. Mendel and Morgan
       d. Watson and Crick
       e. Hershey and Chase

Labeling

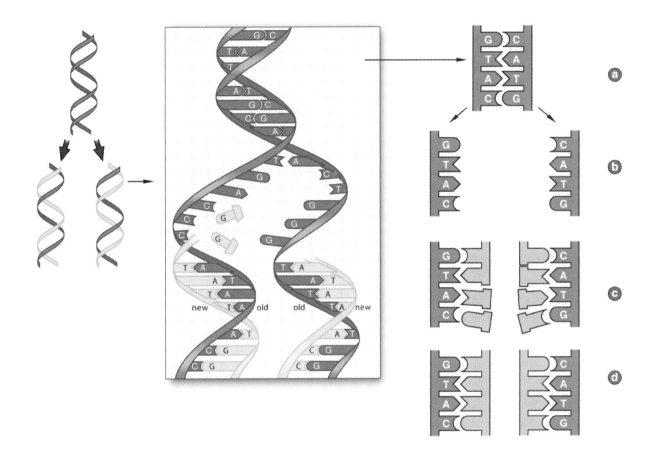

E **49.** The replication illustrated here is termed
    a. dominant.
    b. recessive.
  * c. semiconservative.
    d. conservative.
    e. hemiconservative.

E **50.** In step "b," the original strands have separated because
  * a. the hydrogen bonds between bases were broken.
    b. the sugar-phosphate linkages broke.
    c. the polymerases stopped functioning.
    d. the bases repelled each other.
    e. water changed the bases into their subunits.

E **51.** In step "c," which bonding is the only one that is possible?
    a. A with C
  * b. G with C
    c. C with T
    d. T with G
    e. A with G

E **52.** When step "d" is completed, the two DNA molecules produced will be
    a. identical to each other but not to the parent DNA.
    b. identical to the parent DNA but not to each other.
    c. different from each other and the parent DNA.
  * d. identical to each other and to the parent DNA.
    e. identical to each other and almost the same as the parent DNA.

CHAPTER 10
GENE EXPRESSION AND CONTROL

Multiple-Choice Questions

MAKING AND CONTROLLING THE CELL'S PROTEINS

M 1. A nucleotide sequence that a cell can convert to an RNA or protein product is called a(n)
   a. codon.
   b. intron.
   c. messenger.
   * d. gene.
   e. enzyme.

E 2. The DNA molecule is made up of how many strands?
   a. 1
   * b. 2
   c. 3
   d. 6
   e. 12

M 3. The flow of information from DNA to protein
   a. is reversible.
   b. involves transcription only.
   c. explains evolution.
   d. was discovered by Gregor Mendel.
   * e. uses forms of RNA in the process.

HOW IS RNA TRANSCRIBED FROM DNA?

E 4. _?_ molecules carry protein-assembly instructions from the nucleus to the cytoplasm.
   a. Template DNA
   * b. Messenger RNA
   c. Transfer RNA
   d. Ribosomal RNA
   e. all of these

E 5. The RNA molecule is made up of how many strands?
   * a. 1
   b. 2
   c. 3
   d. 6
   e. 12

D 6. The changing of a business letter from shorthand to typewritten copy is analogous to
   a. translation of mRNA.
   * b. transcription of DNA.
   c. protein synthesis.
   d. deciphering the genetic code.
   e. replication of DNA.

E 7. All the different kinds of RNA are transcribed in the
   a. mitochondria.
   b. cytoplasm.
   c. ribosomes.
   * d. nucleus.
   e. endoplasmic reticulum.

E 8. The form of RNA that carries the code from the DNA to the site where the protein is assembled is called
   * a. messenger RNA.
   b. nuclear RNA.
   c. ribosomal RNA.
   d. transfer RNA.
   e. structural RNA.

M 9. The nitrogenous base found in DNA but not in RNA is
   a. adenine.
   b. cytosine.
   c. guanine.
   d. uracil.
   * e. thymine.

D 10. DNA and RNA are alike in
   a. the pentose sugar.
   b. all the nitrogenous bases used to assemble the genetic code.
   c. the number of strands.
   d. their function in genetics.
   * e. none of these

E 11. Which substance is found in RNA but not in DNA?
   a. thymine
   b. deoxyribose
   * c. uracil
   d. guanine
   e. cytosine

E 12. The nitrogenous base found in RNA but not in DNA is
   a. adenine.
   b. cytosine.
   c. guanine.
   * d. uracil.
   e. thymine.

E 13. Uracil will pair with
   a. ribose.
   * b. adenine.
   c. cytosine.
   d. thymine.
   e. guanine.

M 14. The synthesis of an RNA molecule from a DNA template strand is
   a. replication.
   b. translation.
   * c. transcription.
   d. DNA synthesis.
   e. metabolism.

E 15. The relationship between strands of RNA and DNA is
   a. antagonistic.
   b. opposite.
   * c. complementary.
   d. an exact duplicate.
   e. unrelated.

M 16. Transcription
   a. occurs on the surface of the ribosome.
   b. is the final process in the assembly of a protein.
* c. occurs during the synthesis of any type of RNA from a DNA template.
   d. is catalyzed by DNA polymerase.
   e. all of these

M 17. Transcription
   a. involves both strands of DNA as templates.
   b. uses the enzyme DNA polymerase.
   c. results in a double-stranded end product.
* d. produces three different types of RNA molecules.
   e. all of these

M 18. Transcription starts at a region of DNA called a(n)
   a. sequencer.
* b. promoter.
   c. activator.
   d. terminator.
   e. transcriber.

M 19. Which of the following adds RNA nucleotides, one at a time, during transcription?
* a. RNA polymerase
   b. DNA polymerase
   c. phenylketonuria
   d. transfer RNA
   e. all of these

D 20. Before leaving the nucleus, the RNA molecule
   a. acquires a poly-A tail.
   b. breaks loose from the terminator signal on the template.
   c. becomes capped.
   d. is stripped of its introns.
* e. all of these

M 21. In transcription,
   a. several RNA molecules are made from the same DNA molecule.
   b. promoters are needed so that RNA can bind to DNA.
   c. DNA produces messenger RNA.
   d. a specific enzyme called RNA polymerase is required.
* e. all of these

M 22. The portion of the DNA molecule that is translated is composed of
   a. introns.
   b. anticodons.
* c. exons.
   d. transcriptons.
   e. exons and transcriptons.

D 23. The portion of the DNA molecule that is not translated and is a noncoding portion of DNA is composed of
* a. introns.
   b. anticodons.
   c. exons.
   d. transcriptons.
   e. exons and transcriptons.

M 24. Before messenger RNA is mature,
   a. all exons are deleted and removed.
* b. a cap and a tail are provided.
   c. anticodons are assembled.
   d. the transfer RNA transfers the messenger RNA to the ribosome.
   e. the single RNA strand duplicates itself in much the same way as DNA.

M 25. If the DNA triplets were ATG-CGT, the mRNA codons would be
   a. AUG-CGU.
   b. ATG-CGT.
* c. UAC-GCA.
   d. UAG-CGU.
   e. none of these

D 26. If the DNA triplets were ATG-CGT, the tRNA anticodons would be
* a. AUG-CGU.
   b. ATG-CGT.
   c. UAC-GCA.
   d. UAG-CGU.
   e. none of these

D 27. Which of the following could NOT be an RNA transcript?
   a. AUGCGU
* b. ATGCGT
   c. UACGCA
   d. UAGCGU
   e. GCGUUU

M 28. In transcription,
   a. several amino acids are assembled by the messenger RNA molecules at one time.
* b. a special sequence called a promoter is necessary for transcription to begin.
   c. certain polypeptide sequences are governed by one ribosome, whereas other sequences are produced by other ribosomes.
   d. the transfer RNA molecules arrange the messenger RNA codons into the appropriate sequence.
   e. none of these

DECIPHERING mRNA

D 29. The genetic code
   a. is universal for all organisms.
   b. is based upon 64 codons made of sequences of three nucleotides.
   c. also comes equipped with stop codons.
   d. is redundant; that is, most amino acids have more than one codon.
* e. all of these

E 30. The genetic code is made up of units consisting of how many nucleotides?
    a. 2
*   b. 3
    c. 5
    d. 6
    e. 12

D 31. If the codon consisted of only two nucleotides, there would be how many possible codons?
    a. 4
    b. 8
*   c. 16
    d. 32
    e. 64

D 32. The insertion of how many nucleotides into a genetic sequence does less damage to the code than the insertion of other numbers of nucleotides?
    a. 1
    b. 2
*   c. 3
    d. 4
    e. 5

E 33. There are how many different kinds of amino acids in proteins?
    a. 3
    b. 6
    c. 12
*   d. 20
    e. 28

M 34. There are how many different kinds of RNA codons?
    a. 3
    b. 12
    c. 28
*   d. 64
    e. 120

E 35. There are how many different kinds of RNA nucleotides?
    a. 3
*   b. 4
    c. 5
    d. 6
    e. 12

E 36. The concept that a set of three nucleotides specifies a particular amino acid provides the basis for
    a. the one gene, one enzyme hypothesis.
    b. the one gene, one polypeptide hypothesis.
*   c. the genetic code.
    d. biochemical reactions among nucleic acids.
    e. all of these

M 37. Of all the different codons that exist, three of them
    a. are involved in mutations.
    b. do not specify a particular amino acid.
    c. cannot be copied.
    d. provide punctuation or instructions such as "stop."
*   e. do not specify a particular amino acid and signal instructions such as "stop."

D 38. The wobble effect
    a. explains why and how there can be 31 kinds of transfer RNA molecules.
    b. allows the third codon to vary if the first two codons in the anticodon follow the base-pair rule.
    c. indicates that transfer RNA combines with either the small or large subunit of ribosomes.
*   d. explains freedom in codon-anticodon pairing.
    e. explains why and how there can be 31 kinds of transfer RNA molecules, allows the third codon to vary if the first two codons in the anticodon follow the base-pair rule, and indicates that transfer RNA combines with either the small or large subunit of ribosomes.

E 39. Each "word" in the mRNA language consists of how many letters?
*   a. 3
    b. 4
    c. 5
    d. more than 5
    e. none of these

D 40. If each nucleotide coded for a single amino acid, how many different types of amino acids could be combined to form proteins?
*   a. 4
    b. 16
    c. 20
    d. 64
    e. none of these

M 41. Which of the following carries amino acids to ribosomes, where amino acids are linked into the primary structure of a polypeptide?
    a. mRNA
*   b. tRNA
    c. hnRNA
    d. rRNA
    e. all of these

M 42. Transfer RNA differs from other types of RNA because it
    a. transfers genetic instructions from cell nucleus to cytoplasm.
    b. specifies the amino acid sequence of a particular protein.
*   c. carries an amino acid at one end.
    d. contains codons.
    e. none of these

D 43. The wobble effect pertains to the matching of
*   a. codons with anticodons.
    b. codons with exons.
    c. exons with introns.
    d. template DNA with messenger RNA.
    e. messenger RNA with ribosomal RNA.

E   44.   Eukaryotic ribosomes function as
         a. a single unit.
    *   b. two-part units.
         c. three-part units.
         d. four-part units.
         e. a multidivisional unit.

D   45.   In most species, all mRNA transcripts begin with
         a. methionine.
         b. a ribosome.
    *   c. AUG.
         d. the P site.
         e. an anticodon.

FROM mRNA TO PROTEIN

D   46.   Which of the following statements is FALSE?
         a. In chain elongation, the amino acids are added to
            the chain according to the sequence in the
            messenger RNA.
         b. The messenger RNA molecule is stationary, and
            series of ribosomes called polysomes travel along
            the molecule manufacturing series of polypeptides
            at the same time.
         c. The shape of transfer RNA molecules is uniform
            and is maintained by hydrogen bonds.
         d. Enzymes found in the ribosome catalyze the
            formation of the bonds in the new polypeptide.
    *   e. Polypeptide assembly is reversible.

M   47.   A polysome is
         a. one of the units of a ribosome.
         b. the nuclear organelle that synthesizes RNA.
         c. an organelle that functions similarly to a ribosome
            during meiosis.
         d. the two units of a ribosome considered together.
    *   e. an mRNA molecule with several ribosomes
            attached.

MUTATED GENES AND THEIR PROTEIN PRODUCTS

M   48.   A gene mutation
         a. is a change in the nucleotide sequence of DNA.
         b. may be caused by environmental agents.
         c. may arise spontaneously.
         d. can occur in any organism.
    *   e. all of these

D   49.   Which event may occur in all viruses, prokaryotes,
         and eukaryotes?
         a. duplication
         b. aneuploidy
         c. translocation
    *   d. mutation
         e. all of these

E   50.   Mutations can be
         a. random.
         b. beneficial.
         c. lethal.
         d. heritable.
    *   e. all of these

M   51.   Frameshift mutations may involve
         a. substitution of nucleotides.
         b. substitution of codons.
         c. substitution of amino acids.
    *   d. insertion or deletion of one to several base pairs.
         e. all of these

M   52.   Sickle-cell anemia has been traced to what type of
         mutation?
         a. frameshift
         b. transposable element
         c. mutagenic
    *   d. base-pair substitution
         e. viral

D   53.   The difference between normal and sickle-cell
         hemoglobin is based upon
         a. the number of amino acids in the molecule.
    *   b. the substitution of one amino acid for another.
         c. the number and orientation of the amino acid
            chains attached to the heme portion of the
            molecule.
         d. the number of oxygen molecules that can be
            carried.
         e. the type of bone marrow that produces it.

M   54.   In a mutation,
         a. the new codon may specify a different amino acid
            but may not change the function of the new
            protein produced.
         b. the new codon may specify the same amino acid
            as the old codon.
         c. the new codon and resulting amino acid may
            destroy the function of the protein specified.
         d. the new codon may have no serious effect.
    *   e. All of these may be true.

CONTROLS OVER GENE EXPRESSION

E   55.   Molecules that interact with DNA to alter gene
         expression are
         a. operons.
         b. promoters.
    *   c. regulatory proteins.
         d. repressor amines.
         e. carbohydrates.

M   56.   Repressor proteins
         a. prevent binding of RNA polymerase to DNA.
         b. can be inactivated by an inducer such as lactose.
         c. provide negative control.
         d. prevent binding of RNA polymerase to DNA and
            can be inactivated by an inducer such as lactose.
    *   e. prevent transcription and bind to operators.

D 57. The lactose operon includes
     a. an operator.
     b. three structural genes that manufacture lactose-metabolizing enzymes.
     c. a promoter.
     d. a repressor molecule.
    * e. all of these except "a repressor molecule"

E 58. The obvious advantage of the lactose operon system is that
     a. lactose is not needed as energy for bacteria.
    * b. lactose-metabolizing enzymes need not be made when lactose is not present.
     c. the bacteria will make lactose only in the presence of the proper enzymes.
     d. milk is not needed for adult humans' diet.
     e. glucose can substitute for lactose in the diet of intolerant persons.

D 59. The lactose operon
    * a. requires the presence of milk in the environment of the bacteria.
     b. is turned on before a baby is born.
     c. is a control mechanism that enables vertebrates to digest milk.
     d. causes the production of gas in the digestive tract of milk-drinking animals.
     e. is an excellent model for explaining control mechanisms for eukaryotic forms.

M 60. In prokaryotes such as bacteria, most of the control of gene expression is at the _?_ level.
    * a. transcriptional
     b. transcript-processing
     c. transport
     d. translational
     e. post-translational

D 61. Which of the following is part of a control mechanism to prevent transcription?
     a. promoter
    * b. repressor
     c. structural genes that produce lactase
     d. operator
     e. all of these

M 62. During the early part of a young mammal's life, the *E. coli* in the young offspring's intestinal tract are exposed to high levels of which of the following that later generations of *E. coli* will never be exposed to?
     a. glucose
     b. ribose
     c. cellulose
    * d. lactose
     e. fructose

E 63. The model of the prokaryote operon explains the regulation of which of the following?
     a. replication
    * b. transcription
     c. induction
     d. Lyonization
     e. none of these

M 64. In the prokaryotic lac operon model, it is usually the _?_ that inactivates the repressor protein.
     a. lactose digesting enzyme
     b. product
    * c. lactose
     d. promoter
     e. operator

M 65. When a gene transcription occurs, which of the following is produced?
     a. more DNA
     b. protein or polypeptide sequences
    * c. messenger RNA
     d. enzymes
     e. genetic defects

D 66. Which of the following is NOT actually a part of an operon?
     a. promoter
     b. gene for permease
     c. operator
     d. gene for acetylase
    * e. regulator genes

D 67. A regulator gene produces which of the following?
    * a. repressor protein
     b. regulatory enzyme
     c. promoter
     d. operator
     e. transcriber

E 68. A repressor protein binds with
     a. messenger RNA.
    * b. the operator.
     c. the regulator.
     d. a product.
     e. a substrate.

D 69. Genes located in different regions of the body during embryonic development may
     a. be turned on and off.
     b. never be turned on.
     c. be turned on and left on.
     d. be activated for only a short time in one cell and a long time in another cell.
    * e. all of these

M 70. Which of the following terms refers to the processes by which cells with identical genotypes become structurally and functionally distinct from one another?
     a. metamorphosis
     b. metastasis
     c. cleavage
    * d. differentiation
     e. induction

M 71. Homeotic genes are generally in control of
     a. X chromosome inactivation.
    * b. formation of organs and tissues.
     c. hormone synthesis.
     d. dosage compensation.
     e. all of these

M 72. In mammals, X chromosome inactivation results in
   a. a total shut down of both female X chromosomes.
   b. only the shut down of the X chromosome derived from the father.
   c. only the shut down of the X chromosome derived from the mother.
* d. the shut down of either the X from the father or the X from the mother.
   e. death of the female.

M 73. A normal mammalian female
* a. usually has one Barr body.
   b. is a mosaic for the X-linked traits she inherits.
   c. uses the paternal X chromosome for a Barr body.
   d. uses the maternal X chromosome for a Barr body.
   e. always has one Barr body and is a mosaic for the X-linked traits she inherits.

M 74. A calico cat illustrates
   a. hybridization.
   b. dosage compensation.
* c. mosaic phenotype.
   d. environmental effects on fur color enzymes.
   e. incomplete dominance.

E 75. The mosaic effect in human females can be observed in
   a. skin color.
   b. hair color.
   c. distribution of fat cells.
* d. distribution of sweat glands.
   e. all of these

Matching Questions

D 76. Matching I. Choose the best matching element.
   1. ___ anticodon
   2. ___ rRNA
   3. ___ codon
   4. ___ ribosome
   5. ___ genetic code
   6. ___ termination
   7. ___ messenger RNA
   8. ___ polysome
   9. ___ promoters
   10. ___ transcription
   11. ___ translation
      A. brought about by one of three codons
      B. RNA-directed synthesis of polypeptide chains
      C. sites at which RNA polymerases can bind and initiate transcription
      D. binds to small subunit platform of a ribosome
      E. guided and catalyzed by RNA polymerases

   F. polypeptide chain elongation proceeds independently at each body in this cluster
   G. all of the mRNA codons
   H. a tRNA triplet opposite an amino acid
   I. complexed with protein to form ribosomes
   J. "workbenches" upon which polypeptides are assembled
   K. a set of three mRNA nucleotides

Answers: 1. H   2. I   3. K   4. J
          5. G   6. A   7. D   8. F
          9. C   10. E   11. B

M 77. Matching II. Choose the one most appropriate answer for each.
   1. ___ Barr body
   2. ___ histones
   3. ___ nonionizing radiation
   4. ___ X chromosome inactivation
   5. ___ calico cat
   6. ___ alkylating agent
   7. ___ repressor protein
      A. a condensed X chromosome
      B. methyl group can attach here, providing chemical control
      C. attaches or detaches from operator to regulate transcription
      D. can change bonding properties of thymine and cytosine
      E. an example of dosage compensation
      F. chemicals that can cause transfer of methyl groups to DNA
      G. mosaic effect arising from random X chromosome inactivation

Answers: 1. A   2. B   3. D   4. E
          5. G   6. F   7. C

Classification Questions

Answer questions 78–82 in reference to the five RNA codons listed below.

    a. AUG
    b. UAA
    c. UUU
    d. UUA
    e. AAA

D   **78.** This codon terminates a coding region.

D   **79.** The anticodon AAA would pair with this codon.

M   **80.** A single mutation involving the second letter of codon AUA would convert it to this codon.

D   **81.** A DNA codon of ATT would be complementary to this RNA codon.

D   **82.** This codon codes for an amino acid and indicates the beginning of a coding region.

Answers: 78. b   79. c   80. e

            81. b   82. a

Answer questions 83–87 in reference to the five items of gene regulation listed below:

    a. lac operon
    b. operator
    c. promoter
    d. lactose
    e. repressor

M   **83.** This item contains promotor, operator, and three genes specifying enzymes.

D   **84.** A repressor protein can shut down transcription by binding to this item.

M   **85.** A type of regulatory protein that can prevent transcription.

D   **86.** When the repressor is inactivated, RNA polymerase can bind to this item and allow transcription to occur.

D   **87.** A molecule that can activate the lac operon is represented by this item.

Answers: 83. a   84. b   85. e

            86. c   87. d

Selecting the Exception

D   **88.** Four of the five answers listed below are steps in the process of transcription. Select the exception.
    a. cap put on one end
    b. introns snipped out
*   c. action by DNA polymerase
    d. poly-A tail placed on one end
    e. exons spliced together

D   **89.** Four of the five answers listed below are related pairings. Select the exception.
    a. double-stranded DNA—messenger RNA
    b. purine—pyrimidine
    c. codon—anticodon
    d. small subunit—large subunit
*   e. promoter—terminator

D   **90.** Four of the five answers listed below are chromosomal abnormalities. Select the exception.
    a. translocation
*   b. elongation
    c. duplication
    d. deletion
    e. inversion

D   **91.** Four of the five answers listed below are components of a nucleotide. Select the exception.
    a. pentose sugar
*   b. amino acid
    c. pyrimidine
    d. phosphate group
    e. purine

D   **92.** Four of the five answers listed below are related by a common number. Select the exception.
    a. number of nucleotides in a codon
    b. number of building blocks (parts) in a nucleotide
    c. number of stop codons
*   d. number of types of DNA
    e. number of types of RNA

D   **93.** Three of the four answers listed below are steps in translation. Select the exception.
    a. initiation
*   b. replication
    c. chain elongation
    d. termination

D   **94.** Four of the five answers listed below are features of the lactose operon. Select the exception.
    a. regulator
*   b. terminator
    c. operator
    d. promoter
    e. gene that produces enzymes

Labeling

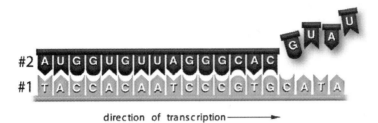

direction of transcription ———————►

#2 AUGGUGUUAGGGCACGUAU

E **95.** In this depiction of transcription, strand # _?_ is _?_ because it _?_.
   a. 1; RNA; is single-stranded.
* b. 2; RNA; contains uracil.
   c. 2; RNA; contains thymine.
   d. 1; RNA; has no uracil (U).
   e. 2; DNA; contains adenine (A).

E **96.** The start codon of RNA is
   a. TAC.
   b. ATA.
   c. UAU.
   d. GUG.
* e. AUG.

E **97.** If the fourth base from the left (G) in RNA were deleted, what would the new fourth codon be?
   a. GGG.
* b. GGC.
   c. UGU.
   d. UAU.
   e. UUA.

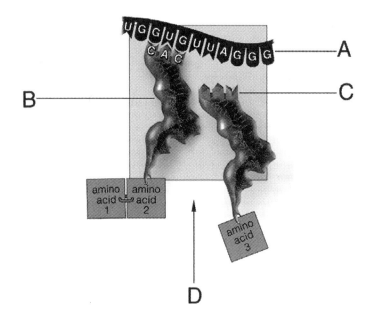

E   **98.**   Messenger RNA is indicated by the letter _?_ .

E   **99.**   The base sequence at letter "C" will be
　　　　　a. AAT.
　　　　　b. CCG.
　　　　　c. TTA.
　　　　　d. UUA.
　　*　　e. AAU.

E   **100.**   The joining of amino acid 2 to amino acid 3 (letter "D") will be by
　　　　　a. an ionic bond.
　　　　　b. protein linkage.
　　*　　c. a peptide bond.
　　　　　d. hydrogen linkage.
　　　　　e. a hook.

Answers:　　98. A

CHAPTER 11
STUDYING AND MANIPULATING GENOMES

Multiple-Choice Questions

A MOLECULAR TOOLKIT

M 1. Recombinant DNA technology
   a. uses bacteria to make copies of the desired product.
   b. splices DNAs together.
   c. is possible only between closely related species.
   * d. uses bacteria to make copies of the desired product and splices DNAs together.
   e. uses bacteria to make copies of the desired product, splices DNAs together, and is possible only between closely related species.

E 2. Small circular molecules of "extra" DNA in bacteria are called
   * a. plasmids.
   b. desmids.
   c. pili.
   d. F particles.
   e. transferins.

D 3. Plasmids
   a. are self-reproducing circular molecules of DNA.
   b. are sites for inserting genes for amplification.
   c. may be transferred between different species of bacteria.
   d. may confer the ability to donate genetic material when bacteria conjugate.
   * e. all of these

M 4. Formation of recombinant DNA includes _?_.
   a. host cells
   b. DNA fragments
   c. plasmid DNA with sticky ends
   d. recombinant plasmids
   * e. all of these

M 5. In order for DNA molecules to undergo recombination,
   a. they must be from the same species.
   b. their strands must separate as in replication.
   * c. they must be cut and spliced at specific nucleotide sequences.
   d. they undergo lysis.
   e. they must be identical.

E 6. Enzymes used to cut genes in recombinant DNA research are called
   a. ligases.
   * b. restriction enzymes.
   c. transcriptases.
   d. DNA polymerases.
   e. replicases.

M 7. The "natural" use of restriction enzymes by bacteria is to
   a. integrate viral DNA.
   * b. destroy viral DNA.
   c. repair "sticky ends."
   d. copy the bacterial genes.
   e. clone DNA.

D 8. Which of the following is FALSE?
   a. Gene transfer and recombination is a common occurrence in nature.
   b. The transfer of genetic material from one organism to another is dependent upon enzymes that cut and tie genes.
   c. Rather than causing lysis of bacteria, some bacteriophages may be incorporated into the bacterial genome.
   * d. The insertion of gene fragments can be accomplished only in the laboratory under artificial conditions.
   e. Once a gene has been incorporated into a bacterium, it may undergo amplification.

M 9. The fragments of chromosomes split by restriction enzymes
   a. have fused ends.
   b. have specific sequences of nucleotides.
   c. have sticky ends.
   d. form a circle.
   * e. have specific sequences of nucleotides and sticky ends.

M 10. Restriction enzymes
   * a. cut double-stranded DNA at particular nucleotide sequences.
   b. function only at "sticky ends."
   c. produce uniform lengths of DNA.
   d. function only in genetic laboratories.
   e. none of these

M 11. Which of the following enzymes joins the paired "sticky ends" of DNA fragments?
   a. reverse transcriptase
   b. restriction enzymes
   * c. DNA ligase
   d. DNA polymerase
   e. transferase

M 12. RNA can manufacture DNA via the action of
   a. DNA polymerase.
   b. RNA polymerase.
   * c. reverse transcriptase.
   d. ligase.
   e. restriction endonuclease.

D   13.   Because it has no introns, researchers prefer to use _?_ when working with human genes.
*   a.   cDNA
     b.   restricted DNA
     c.   hybridized DNA
     d.   RFLPs
     e.   viral DNA

HAYSTACKS TO NEEDLES

M   14.   A collection of cells that hosts fragments of DNA from a particular organism is called
     a.   copied DNA.
     b.   transcribed DNA.
     c.   DNA amplification.
*   d.   a gene library.
     e.   plasmid DNA.

D   15.   Probes for cloned genes use
*   a.   complementary nucleotide sequences labeled with radioactive isotopes.
     b.   certain media with specific antibodies.
     c.   specific enzymes.
     d.   certain bacteria sensitive to the genes.
     e.   all of these

D   16.   Multiple copies of DNA can be produced by
     a.   cloning a DNA library.
     b.   genetic amplification.
     c.   the use of reverse transcriptase.
     d.   the action of DNA polymerase.
*   e.   all of these

E   17.   Which of the following methods of DNA amplification does NOT require cloning?
     a.   reverse transcription
*   b.   polymerase chain reaction
     c.   cloned DNA
     d.   reverse transcription and polymerase chain reaction
     e.   polymerase chain reaction and cloned DNA

D   18.   For polymerase chain reaction to occur,
     a   isolated DNA molecules must be primed.
     b.   all DNA fragments must be identical.
     c.   the DNA must be separated into single strands.
     d.   a sticky end must be available for the ligase enzyme to function.
*   e.   isolated DNA molecules must be primed and the DNA must be separated into single strands.

M   19.   The method used to produce single strands of DNA
     a.   is known as amplification.
*   b.   involves heating a solution of DNA.
     c.   uses restriction enzymes.
     d.   isolates DNA molecules from the nucleus.
     e.   requires DNA ligase.

DNA SEQUENCING

M   20.   The DNA fragments produced by automated DNA sequencing are identified using
     a.   radioactive probes.
*   b.   laser beams.
     c.   ultracentrifugation.
     d.   electron microscopy.
     e.   restriction enzymes.

E   21.   The separation of DNA fragments on the basis of size as they move through a gelatin medium is called
     a.   probing.
*   b.   gel electrophoresis.
     c.   ultracentrifugation.
     d.   electron transfer.
     e.   enzyme digestion.

FIRST JUST FINGERPRINTS, NOW DNA FINGERPRINTS

M   22.   Separation of DNA fragments by gel electrophoresis
     a.   requires priming.
     b.   is controlled by the length of the fragment.
     c.   provide a banding pattern.
     d.   is the basis for a DNA fingerprint.
*   e.   All are correct except "requires priming."

D   23.   DNA fingerprinting is based on the slight differences in _?_ that occur in the human genome.
     a.   sex chromosomes
     b.   base pairings
*   c.   tandem repeats
     d.   blood and semen DNA
     e.   bonding of DNA to RNA

TINKERING WITH THE MOLECULES OF LIFE

M   24.   In 1972, Paul Berg and his associates were able to
     a.   determine the difference between DNA from a human and a chimp.
*   b.   recombine DNA from different species.
     c.   sequence DNA using a robot.
     d.   make artificial DNA.
     e.   create life in a test tube.

E   25.   The goal of the Human Genome Project was to
     a.   determine the number of chromosomes in humans.
     b.   make recombinant DNA from human chromosomes.
*   c.   determine the location of genes on human chromosomes.
     d.   explore the use of nonhuman DNA to cure human diseases.
     e.   confirm the number of human genes as between 50,000 and 100,000.

D 26. The Human Genome Project sought to
* a. identify the nucleotide sequence of all human genes.
b. develop a complete DNA library for a human gene.
c. develop genetic markers for all genetic diseases.
d. catalog all the varieties of human alleles.
e. identify all humans that possess genetic defects.

M 27. Gene therapy
a. has not yet been used successfully with mammals.
b. is a surgical technique that separates chromosomes that have failed to segregate properly during meiosis II.
c. has been used successfully to treat victims of Huntington's disorder by removing the dominant damaging autosomal allele and replacing it with a harmless one.
* d. replaces defective alleles with normal ones.
e. all of these

PRACTICAL GENETICS

E 28. One of the first successful, large-scale applications of genetic engineering was the commercial production of
a. clotting factor.
* b. insulin.
c. hemoglobin.
d. strawberries.
e. carrot seedlings.

M 29. When the gene for rat somatotropin was injected into mouse eggs,
a. nothing happened because these two animals are different species.
b. the mice grew up as dwarfs.
c. the gene integrated into the mice chromosomes but did not express itself.
* d. the mice grew up to be larger than normal.
e. federal authorities immediately prohibited any further such research.

D 30. The term "biotech barnyards" most likely refers to
* a. the production of human products by farm animals.
b. the development of new species of farm animals.
c. the increase of milk, egg, wool, etc., production.
d. ultramodern methods of rearing more animals on less feed.
e. creation of transgenic animals that can produce several products.

WEIGHING THE BENEFITS AND RISKS

D 31. The transferring of an organ from one species to another is called
* a. xenotransplantation.
b. eugenics.
c. illegal.
d. genomics.
e. cloning.

Classification Questions

Answer questions 32–36 in reference to the five items listed below.
a. restriction enzymes
b. recombinants
c. plasmids
d. clones
e. restriction sites

M 32. Bacterial populations containing thousands or millions of identical copies of one to several genes are these.

D 33. When one uses the techniques of genetic engineering to move a novel or foreign piece of DNA into the DNA of an organism, these new DNA regions are known as _?_.

M 34. The pieces of DNA that are moved by a genetic engineer from one organism to another are first incorporated into these.

E 35. The sole function of these is to cut apart foreign DNA molecules.

D 36. These may contain all of the other entities listed.

Answers: 32. d 33. b 34. c

35. a 36. d

Answer questions 37–41 in reference to the four items listed below.
a. cDNA
b. a restriction enzyme
c. reverse transcriptase
d. a DNA library

M 37. This is from a viral source and catalyzes reactions to construct DNA strands from mRNA.

M 38. Any DNA copied from mRNA transcripts is known as this.

M 39. A protein whose only function is to cut apart foreign DNA entering a cell is this.

M 40. Collections of DNA fragments produced by restriction enzymes and incorporated into cloning vectors is this.

M 41. A strand assembled by reverse transcriptase.

Answers: 37. c 38. a 39. b

40. d 41. a

Selecting the Exception

M   **42.**   Four of the five answers listed below are aspects of the "molecular toolkit." Select the exception.
    a. ligase
    b. reverse transcriptase
    c. restriction
*   d. replicase
    e. DNA polymerase

M   **43.**   Four of the five statements listed below are true of cloned DNA. Select the exception.
    a. The plasmid used is the cloning vector.
    b. Identical copies are produced.
*   c. Cloned DNA is produced by reverse transcriptase.
    d. Multiple copies are produced.
    e. Cloned DNA is manufactured in bacteria cells.

M   **44.**   Four of the five answers listed below are aspects of the process known as gene splicing. Select the exception.
    a. cloning vector
    b. restriction enzymes
    c. sticky ends
    d. exposed base pairs
*   e. crossing over

CHAPTER 12
PROCESSES OF EVOLUTION

Multiple-Choice Questions

EARLY BELIEFS, CONFOUNDING DISCOVERIES

E **1.** The great Chain of Being developed from ideas
     * a. of Europeans.
       b. written down rather recently.
       c. of Americans only.
       d. told by primitive tribes.
       e. derived from the scientific method.

D **2.** People embracing the idea of the great Chain of Being did NOT believe in which of the following?
       a. Spiritual beings were a part of the Chain.
       b. Life forms were designed and forged at the same time at one center of creation..
     * c. Organisms could appear, disappear, or move up and down the Chain.
       d. Each species was "fixed" at creation.
       e. All the "links" would eventually be discovered.

M **3.** Scientists began to question the perfection of the Chain of Being because of
       a. the discovery of new organisms in new parts of the world.
       b. the presence of vestigial structures in some organisms.
       c. the existence of fossil forms.
       d. similarities in the structures found in different forms of life.
     * e. all of these

M **4.** The distribution of different organisms over the surface of the Earth
     * a. offers evidence for evolution.
       b. provides evidence for a single center of evolution.
       c. appears to be simply a matter of chance.
       d. is not affected by biogeographical features.
       e. is primarily the result of human activities.

E **5.** The study of the patterns in the geographic distribution of plants and animals around the world is
       a. diversity.
     * b. biogeography.
       c. ecology.
       d. natural history.
       e. environmentalism.

M **6.** The forelimbs of early mammals were similar in all features EXCEPT
       a. embryonic origin.
       b. position on the body.
       c. number.
     * d. function.
       e. composition.

M **7.** Ancient whales as seen from fossil evidence have
       a. wings.
       b. one pair of internal legs.
       c. two pairs of internal legs.
     * d. ankle bones.
       e. two pairs of vestigial legs that are seen externally.

E **8.** The oldest fossils
       a. demonstrate the widest distribution.
       b. represent the most highly evolved plants and animals.
     * c. are found buried deepest in the ground.
       d. are found in Africa.
       e. are primitive marine vertebrates.

M **9.** Fossils
     * a. are found in underground rock layers.
       b. are distributed underground, with the oldest forms near the top.
       c. have more complex structure the deeper they are buried.
       d. are the same throughout the world no matter where they are found.
       e. that are most like living organisms are found deepest in the ground.

M **10.** Fossils found in the lowest geological strata are generally the most
       a. advanced.
       b. complex.
     * c. primitive.
       d. widespread.
       e. specialized.

M **11.** The theory of catastrophism
       a. was proposed by Buffon.
       b. indicates that a series of disasters necessitated separate acts of creation to replace species that became extinct.
       c. states that one worldwide disaster led to massive extinction and subsequent replacement by a new creation.
     * d. held that after a series of massive extinctions the world was repopulated by the survivors of existing species.
       e. has absolutely no basis in fact because extinctions just happen with no apparent patterns.

M 12. Cuvier, an anatomist and paleontologist, proposed that
       a. all present-day organisms have descended, with adaptations, from one—or possibly a few—original organisms.
    * b. the Earth's history has been marked by several periods when destruction of populations was widespread and that, after each such period, the earth was repopulated.
       c. evolutionary changes in organisms are caused by use and disuse.
       d. although evolution is responsible for all the changes that happen to species, God created the original members of each species.
       e. none of these

D 13. There is no convincing fossil evidence for which of the following?
       a. evolution
       b. extinction
       c. change
    * d. catastrophism
       e. uniformitarianism

M 14. Which of the following statements is TRUE?
       a. The fossil record supports Cuvier's theory of catastrophism.
    * b. According to the theory of catastrophism, a single time of creation had populated the entire world.
       c. According to the theory of catastrophism, new species developed out of the survivors of the catastrophes.
       d. The theory of catastrophism was based upon observable responses that organisms made to catastrophes.
       e. According to catastrophism, there were several distinct periods of creation following each catastrophe.

E 15. According to Lamarck, the characteristics of organisms changed because of
       a. chance.
    * b. an innate drive for perfection that produced acquired changes.
       c. extinction of competitors.
       d. special acts of creation.
       e. genetic mutation.

M 16. Lamarck's contribution to the theory of evolution was the concept of
       a. natural selection.
       b. catastrophism.
    * c. inheritance of acquired characteristics.
       d. mutation.
       e. geographic distribution of organisms.

D 17. Which of the following would be a modern example of Lamarckianism?
       a. A strain of houseflies resistant to insecticides emerges.
       b. Squirrels separated by a river are found to be unable to interbreed.
    * c. A son is born with a portion of his right index finger missing, the same portion cut off from his father's hand in an accident.
       d. A strain of houseflies resistant to insecticides emerges; and squirrels separated by a river are found to be unable to interbreed.
       e. A strain of houseflies resistant to insecticides emerges; squirrels separated by a river are found to be unable to interbreed; and a son is born with a portion of his right index finger missing, the same portion cut off from his father's hand in an accident.

M 18. Lamarck believed
       a. that life was created long ago in a simple state.
       b. in the inheritance of acquired characteristics.
       c. that giraffes' necks elongated in response to stretching.
       d. that environmental pressures bring about changes in organisms.
    * e. all of these

M 19. Which of the following has no part in today's concept of natural selection?
    * a. inheritance of acquired characteristics
       b. struggle for existence
       c. inherited variation
       d. overproduction of offspring
       e. survival of the best adapted

D 20. Which is NOT a part of Lamarck's theory?
       a. The environment controls and modifies traits.
       b. Characteristics acquired by organisms throughout their lifetimes are transmitted to their offspring.
       c. Organs that are used extensively tend to improve and are found in offspring, whereas those not used will diminish and are not passed on to the offspring.
    * d. Those organisms that are best adapted have a better chance to reproduce than those equipped with inferior adaptations.
       e. All of these are a part of Lamarck's theory.

M 21. Charles Darwin
       a. at first was interested in a career in medicine.
       b. studied to become a clergyman.
       c. followed his avocation as a naturalist.
    * d. all of these
       e. none of these

E 22. Darwin's mentor, who obtained a position on HMS *Beagle* for Darwin, was
       a. Alfred Wallace.
    * b. John Henslow.
       c. Jean-Baptiste Lamarck.
       d. Georges Cuvier.
       e. Charles Lyell.

D 23. The value to Darwin of Lyell's ideas on the geologic history of the Earth was the
a. evidence from fossils.
b. record of catastrophic changes that encouraged evolution.
c. confirmation of Lamarck's theories.
* d. enormous lengths of time required for geologic events.
e. proof of several sites of creation.

M 24. Which theory was helpful to Darwin in the formulation of his theory of evolution?
a. catastrophism
b. inheritance of acquired characteristics
* c. the theory of uniformity
d. continental drift
e. special creationism

E 25. Glyptodonts were fossil forms that resembled
a. ostriches.
* b. armadillos.
c. kangaroos.
d. turtles.
e. sloths.

D 26. After his return to England, Darwin pondered which of the following questions most heavily?
* a. What is the possible evidence that life evolves?
b. Does the fossil evidence support the theory of uniformity?
c. Are the extinct and living armadillos the same species?
d. Did Galápagos finches have a common mainland ancestor?
e. Will natural selection work in England?

E 27. Thomas Malthus proposed that
a. the food supply multiplied faster than the population.
* b. the population multiplied faster than the food supply.
c. the food supply and population multiplied at the same rate.
d. artificial selection was the key to evolution.
e. natural selection was the key to evolution.

M 28. The place Darwin visited on his trip around the world that had the greatest impact on his thinking was
a. the Canary Islands.
b. Africa.
c. the Hawaiian Islands.
* d. the Galápagos Islands.
e. Brazil.

M 29. The most important evidence that Darwin used to develop his theory of natural selection came from
a. the Argentine pampas.
b. his boyhood neighborhood in England.
* c. the Galápagos Islands.
d. Australia and New Zealand.
e. South America.

M 30. Galápagos finches are examples of
a. scavengers.
b. morphological isolation.
* c. adaptation.
d. punctuated equilibrium.
e. catastrophism.

E 31. Darwin's finches were found on the _?_ Islands.
* a. Galápagos
b. Canary
c. Philippine
d. Hawaiian
e. Aleutian

E 32. The feature of Darwin's finches that underwent variation was the
a. feet.
* b. beaks.
c. feathers.
d. structure of the eggs.
e. all of these

D 33. Darwin's theory of evolution
a. was the first theory to propose natural selection.
b. is no longer accepted by biologists.
* c. failed to account for the sources of variability.
d. did not account for differential survival and reproduction.
e. was based upon the chances of mutation occurring.

D 34. Which of the following was NOT one of Darwin's observations?
* a. Most individuals have an equal chance to survive and reproduce.
b. Changes in organisms were gradual and took place over long periods of time.
c. Members of the same species may exhibit considerable variation.
d. Some characteristics are heritable and passed on to offspring.
e. Some characteristics afford their possessor a better chance of survival.

D 35. Natural selection operates to produce changes in
a. individuals.
* b. populations.
c. races.
d. phyla.
e. animals only.

D 36. Which of the following is NOT a factor involved in the theory of evolution?
a. All organisms reproduce beyond the limits of the environment that supports them.
* b. Food supplies keep pace with the growth of populations feeding upon them.
c. Populations of organisms tend to remain relatively stable through time.
d. There is much variation in the characteristics of organisms making up a population.
e. Some traits are more adaptive than others.

D   37.   One part of Darwin's theory is that individuals with certain traits have an increased competitive edge. The source of these traits is
        a.   adaptation to the stress.
        b.   development over a lifetime.
    *   c.   inherited at birth.
        d.   mutation after birth.
        e.   all of these

M   38.   The operation of natural selection depends upon the fact that
        a.   the strong always survive, whereas the weak always die.
    *   b.   some individuals have a better chance to produce more offspring.
        c.   mutations are always harmful.
        d.   acquired characteristics are inherited.
        e.   reproduction of all members of a species is virtually the same.

M   39.   Which of the following is NOT a component of Darwin's principle of natural selection?
    *   a.   New alleles are constantly produced through mutation.
        b.   Populations exhibit great variation.
        c.   Organisms produce more offspring than can be sustained by the environment.
        d.   Over time, adaptive phenotypes increase in frequency within a population.
        e.   Natural populations have an inherent reproductive capacity.

D   40.   Natural selection
        a.   actively combs through a population searching for the best combination of genes.
        b.   is a haphazard process based upon chance.
        c.   involves differential survival.
        d.   involves differential reproduction.
    *   e.   involves both differential survival and differential reproduction.

E   41.   The person credited with being the codiscoverer of evolution was
    *   a.   Alfred Wallace.
        b.   Charles Lyell.
        c.   Thomas Malthus.
        d.   James Hutton.
        e.   John Henslow.

THE NATURE OF ADAPTATION

D   42.   Long-term adaptation
        a.   is inheritable.
        b.   includes aspects of form and function.
        c.   is the outcome of natural selection.
        d.   improves the odds of survival and reproducing.
    *   e.   includes all of these.

M   43.   The South American tomato is useful in hybridization because of its
        a.   large, leafy surfaces.
    *   b.   tolerance to salty water in soil.
        c.   ability to endure extreme heat.
        d.   drought resistance.
        e.   all of these

M   44.   Llamas can thrive at the high Andean altitudes because they
        a.   have heavy fur coats.
        b.   are very sure-footed on the steep slopes.
    *   c.   can bind oxygen to their hemoglobin better.
        d.   make more red blood cells per milliliter.
        e.   drink little water.

INDIVIDUALS DON'T EVOLVE, POPULATIONS DO

M   45.   Which of the following is a group of individuals of the same species for which there are no restrictions to random mating among its members?
        a.   individual
        b.   species
    *   c.   population
        d.   polyploid
        e.   all of these

D   46.   Members of a population would be LEAST likely to have which of the following in common?
        a.   phenotype
        b.   morphological traits
    *   c.   genotype
        d.   physiological traits
        e.   behavioral traits

D   47.   Only identical twins have the same
    *   a.   genotype.
        b.   phenotype.
        c.   traits.
        d.   genotype and phenotype.
        e.   genotype, phenotype, and traits.

D   48.   Which of these statements is TRUE?
        a.   Environment can readily alter some genotypes.
    *   b.   Genotype is seen in phenotype.
        c.   Genetic variation is easier seen than phenotypic variation.
        d.   Variation dies with individuals.
        e.   Phenotype is seen physically in the genotype.

D   49.   Which of the following is considered a USUAL cause of variation in sexually reproducing organisms?
        a.   changes in chromosome number
        b.   mutation
        c.   independent assortment of chromosomes
        d.   crossing over
    *   e.   both independent assortment of chromosomes and crossing over

D 50. Genetic variation is the result of all EXCEPT which one of the following?
a. alteration in chromosome structure or number
b. gene mutation
c. independent assortment
* d. the role of environment in controlling genetic expression
e. crossing over and genetic recombination

M 51. Microevolution is the result of
a. gene flow.
b. genetic drift.
c. mutation.
d. natural selection.
* e. all of these

M 52. New combinations of genes may be produced by
a. immigration.
b. mutation.
c. crossing over.
d. sexual reproduction.
* e. all of these

M 53. Introduction of previously nonexistent genes into a population may be accomplished by
a. nonrandom mating.
* b. mutation.
c. sexual recombination.
d. the founder effect.
e. the bottleneck effect.

M 54. Which of the following is NOT a major process of microevolution?
a. mutation
* b. divergence
c. genetic drift
d. gene flow
e. natural selection

E 55. New alleles arise by
* a. mutation.
b. migration.
c. genetic drift.
d. random mating.
e. independent assortment.

E 56. New genes arise from
a. genetic drift.
* b. mutation.
c. gene flow.
d. recombination.
e. natural selection.

D 57. New alleles that appear by mutation
a. are inherently disadvantageous to their bearers.
b. are seldom advantageous or disadvantageous in themselves.
c. either have or lack survival value only in the context of their environment.
* d. are seldom advantageous or disadvantageous in themselves and either have or lack survival value only in the context of their environment.
e. are inherently disadvantageous to their bearers and are seldom advantageous or disadvantageous in themselves.

E 58. Which of the following is a source of new alleles within a population?
a. genetic recombination
b. meiosis
* c. mutation
d. genetic drift
e. gene flow

M 59. Whether a mutation is ultimately considered harmful, neutral, or lethal is often determined by
a. phenotype.
b. the will of the individual.
c. the Hardy-Weinberg formula.
* d. environment.
e. fate.

WHEN IS A POPULATION *NOT* EVOLVING?

M 60. Which statement is NOT true?
a. Migration leads to genetic variation.
* b. Dominant genes always occur more frequently in a population than recessive genes.
c. Nonrandom mating may result in changes in gene frequency.
d. The Hardy-Weinberg law applies to large, stable populations.
e. Crossing over increases variation.

E 61. The Hardy-Weinberg rule is valuable for the calculation of changes in
a. population size.
b. speciation.
* c. allele frequencies.
d. mutation.
e. dimorphism.

E 62. Which of the following is an example of random mating?
a. The largest and strongest males develop a harem.
b. A female bird will mate only with males that perform the best courtship displays.
c. Members of a sorority usually marry fraternity brothers.
* d. Some males mate with any females they encounter.
e. Cousins marry cousins.

D   63. The genetic equilibrium of a population can be upset
          by all EXCEPT which of the following?
          a. mutations
          b. migration
      *   c. random mating
          d. genetic drift
          e. small population

D   64. If the frequency of a recessive gene in a population
          under genetic equilibrium is 40 percent, in the next
          generation the frequency of that gene would be
          a. 20 percent.
      *   b. 40 percent.
          c. 80 percent.
          d. 100 percent.
          e. dependent upon other factors, so it cannot be
              predicted but must instead be reevaluated each
              generation.

D   65. If the frequency of a recessive allele is 36 percent, the
          frequency of the dominant allele would be what
          percent?
          a. 5
          b. 8
          c. 25
          d. 48
      *   e. 64

M   66. In the Hardy-Weinberg equation, the term "q^2" refers
          to the frequency of
          a. a recessive allele of a given locus.
      *   b. the homozygous recessive genotype at a given
              locus.
          c. recessive alleles in a population.
          d. heterozygotes in a population.
          e. dominant alleles.

D   67. If the frequency of the recessive allele is 30 percent,
          the frequency of the heterozygous carrier would be
          what percent?
      *   a. 42
          b. 9
          c. 27
          d. 60
          e. 80

D   68. In a population that is in Hardy-Weinberg equilibrium,
          the frequency of the homozygous recessive genotype
          is 0.49. The percentage of the population that is
          heterozygous is
          a. 51.
          b. 49.
      *   c. 42.
          d. 7.
          e. 3.

D   69. Of 400 people who dwell on a Pacific island, 16 are
          homozygous recessive for a trait that has only two
          different types of alleles in the population. The
          number of heterozygous people is
          a. 256.
          b. 32.
          c. 64.
      *   d. 128.
          e. 384.

NATURAL SELECTION REVISITED

M   70. Directional selection occurs when
          a. the environment controls which organisms will
              survive.
          b. humans determine which organisms will survive.
          c. the extremes of the population have a lesser
              chance to survive.
          d. the extremes of the population have a better
              chance to survive.
      *   e. the organisms on one extreme of the population
              have a better chance to survive than those on the
              other extreme.

M   71. An insect that exhibits resistance to a pesticide
          a. developed the resistance in response to the
              pesticide.
          b. mutated when exposed to the pesticide.
      *   c. inherited genes that made it resistant to the
              pesticide.
          d. none of these
          e. all of these

M   72. When DDT was first introduced, insects were very
          susceptible to it. The development of resistance to
          DDT by insects was the result of
          a. special creation.
      *   b. natural selection of forms that expressed genes for
              resistance.
          c. the high biotic potential of insects.
          d. a naturally occurring example of inheritance of
              acquired characteristics.
          e. mutation induced by DDT.

M   73. Stabilizing selection occurs when
          a. the environment controls which organisms will
              survive.
          b. humans determine which organisms will survive.
      *   c. the extremes of the population have a lesser
              chance to survive.
          d. the extremes of the population have a better
              chance to survive.
          e. the organisms on one extreme of the population
              have a better chance to survive than those on the
              other extreme.

M 74. In an unchanging environment, selection in a well-adapted population is
a. directional.
b. disruptive.
* c. stabilizing.
d. absent.
e. unpredictable.

E 75. In a certain bird species, clutch size (the number of eggs laid by a female in one breeding season) ranges from four to eight, and the most frequent clutch size is six. This phenomenon is an example of
a. sexual selection.
* b. stabilizing selection.
c. disruptive selection.
d. directional selection.
e. mutation.

M 76. The famous "bell-shaped curve" that usually results when test scores are plotted against number of students is an example of what type of selection?
a. disruptive
* b. stabilizing
c. divergent
d. variable
e. directional

M 77. In stabilizing selection,
a. differential survival and reproduction favor the extremes of the population.
b. humans are the chief factor controlling which organisms survive and reproduce.
* c. the most common type of organisms survive and reproduce.
d. the characteristics of a population move in one direction or another through time.
e. variability is encouraged in a population and unusual forms are more common.

MAINTAINING VARIATION IN A POPULATION

D 78. Male mallards have had emerald green head feathers and wings with metallic blue patches for hundreds of years, whereas female mallards have been drab, brown-feathered ducks. This phenotypic situation suggests that mallards may be an example of
a. directional selection.
b. polyploidy.
c. allopatric speciation.
* d. disruptive selection.
e. sexual isolation.

D 79. Balanced polymorphism is a type of
a. disruptive selection.
b. sexual selection.
c. directional selection.
d. reproductive isolation.
* e. stabilizing selection.

D 80. The persistence of the sickle-cell anemia allele in the African population is the result of
a. a high rate of mutation of the normal allele to the sickle-cell anemia allele.
* b. the advantage of the heterozygous form over the homozygous forms.
c. nonrandom mating.
d. a decline in the occurrence of malaria in Africa.
e. interbreeding.

M 81. The Hb^S allele (sickle cell) occurs at a higher frequency in Africa than it does in the United States because
a. it is a dominant allele in Africa and a recessive one in the United States.
b. genetic recombination occurs at different rates in different human populations.
* c. natural selection favors heterozygotes in Africa but favors homozygous normal individuals in the United States.
d. the African population is descended from a small group of individuals who possessed the allele at a high frequency.
e. persons with the allele are not allowed to immigrate.

E 82. The difference in the appearance of the male and the female is known as
a. polymorphism.
* b. sexual dimorphism.
c. the dioecious condition.
d. the monoecious condition.
e. a primary sexual characteristic.

E 83. Male northern sea lions are nearly twice the size of females because
a. males live longer than females.
b. predators of the sea lions favor males.
* c. healthy and vigorous males compete to mate with females.
d. each male must protect the one female with which he mates.
e. females outlive males.

M 84. Sexual dimorphism has arisen as a result of
a. stabilizing selection.
b. kin selection.
* c. sexual selection.
d. directional selection.
e. disruptive selection.

D 85. For most species that exhibit sexual dimorphism, the selection of a mate is the responsibility of the
a. male.
b. parents.
* c. female.
d. larger individual, no matter the species.
e. more colorful individual.

GENETIC DRIFT—THE CHANCE CHANGES

M 86. The evolutionary force that operates primarily through chance is
      a. natural selection.
  * b. genetic drift.
      c. isolation.
      d. mating preference.
      e. sexual dimorphism.

M 87. Genetic drift
      a. may lead to a loss of variation in a population.
      b. requires small populations.
      c. occurs in populations with the founder effect.
      d. may occur when conditions produce the bottleneck effect.
  * e. all of these

M 88. The influence of genetic drift on allele frequencies increases as
      a. gene flow increases.
  * b. population size decreases.
      c. mutation rate decreases.
      d. the number of heterozygous loci increases.
      e. as the population ages.

M 89. The introduction of a small population onto an island that results in a limited gene pool for a population is an example of
      a. the Hardy-Weinberg law.
      b. genetic drift.
      c. the bottleneck effect.
  * d. the founder principle.
      e. the effect of genetic isolation.

D 90. The biological impact of the "founder effect" is based upon
      a. absence of gene flow.
      b. chance.
      c. migration.
      d. reduction of genetic diversity.
  * e. all of these

M 91. The sharp reduction of the gene pool and the numbers of a population through a severe epidemic is an example of
      a. natural selection.
      b. genetic isolation.
  * c. the bottleneck effect.
      d. the founder principle.
      e. all of these

D 92. If you sampled the genetic characteristics of a large population and found that of the 50 loci analyzed there was very little if any variation, the most likely explanation would be that
      a. a uniform environment selected for these alleles.
      b. there has been a lack of migration and the genetic equilibrium stabilized the population.
      c. strong selection pressures eliminated alternative alleles.
  * d. a bottleneck effect may have occurred in the past to reduce the variability in the population.
      e. a combination of low mutation rates and differential sexual selection produced these results.

M 93. When a population goes through a bottleneck,
  * a. genetic drift is pronounced.
      b. mutation rates increase.
      c. extinction rates decrease.
      d. natural selection decreases in intensity.
      e. population numbers increase.

M 94. When all of the individuals of a population have become homozygous for one allele only at a locus, we say that _?_ has occurred.
  * a. fixation
      b. extinction
      c. mutation
      d. evolution
      e. drift

GENE FLOW—KEEPING POPULATIONS ALIKE

M 95. Gene flow
      a. makes adjacent populations more similar.
      b. acts to prevent speciation.
      c. is a microevolutionary process.
      d. counteracts the effects of mutation, natural selection, and genetic drift.
  * e. all of these

M 96. Gene flow
  * a. keeps separated populations genetically similar.
      b. speeds up the divergence of two populations.
      c. increases the genetic variation between populations.
      d. is promoted by isolating mechanisms.
      e. increases the likelihood of natural selection.

D 97. What accounts for the fact that polydactylism is prevalent and Tay-Sachs disease virtually absent in one human population in the United States while Tay-Sachs disease is prevalent and polydactylism virtually absent in another?
   a. Natural selection has promoted these differences because humans live in many different environments.
   b. Mutation rates differ among different loci.
 * c. There is little gene flow between the two populations.
   d. The populations are small, and therefore genetic drift is a major factor in the determination of allele frequencies.
   e. The two populations have a high inbreeding rate.

D 98. A general warming trend in northern climates might decrease the ice bridges that usually form between islands in the upper Great Lakes. Because animals travel across these bridges, this warming could result in
 * a. decreased gene flow.
   b. more genetic heterogeneity.
   c. healthier populations of animals.
   d. more mutations.
   e. all of these

Matching Questions

M 99. Matching I. Choose the most appropriate answer for each.
   1. ___ Cuvier
   2. ___ Darwin
   3. ___ Lamarck
   4. ___ Lyell
   5. ___ Malthus
      A. wrote Principles of Geology
      B. developed the theory of catastrophism
      C. believed that giraffes have long necks because their short-necked ancestors stretched their necks and passed this change on to their offspring
      D. was a naturalist who sailed on the *Beagle* and studied finches
      E. wrote Essay on the Principle of Population

Answers: 1. B   2. D   3. C   4. A
           5. E

D 100. Matching II. Choose the most appropriate letter for each.
   1. ___ $p + q$
   2. ___ species
   3. ___ directional selection
   4. ___ gene pool
   5. ___ balanced polymorphism
   6. ___ p^2
   7. ___ $2pq$
   8. ___ genetic equilibrium
   9. ___ q^2
      A. a reference point that implies stability of gene frequencies through generations
      B. encompasses all of those actually or potentially interbreeding populations that are reproductively isolated from other such groups
      C. the genes of an entire population
      D. the frequency of homozygous dominants in a population
      E. the frequencies of dominant and recessive alleles in a population
      F. the frequency of heterozygotes in a population
      G. the frequency of homozygous recessives in a population
      H. HbA and HbS in regions where malaria is found
      I. pesticide-resistant pests

Answers: 1. E   2. B   3. I   4. C
           5. H   6. D   7. F   8. A
           9. G

Classification Questions

Answer questions 101–104 in reference to the four evolutionary processes listed below.

    a. mutation
    b. gene flow
    c. genetic drift
    d. natural selection

M **101.** This is most likely to lead to the loss of genetic variation in a small population.

E **102.** This process produces new genetic variation within a species.

M **103.** This process can rapidly offset the effects of genetic isolation when two populations come into secondary contact.

D **104.** The reduced contribution of one phenotype in comparison to another to the next generation is an example of this.

Answers: 101. c   102. a   103. b

           104. d

Selecting the Exception

M **105.** Four of the five people listed below were biologists. Select the exception.
    a. Lamarck
*   b. Lyell
    c. Wallace
    d. Cuvier
    e. Darwin

M **106.** Four of the five answers below support the concept of evolution. Select the exception.
    a. biogeography
    b. fossils
    c. comparative anatomy
    d. natural selection
*   e. catastrophism

M **107.** Four of the five answers below are true of Darwin's voyage. Select the exception.
    a. It lasted five years.
*   b. He wrote the final draft of a book on species.
    c. He sailed aboard the HMS *Beagle.*
    d. He embarked from England when he was 22 years old.
    e. He visited the mainland of South America.

D **108.** Four of the five answers below are consistent with Darwin's theory of natural selection. Select the exception.
    a. All populations tend to overproduce.
    b. Some members are more adapted to the rigors of competition.
    c. Limited resources put limits on population growth.
*   d. Variation in individuals is not inheritable.
    e. Traits appear and disappear.

M **109.** Four of the five answers listed below are sources of variation in a population. Select the exception.
    a. mutation
    b. sexual reproduction
    c. crossing over
    d. independent assortment
*   e. law of dominance

D **110.** Four of the five answers listed below are characteristics of an unchanging, nonevolving population. Select the exception.
    a. random mating
    b. no mutation
*   c. differential survival
    d. no migration or gene flow
    e. infinitely large population

E **111.** Four of the five answers listed below are characteristics of mutations. Select the exception.
*   a. predictable
    b. lethal or beneficial
    c. random
    d. effects depend upon environment
    e. heritable

D **112.** Four of the five answers listed below are portions of the theory of natural selection. Select the exception.
    a. Variation is heritable.
    b. Heritable traits vary in adaptability.
    c. More organisms are produced than can survive.
*   d. The largest and strongest always contribute more genes to the next generation.
    e. Natural selection is the result of differential reproduction.

M **113.** Four of the five answers listed below are types of selection exhibited by nature. Select the exception.
*   a. artificial
    b. disruptive
    c. stabilizing
    d. directional
    e. sexual

D **114.** Four of the five answers listed below can upset genetic equilibrium. Select the exception.
*   a. interbreeding
    b. genetic drift
    c. mutation
    d. natural selection
    e. gene flow

Labeling

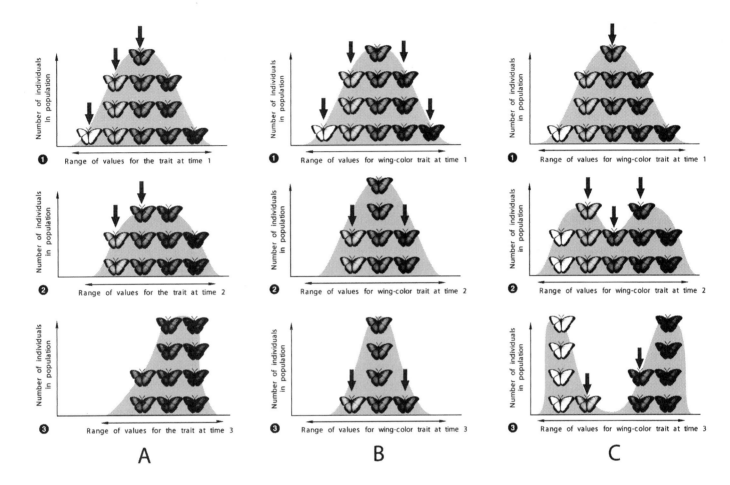

E **115.** "Stabilizing selection" is depicted in the diagram labeled with the letter _?_.

E **116.** The illustration designated with the letter "A" shows selection against

   * a. light-colored butterflies.
     b. tasty butterflies.
     c. bad-tasting butterflies.
     d. noncompetition.
     e. dark-colored butterflies.

E **117.** If the results of a biology exam showed a "bimodal curve," it would resemble the illustration at letter _?_.

E **118.** "Directional selection" is depicted in the diagram labeled with the letter _?_.

Answers: 115. B   117. C   118. A

CHAPTER 13
EVOLUTIONARY PATTERNS, RATES, AND TRENDS

Multiple-Choice Questions

FOSSILS—EVIDENCE OF ANCIENT LIFE

M **1.** The fossil record is incomplete because
    a. very few organisms were preserved as fossils.
    b. organisms tend to decay before becoming a fossil.
    c. animals with hard parts are preserved more easily.
    d. geologic processes may destroy fossils.
  * e. all of these

E **2.** Fossils would include
    a. skeletons.
    b. shells.
    c. seeds.
    d. tracks.
  * e. all of these

M **3.** Which of the following organisms would you most likely expect to find preserved as a fossil?
    a. a jellyfish
  * b. a shelled arthropod such as a trilobite
    c. an earthworm
    d. a nematode
    e. a protistan such as an amoeba

M **4.** Which of the following statements is TRUE?
    a. Many fossils have not been discovered, whereas others may have been destroyed.
    b. Some types of organisms are more likely to be preserved than others.
    c. Some environments are more conducive to preserving.
    d. Many fossils have not been discovered, whereas others may have been destroyed; and some types of organisms are more likely to be preserved than others.
  * e. Many fossils have not been discovered, whereas others may have been destroyed; some types of organisms are more likely to be preserved than others; and some environments are more conducive to preserving.

M **5.** Which of the following habitats is most likely to be rich in fossils?
    a. eroding hillsides
    b. deserts
    c. polar ice caps
  * d. bed of a former shallow sea
    e. rocky plateau

DATING PIECES OF THE PUZZLE

M **6.** The geologic time scale is subdivided on the basis of
    a. the appearance of different radioactive isotopes in different strata.
    b. levels of background extinction.
  * c. periods of mass extinction.
    d. the appearance of different radioactive isotopes in different strata and levels of background extinction.
    e. the appearance of different radioactive isotopes in different strata, levels of background extinction, and periods of mass extinction.

M **7.** Macroevolution involves all EXCEPT which one of the following?
    a. the development of higher taxa
    b. periods of massive extinction at the end of geologic periods
    c. the concept of punctuated equilibrium
  * d. gradual differentiation that leads to speciation
    e. large changes

EVIDENCE FROM BIOGEOGRAPHY

E **8.** The large, ancient land mass that contained all the continents was called
    a. Laurasia.
  * b. Pangea.
    c. Glossopteris.
    d. Atlantis.
    e. all of these

D **9.** Plate tectonic theory is based on
    a. a thermal convection model, in which cool material in the Earth's mantle rises and spreads laterally beneath the crustal plates.
    b. the idea that the Earth's crust is fragmented into rigid crusts that are sinking slowly beneath crustal plates.
    c. rock stratification.
  * d. Earth's crustal movements.
    e. the ideas of catastrophism.

M **10.** The older idea that geologic processes have formed the Earth's surface by gradual, evenly repetitive change is known as
    a. the theory of catastrophism.
    b. plate tectonics.
    c. continental drift.
  * d. the theory of uniformity.
    e. the theory of relativity.

D 11. Diversity of living organisms would be increased by
    a. continental drift.
    b. the formation of Pangea.
    c. seafloor spreading.
    d. movement of Gondwana.
  * e. all but "formation of Pangea."

MORE EVIDENCE FROM COMPARATIVE MORPHOLOGY

M 12. Which of the phrases below completes the stem of the following statement INCORRECTLY? The use of comparative morphology as a demonstration of evolution
    a. assumes that the forms being compared had a common ancestor.
    b. is based upon the premise that an organism's body form is a product of evolution.
    c. can compare embryonic as well as adult structures.
  * d. can compare the life expectancies of ancestors.
    e. provides that certain developmental constraints during evolution limit the range of forms possible as adults.

M 13. The convergence in external morphology of bats, birds, and insects is attributed to
    a. reduced genetic variability in these groups.
  * b. selection pressures that are common to these groups.
    c. reproductive isolation of these groups.
    d. identical genes in all three groups.
    e. use and disuse of the limbs.

M 14. Which of the following serve as examples of morphological convergence?
  * a. bats, birds, and insects
    b. panthers and tigers
    c. apes and monkeys
    d. sharks, skates, and rays
    e. mice, rats, and gerbils

M 15. Evolutionary relationships, when determined solely by the study of comparative morphology, may be due to
    a. morphological divergence.
  * b. morphological convergence.
    c. adaptive radiation.
    d. extinction.
    e. homology.

D 16. The wings of a bird and the wings of a butterfly are _?_ and show morphological _?_.
    a. homologous; convergence
  * b. analogous; convergence
    c. homologous; divergence
    d. analogous; divergence
    e. homologous; diversity

D 17. Which of the following would be considered more primitive based upon the structure of their limbs?
    a. bats
  * b. early reptiles
    c. porpoises
    d. penguins
    e. birds

M 18. The bones in the forelimbs of a mammal
  * a. can often be traced to a common ancestor.
    b. offer no evidence to support the theory of evolution.
    c. perform the same function no matter which species they are in.
    d. may exhibit either analogy or homology but not both when compared to the forelimb of another animal.
    e. show convergence with some invertebrate structures.

D 19. Which of the following structures are analogous but NOT homologous to each other?
  * a. wing of a bird and the wing of a butterfly
    b. bones of the wing of a bird and the bones of the wing of a bat
    c. the dewclaw of a dog and the little toe of a human
    d. the flipper of an aquatic animal and the arm of a human
    e. All of these are analogous but not homologous.

M 20. Bats, birds, and insects together exhibit
    a. morphological divergence.
    b. parallel evolution.
  * c. morphological convergence.
    d. regression.
    e. coevolution.

EVIDENCE FROM PATTERNS OF DEVELOPMENT

D 21. The study of comparative embryology has revealed the conservative nature of the genes responsible for
    a. food procurement.
    b. reproductive behavior.
  * c. embryonic development.
    d. size.
    e. intelligence.

D 22. The fact that many vertebrate embryos are more similar to one another than their respective adult stages are to one another may ultimately be due to
    a. environment.
    b. hormones.
    c. microevolution.
  * d. genes.
    e. speciation.

M 23. The variation in the forms of adult vertebrates probably arose through mutations in _?_ genes.
  a. dominant
* b. master
  c. oncogenic
  d. promoter
  e. operator

EVIDENCE FROM DNA, RNA, AND PROTEINS

M 24. Which mutations are NOT subject to natural selection?
  a. lethal
  b. physiological
* c. neutral
  d. morphological
  e. beneficial

M 25. Neutral mutations
* a. are not subjected to selection.
  b. occur at different rates at different times during evolution.
  c. confer a disadvantage.
  d. do not occur; either a gene enhances survival or it does not.
  e. account for the difference between hemoglobin in normal blood and that found in sickle-cell anemia.

D 26. Neutral mutations
  a. code for different proteins.
* b. allow the time of divergence between different forms to be pinpointed.
  c. can be used to accurately establish the relationship between widely differing animals.
  d. are responsible for the variation in the various hemoglobin molecules found in mammals.
  e. cannot give us any indication of the rates and degrees of evolutionary change.

M 27. The concept of a molecular clock is based on the idea that
* a. neutral mutations occur at regular rates.
  b. genetic relatedness can be determined by timing antibody-antigen reactions.
  c. radioactive isotopes decay at a constant rate.
  d. speciation is a rapid event.
  e. cytochrome c is very similar in primates.

M 28. Which of the following is NOT a useful indicator of phylogenetic relatedness?
  a. base sequences in DNA
  b. amino acid sequences in a protein
* c. similar ecological requirements
  d. similar embryonic development
  e. morphological divergence

D 29. Comparisons of protein similarity between species can reveal the degree of genetic kinship because
  a. the number of protein variations is limited.
* b. specific amino acids are dictated by known nucleotide sequences.
  c. gel electrophoresis converts proteins to nucleotides.
  d. protein can be hybridized with DNA.
  e. DNA is made by directions stored in proteins.

D 30. DNA-DNA hybridization studies
  a. depend upon determining the exact sequence of nucleotides in a gene.
  b. can be done using a simple tissue homogenizer and computer-assisted analysis.
  c. involve generating new nucleotide sequences by using ultracentrifugation.
* d. measure the amount of heat necessary to separate two single strands of DNA that have been allowed to fuse together.
  e. give little clue as to how genes mutate.

M 31. The most conclusive evidence used in establishing the relationship of closely related species is
  a. fossil remains.
  b. taxonomy.
* c. DNA-DNA hybridization.
  d. homologous structures.
  e. analogous structures.

REPRODUCTIVE ISOLATION, MAYBE NEW SPECIES

E 32. The word "species" could be translated
  a. group.
* b. kind.
  c. portion.
  d. type.
  e. section.

E 33. The word "phenotype" designates the
  a. portion of the genes that are not expressed.
  b. type of genes an organism possesses.
  c. amount of change seen from one generation to the next.
* d. observable aspects of any individual organism.
  e. extent of mutation.

M 34. In the biological species concept of Ernst Mayer, what aspect of a population is critical to determining a species?
  a. physical appearance
  b. similar behavior patterns
* c. interbreeding capabilities
  d. polyploidy
  e. similar genotypes

M 35. Members of the same species would be expected to
   a. look exactly alike.
   b. be reproductively isolated from one another.
   * c. share the same gene pool.
   d. have the same phenotype.
   e. resist evolution.

M 36. A species is composed of
   a. related organisms.
   b. a group of reproductive females.
   * c. populations that have the potential to interbreed and produce fertile offspring.
   d. organisms located in the same habitat.
   e. all males and females in the same geographical range with the same ecological requirements.

M 37. Two individuals are members of the same species if they
   a. possess the same number of chromosomes.
   b. breed at the same time.
   c. are phenotypically indistinguishable.
   * d. can mate and produce fertile offspring.
   e. live together.

M 38. Complete reproductive isolation is evidence that what has occurred?
   a. extinction
   * b. speciation
   c. polyploidy
   d. hybridization
   e. gene flow

D 39. Which of the following will NOT promote speciation?
   a. gamete differences
   * b. gene flow
   c. season of fertility
   d. natural selection
   e. genetic drift

D 40. Speciation occurs
   * a. after populations become reproductively isolated and diverge.
   b. when mutations generate observable differences.
   c. when transitional forms develop between different populations.
   d. when natural selection pressures reach their maximum.
   e. when humans intervene and establish new breeds.

D 41. Divergence may lead to
   a. genetic drift.
   * b. speciation.
   c. balanced polymorphism.
   d. gene flow.
   e. genetic equilibrium.

E 42. The term "reproductive isolation mechanism" refers to
   a. specific areas where males compete or display for females.
   b. the process by which sexual selection evolves within a population.
   * c. a blockage of gene flow between populations.
   d. the inability of a species to continue reproduction.
   e. sexual sterility.

D 43. Which of the following is NOT an example of an isolating mechanism?
   a. species-specific courtship rituals
   * b. Hardy-Weinberg equilibrium
   c. incompatible reproductive structures
   d. earthquakes and floods
   e. all of these

M 44. Incompatibilities between the developing embryo and the maternal organism that cause the embryo to abort spontaneously may prevent individuals of different populations from producing fertile offspring. Such differences may be which of the following?
   * a. isolating mechanisms
   b. allele frequencies
   c. mutations
   d. founder effects
   e. gene flow

M 45. The primary reason for hybrid sterility is
   a. the inability of the hybrid to attract a mate.
   b. the difficulty in finding a suitable habitat in which to survive.
   c. that the hybrids are usually weak and have difficulty surviving to reproductive maturity.
   * d. the difficulty in the pairing of homologous chromosomes.
   e. the inability of the hybrid to develop an appropriate courtship pattern.

E 46. Isolating mechanisms that take effect before or during fertilization could be classified as
   a. hybridizing.
   * b. prezygotic.
   c. genetically divergent.
   d. postzygotic.
   e. persistent.

E 47. The 13-year and 17-year cicadas are isolated by
   a. space.
   b. behavior.
   c. incompatibility of reproductive body parts.
   * d. time.
   e. gamete incompatibility.

M 48. A difference in reproductive timing describes _?_ isolation
   a. behavioral.
   * b. temporal.
   c. mechanical.
   d. gametic.
   e. ecological.

M 49. Members of two different bird species mate and produce viable fertile offspring. The courtship song of the hybrid is not recognized by members of either parent species. This is an example of
   a. speciation.
   b. balanced polymorphism.
   * c. behavioral isolation.
   d. sexual selection.
   e. ecological isolation.

D 50. Suppose you witness the mating of a cat and a dog, obviously two different species, but realize that there will be no viable offspring due to isolating mechanisms that are
a. mechanical.
* b. gametic.
c. behavioral.
d. temporal.
e. ecological.

D 51. During a study of two closely related animals it did not appear as though they were reproductively isolated until the possibility that their different niches could result in _?_ isolation was noted.
* a. ecological
b. gametic
c. temporal
d. behavioral
e. mechanical

E 52. Hybrid inviability is an example of what kind of isolation?
a. gametic
b. prezygotic
c. divergent
d. mechanical
* e. postzygotic

M 53. Mules are exceptional hybrids because
a. they are weak.
b. their survival rate is low.
* c. they are sturdy and strong.
d. they are sterile.
e. their offspring are sterile.

INTERPRETING THE EVIDENCE: MODELS FOR SPECIATION

M 54. Allopatric speciation requires
a. gradual evolutionary changes.
* b. geographic isolation or physical barriers.
c. polyploidy.
d. adaptive radiation.
e. inbreeding.

M 55. The greatest contributor(s) to allopatric isolation is (are)
* a. geographical barriers.
b. differences in reproductive timing.
c. gametic incompatibility.
d. hybrid inviability.
e. behavioral peculiarities.

D 56. The effectiveness of geographical barriers in promoting speciation is related to the
a. size of the barrier.
* b. ability of the organisms to overcome the barrier.
c. speed at which the barrier forms.
d. duration of the barrier before it is torn down.
e. size of the population it separates.

M 57. Changes in the Mississippi River caused by earthquakes are thought to have caused speciation by
a. divergence.
b. parapatry.
* c. allopatry.
d. gene flow.
e. sympatry.

M 58. Speciation caused by the separation of the continents would be by
a. divergence.
b. parapatry.
c. gene flow.
* d. allopatry.
e. sympatry.

M 59. Sympatric speciation occurs
a. gradually.
b. rapidly.
c. in the same homeland.
d. gradually and in the same homeland.
* e. rapidly and in the same homeland.

M 60. Which is NOT necessary for sympatric speciation?
a. organisms living together in same location
b. "same homeland"
* c. physical barriers
d. existing interbreeding population
e. reproductively mature individuals

M 61. The cichlids of the African crater lakes are an example of
a. divergence.
b. parapatry.
c. gene flow.
d. allopatry.
* e. sympatry.

E 62. Sympatric speciation through polyploidy has been a frequent phenomenon in the evolution of
a. insects.
b. mammals.
c. bacteria.
* d. plants.
e. fungi.

M 63. Which of the following can result in instant speciation?
a. development of a physical barrier
* b. polyploidy
c. increase in physical size
d. change in environmental conditions
e. the introduction of a new predator into an area

D 64. Which of the following is accurate concerning polyploidy?
a. It is more common in animals than plants.
b. It is the result of mitotic irregularities.
c. It cannot be passed on to offspring.
* d. It often arises due to nondisjunction.
e. It is limited to no more than three sets of chromosomes.

M   65.   Parapatric speciation would be expected to occur most often
        a. in the same homeland.
    *   b. near a common border between two populations.
        c. within a group of interbreeding populations.
        d. across obvious geographical barriers.
        e. by divergence from a common interbreeding population.

E   66.   The border across which genes can flow between two populations is called the
    *   a. contact zone.
        b. parapatric zone.
        c. zone of speciation.
        d. demilitarized zone.
        e. zone of polyploidy.

PATTERNS OF SPECIATION AND EXTINCTIONS

E   67.   A speciation pattern that exhibits branching of populations is termed
        a. allopatric.
        b. anagenesis.
        c. nondivergent.
        d. hybridizing.
    *   e. cladogenesis.

M   68.   Evolutionists use the term "anagenesis"
        a. to describe a divergence of one species into several.
        b. to indicate branching speciation patterns.
    *   c. for speciation from a single, unbranched line of descent.
        d. to describe a divergence of one species into several and to indicate branching speciation patterns.
        e. to indicate inbreeding.

E   69.   Scientists have traditionally drawn evolutionary diagrams in the form of
        a. interlocking circles.
        b. pyramids.
        c. a set of parallel lines.
    *   d. a tree.
        e. nested squares or boxes.

M   70.   The gradual model of evolutionary change proposes that most morphological change occurs
        a. gradually but without development of new species.
        b. rapidly but without speciation.
    *   c. gradually during speciation.
        d. rapidly, leading to new species.
        e. at a constant pace but with no new species.

M   71.   The punctuation model of evolutionary change proposes that most morphological change occurs
        a. gradually but without development of new species.
        b. rapidly but without speciation.
        c. gradually during speciation.
    *   d. rapidly, leading to new species.
        e. at a constant pace but with no new species.

D   72.   The lack of transitional forms of organisms would be
        a. more expected in the gradual model than in the punctuation model.
    *   b. more expected in the punctuation model than in the gradual model.
        c. equally expected in both models.
        d. expected in neither model.
        e. a reason to abandon the use of all models.

D   73.   Which of the following contributes to adaptive radiation within a lineage?
        a. extinction of competitors
        b. new phenotypic characteristics
        c. genetic uniformity
    *   d. extinction of competitors and new phenotypic characteristics
        e. extinction of competitors, new phenotypic characteristics, and genetic uniformity

D   74.   Which of the following adaptations would be most important for an animal that is to live on land?
        a. three germ layers
        b. a moist skin without scales
    *   c. internal fertilization
        d. external gills with major sense organs concentrated in the head region
        e. external fertilization

M   75.   The acquisition of a key evolutionary innovation by a species gives evidence for the concept of
        a. uniformitarianism.
        b. gradualism.
        c. convergence.
    *   d. adaptive radiation.
        e. special creation.

M   76.   Which of the following could NOT be an explanation for mass extinction?
        a. collisions between the Earth and other bodies in the solar system
        b. continental movements
    *   c. adaptive radiation of new predator species in many lineages
        d. alterations in sea level
        e. plate tectonics

M   77.   Mass extinctions are usually followed by
           a. periods of recovery.
           b. adaptive radiations.
           c. smaller extinctions.
      *   d. slowly recovering biodiversity as new species fill
              vacant adaptive zones.
           e. periods of recovery, adaptive radiations, and
              smaller extinctions.

ORGANIZING INFORMATION ABOUT SPECIES

D   78.   Classification units of any rank are referred to as
           a. cladistics.
           b. families.
           c. phyla.
      *   d. taxa.
           e. orders.

E   79.   The higher taxa are groupings of
           a. orders.
           b. classes.
           c. families.
           d. phyla.
      *   e. all of these

E   80.   Ever more inclusive groupings of species are
           a. binominal systems.
      *   b. higher taxa.
           c. taxonomies.
           d. systematics.
           e. links of the Chain of Being.

M   81.   Which of the following groups represents the most
           closely related organisms?
           a. kingdoms
      *   b. species
           c. orders
           d. genera
           e. taxa

M   82.   Organisms "X" and "Y" are suspected to be the same
           species. Which of the following will provide the
           ultimate proof?
      *   a. interbreeding
           b. anatomy
           c. physiology
           d. ecology
           e. behavior

E   83.   Scientific names of organisms are written in
           a. French.
           b. English.
      *   c. Latin.
           d. German.
           e. Swedish.

E   84.   Which of the following is written correctly?
           a. *Felis* domestica
           b. Felis Domestica
           c. *felis domestica*
      *   d. *Felis domestica*
           e. *felis Domestica*

D   85.   Which of the following is NOT correct?
      *   a. The specific name can be used alone.
           b. The generic name can be used alone.
           c. The specific name must be preceded by a generic
              name.
           d. A family includes related genera.
           e. The kingdom is the most inclusive category.

M   86.   "House fly" is the _?_ applied to a small, pestiferous
           insect that is often an uninvited guest at dinner.
           a. scientific name
           b. genus and species
           c. universal name
      *   d. English common name
           e. Latin name

E   87.   Which of the following includes all the others?
           a. family
      *   b. phylum
           c. species
           d. class
           e. order

E   88.   Which of the following includes all related genera?
      *   a. family
           b. phylum
           c. species
           d. class
           e. order

M   89.   Which of the following is the least inclusive category?
           a. family
           b. order
      *   c. species
           d. kingdom
           e. genus

M   90.   The only taxonomic category in which microevolution
           can occur is the
           a. genus.
      *   b. species.
           c. kingdom.
           d. family.
           e. class.

M   91.   Phylogeny refers to what aspects of individuals?
           a. morphological traits
      *   b. evolutionary relationships
           c. physiological characteristics
           d. behavioral features
           e. all of these

D   92.   Phylogenetic reconstruction
           a. is based upon homologous structures.
           b. requires an outgroup for comparison with the
              ingroup.
           c. mimics the scale of nature.
           d. identifies relative relationships.
      *   e. all but "mimics the scale of nature" are correct

D 93. Variations in phylogeny based on fossil records are probably most often due to
   a. imperfections in the fossils themselves.
 * b. differences of interpretation by scientists.
   c. inconsistencies in rock strata.
   d. inaccuracies in radioisotope dating.
   e. mistakes in creation.

D 94. The cladistics approach to discovering phylogeny
   a. assesses the significance of homologous structures.
   b. is concerned about common ancestry.
   c. portrays relative relationships among organisms.
 * d. estimates "who came from whom."
   e. assesses the significance of homologous structures, is concerned about common ancestry, and portrays relative relationships among organisms.

D 95. In a cladogram,
 * a. the axis can be considered to be a time line.
   b. features found in only one of the ingroups are very useful in establishing relationships.
   c. the higher the position of a group on the cladogram, the more distant is the most recent common ancestor.
   d. the lower in a cladogram a group is, the more derived features they have in common.
   e. all of these

D 96. Technically speaking, a cladogram conveys
 * a. portrayals of relative relationships.
   b. lines of descendants.
   c. a tree of ancestors.
   d. a classification scheme.
   e. all of these

Matching Questions

D 97. Matching I. Choose the most appropriate letter for each blank.
   1. ___ analogous structures
   2. ___ scientific name
   3. ___ cladogram
   4. ___ DNA-DNA hybridization
   5. ___ fossil
   6. ___ fungi
   7. ___ molecular clock
   8. ___ bacteria
   9. ___ morphological divergence
   10. ___ phylogeny
   11. ___ plants
   12. ___ three-domain system

   A. schemes that reflect evolutionary relationships among species
   B. branching diagram representing patterns of relationships of whole organisms
   C. adaptations similar in function but of distant lineage
   D. multicelled eukaryotes; nearly all photoautotrophs
   E. buried remains and impressions of organisms that lived in the past
   F. prokaryotes
   G. heterotrophs with extracellular digestion and absorption
   H. Bacteria, Archaea, and Eukarya
   I. has two parts
   J. used to compare DNA of two different species
   K. change in body form
   L. use of accumulated neutral mutations to determine past evolutionary events

Answers: 1. C   2. I   3. B   4. J
   5. E   6. G   7. L   8. F
   9. K   10. A   11. D   12. H

D   **98.** Matching II. Choose the most appropriate letter for each.

    1. ___ clade

    2. ___ species

    3. ___ isolating mechanism

    4. ___ sympatric speciation

    5. ___ polyploidy

    6. ___ punctuation model

    7. ___ mass extinction

    8. ___ allopatric speciation

    9. ___ adaptive radiation

    A. geographic separation of two populations accompanied by gradual divergent evolution between them; reproductive isolation

    B. encompasses all of those actually or potentially interbreeding populations that are reproductively isolated from other such groups

    C. a population occupying the same distribution range undergoes reproductive isolation

    D. morphological changes compressed into brief periods when populations start to diverge

    E. branching pattern of speciation

    F. catastrophic, global loss of species

    G. divergences

    H. inheritance of three or more of each type of chromosome

    I. prevents gene flow between populations

Answers: 1. E   2. B   3. I

            4. C   5. H   6. D

            7. F   8. A   9. G

Classification Questions

Answer questions 99–103 in reference to the five taxonomic categories listed below.

    a. genus
    b. species
    c. order
    d. family
    e. phylum

E   **99.** This category is not included in any of the other listed categories.

E   **100.** This category is included in each of the other categories.

D   **101.** The term "Hominidae" is an example of this.

M   **102.** This category denotes the taxonomic category of *Homo* (humans).

D   **103.** This category usually includes several families.

Answers: 99. e   100. b   101. d

            102. a   103. c

Answer questions 104–108 in reference to the four microevolutionary processes listed below.

    a. mutation
    b. gene flow
    c. genetic drift
    d. natural selection

M   **104.** involves chance

E   **105.** original source of alleles

M   **106.** preserves species cohesion

M   **107.** Darwin's major evolutionary mechanism involving reproductive differences

M   **108.** results from differential survival and reproduction

Answers: 104. c   105. a   106. b

            107. d   108. d

Selecting the Exception

D   **109.** Four of the five answers listed below are habitats favoring fossil preservation. Select the exception.

    * a. deserts
    b. swamp
    c. tar pits
    d. seafloor
    e. caves

E   **110.** Four of the five answers listed below are taxonomic categories. Select the exception.

    a. species
    b. class
    * c. taxon
    d. order
    e. phylum

E **111.** Four of the five answers listed below are related to investigations into evolutionary evidence from comparative biochemistry. Select the exception.
     a. neutral mutations
*   b. homologous structures
     c. molecular clock
     d. protein comparisons
     e. DNA-DNA hybridizations

M **112.** Four of the five answers listed below are used in describing a species. Select the exception.
     a. interbreeding
     b. sexual reproduction
     c. natural
     d. populations
*   e. appearance

D **113.** Three of the four answers listed below promote evolution. Select the exception.
     a. genetic drift
     b. mutation
*   c. gene flow
     d. natural selection
     e. none of these; all answers promote evolution

E **114.** Four of the five answers listed below are types of prezygotic isolating mechanisms. Select the exception.
     a. temporal
*   b. hybrid inviability
     c. mechanical
     d. ecological
     e. gametic

D **115.** Four of the five answers listed below are portions of the theory of natural selection. Select the exception.
     a. Variation is heritable.
     b. Heritable traits vary in adaptability.
     c. More organisms are produced than can survive.
*   d. The largest and strongest always contribute more genes to the next generation.
     e. Natural selection is the result of differential reproduction.

M **116.** Four of the five answers listed below are types of speciation. Select the exception.
*   a. postzygotic
     b. allopatric
     c. parapatric
     d. punctuation
     e. sympatric

E **117.** Four of the five answers listed below can function to isolate populations. Select the exception.
     a. geography
     b. behavior
     c. time
     d. gametes
*   e. external fertilization

Labeling

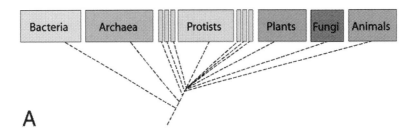

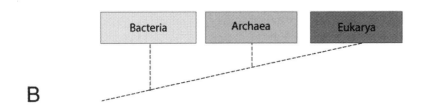

E **118.** The system of "domains" is represented by the letter _?_.

E **119.** The more "traditional" system of classification is represented by the letter _?_.

E **120.** The classification system based on DNA comparisons is represented at letter _?_.

Answers: 118. B   119. A   120. B

CHAPTER 14
EARLY LIFE

Multiple-Choice Questions

ORIGIN OF THE FIRST LIVING CELLS

E 1. Fossil evidence of the earliest living organisms now dates back
    a. 570 million years.
    b. 1.4 billion years.
  * c. about 3.8 billion years.
    d. more than 5 billion years.
    e. to 4004 B.C.

M 2. Life on Earth began how many years ago?
    a. 6,000
    b. 350,000
    c. 35,000,000
    d. 350,000,000
  * e. 3,800,000,000

E 3. The primitive atmosphere did NOT contain
    a. water vapor.
    b. free nitrogen.
    c. free hydrogen.
  * d. free oxygen.
    e. inert gases.

E 4. Many of the organic compounds essential for life, such as amino acids and nucleotides, could NOT assemble spontaneously in the presence of
    a. hydrogen.
  * b. free oxygen.
    c. carbon dioxide.
    d. nitrogen.
    e. argon.

E 5. Organic compounds break down spontaneously in the presence of _?_; hence, life probably never would have emerged if the ancient atmosphere had been the same as today's.
    a. carbon dioxide
    b. hydrogen
  * c. oxygen
    d. nitrogen
    e. silica

E 6. Experiments like those first performed by Stanley Miller in 1953 demonstrated that
    a. DNA forms readily and reproduces itself.
  * b. many of the organic compounds required for life can form under abiotic conditions.
    c. complete, functioning prokaryotic cells are formed after approximately three months.
    d. a lipid-protein film will eventually be formed by thermal convection.
    e. all of these

M 7. Which of the following was NOT included in Miller's reaction chamber, which did contain substances intended to duplicate the atmosphere of ancient Earth?
  * a. carbon dioxide
    b. methane
    c. ammonia
    d. water vapor
    e. methane and ammonia

E 8. Who demonstrated the possibility of producing organic compounds from gases and water if the mixture is bombarded with a continuous spark discharge?
  * a. Miller
    b. Starr
    c. Thompsen
    d. Pauling
    e. Platt

E 9. The Miller experiment designed to study the early synthesis of organic compounds did NOT include which of the following molecules?
    a. methane
    b. ammonia
    c. water
  * d. oxygen
    e. All of these molecules were included in the experiment.

M 10. The primitive template that was thought to be used for forming chains that resemble proteins or nucleic acids was
    a. stratified mica crystals.
  * b. clay compounds.
    c. the bottoms of tidal pools.
    d. dried-out mud flats.
    e. pockets in lava beds.

M 11. Clay compounds were thought to be original sites for the formation of
    a. amino acids.
    b. sugars.
    c. polysaccharides.
  * d. protein chains.
    e. lipid molecules.

M 12. Under abiotic conditions, enzyme-like protein chains formed to serve as
    a. a supply of structural units.
    b. enzymes to catalyze reactions.
    c. subunits in the formation of DNA.
    d. subunits in the formation of RNA.
  * e. a supply of structural units and enzymes to catalyze reactions.

E 13. The first templates for protein synthesis were
   a. complex carbohydrates.
   b. mineral crystals.
* c. layers of clay.
   d. sheets of layered minerals such as mica.
   e. multiple oil liposomes or micelles.

M 14. The most likely molecules to serve as a replacement
       for clay as a template for protein synthesis are
   a. coenzymes.
* b. RNAs.
   c. DNAs.
   d. other proteins.
   e. complex carbohydrates.

D 15. What step occurred first in the evolution of life?
   a. formation of lipid spheres
   b. formation of protein-RNA systems
   c. formation of membrane-bound protocells
* d. spontaneous formation of lipids, proteins,
      carbohydrates, and nucleotides under abiotic
      conditions
   e. formation of ATP

D 16. Which step in the evolution of life is the most complex
       and occurred last?
   a. formation of lipid spheres
   b. formation of protein-RNA systems
* c. formation of membrane-bound protocells
   d. spontaneous formation of lipids, proteins,
      carbohydrates, and nucleotides under abiotic
      conditions
   e. formation of ATP

M 17. Experiments showed that if heated protein chains were
       allowed to cool in water, they would
   a. form nitrogen, which would escape as a gas.
   b. form proteinoids.
* c. form small, stable spheres or microspheres.
   d. clot and form a complex latticework frame for
      chemical reactions.
   e. break down into the original amino acids from
      which the protein chain was made.

E 18. The first organisms
   a. had to be autotrophic.
   b. were parasitic.
* c. obtained energy by anaerobic pathways.
   d. were aerobes.
   e. all of these

D 19. The first organisms
   a. absorbed their food supplies from the organic
      molecules that surrounded them.
   b. were eukaryotes.
   c. utilized fermentation for energy production.
   d. utilized ATP.
* e. all of these except "were eukaryotes."

D 20. The earliest organisms were probably unicellular
   a. autotrophs.
   b. aerobes.
* c. heterotrophs.
   d. eukaryotes.
   e. molds.

M 21. The first organisms were most probably
   a. autotrophic.
   b. multicellular.
   c. protozoans.
* d. prokaryotic.
   e. photosynthetic.

D 22. During the Archean era, divergence of the prokaryotes
       led to all but which of the following?
   a. archaebacteria
   b. eukaryotes
* c. multicelled organisms
   d. eubacteria
   e. additional prokaryotes

D 23. The early atmosphere
   a. was essentially the same as occurs now.
* b. was changed drastically by the liberation of
      oxygen following the evolution of photosynthesis.
   c. was characterized by high concentrations of
      oxygen and ozone.
   d. was characterized by high concentrations of inert
      gases before the evolution of living organisms.
   e. was so dense that life could not evolve.

WHAT ARE EXISTING PROKARYOTES LIKE?

E 24. All EXCEPT which one of the following are
       characteristics of at least some of the bacteria?
   a. photosynthesis
   b. heterotrophy
   c. chemosynthesis
* d. multicellularity
   e. no nucleus

M 25. Which of the following can bacteria use as an energy
       source?
   a. hydrogen sulfide
   b. nitrites
   c. sunlight
   d. ammonia
* e. all of these

E 26. In bacteria, DNA is found
   a. in the nucleus alone.
   b. in organelles alone.
   c. in both the nucleus and organelles.
* d. as a single, circular thread.
   e. as particles scattered throughout the entire
      bacterial cell.

E   27.   Bacteria can obtain their nutrition by
           a. photosynthesis.
           b. breakdown of chemical compounds.
           c. being heterotrophs.
           d. photosynthesis and breaking down chemical
               compounds.
        * e. all of these

M   28.   Prokaryotes (bacteria)
           a. have cell walls composed of cellulose.
           b. reproduce primarily by conjugation.
        * c. have a single chromosome.
           d. are eukaryotic.
           e. have a distinct nucleus.

M   29.   Which of the following concerning bacteria is TRUE?
           a. They are diploid organisms.
           b. They produce gametes.
        * c. They possess circular DNA molecules.
           d. They are eukaryotic.
           e. They are multicellular.

M   30.   Which of the following statements is NOT
           characteristic of bacteria?
        * a. Some have no plasma membrane.
           b. Some may have hairlike structures called pili.
           c. Some may have rigid cell walls.
           d. Some may have flagella and move about.
           e. Some may have a polysaccharide covering.

D   31.   Which of the following distinguishes the bacterial
           flagellum from those of eukaryotes?
           a. quantity per cell
           b. general appearance
           c. function
        * d. the way it moves
           e. all of these

M   32.   Which of the following allow the bacteria to join
           together to transfer genes?
           a. flagella
           b. pores
           c. connecting channels
        * d. pili
           e. stylets

D   33.   In what way does prokaryotic fission resemble
           eukaryotic mitosis?
           a. movement of chromosomes
        * b. genetically identical daughter cells
           c. intracellular mechanisms
           d. genetically identical daughter cells and
               intracellular mechanisms
           e. movement of chromosomes, genetically identical
               daughter cells, and intracellular mechanisms

M   34.   The process by which one bacterial cell transfers DNA
           to another is
           a. fission.
           b. gametic fusion.
        * c. conjugation.
           d. lysis.
           e. none of these

E   35.   One of the newest techniques used to identify bacteria
           is to determine their
           a. diseases.
           b. reproductive types.
           c. metabolic processes.
        * d. nucleotide sequences.
           e. metabolic by-products.

E   36.   Which of the following do anaerobic methanogens
           produce?
           a. carbon monoxide
           b. carbon dioxide
           c. ammonia sulfide
        * d. methane
           e. hydrogen sulfide

E   37.   Which bacterium is most likely to be found in wetland
           mud?
           a. thermophilic
           b. halophilic
           c. cyanobacteria
        * d. methanogen
           e. *E. coli*

M   38.   The methane-producing bacteria belong to
        * a. Archaea.
           b. Prokaryota.
           c. Eukaryota.
           d. Urkaryota.
           e. Bacteria.

M   39.   Which terms accurately describe the archaebacteria?
           a. extinct, aerobic
           b. extinct, anaerobic
           c. present, aerobic
        * d. present, anaerobic
           e. none of these is the correct combination

M   40.   The archaea can be described by all EXCEPT which
           one of the following?
           a. anaerobic
           b. chemosynthetic
        * c. pathogenic
           d. halophilic
           e. heterotrophic

D   41.   Endospores are produced by
           a. chrysophytes.
        * b. bacteria.
           c. protozoans.
           d. viruses.
           e. protists.

M   42.   When conditions are hostile, some bacteria
           a. engage in conjugation.
           b. switch to photosynthesis.
        * c. form endospores.
           d. become pathogenic.
           e. die.

E 43. The organism associated with strong toxin production in improperly sterilized or sealed cans and jars is
   *   a. *Clostridium botulinum.*
        b. *Clostridium tetani.*
        c. fer-de-lance snakes.
        d. certain nettles in Java.
        e. vines and is called curare.

M 44. The bacterium *E. coli*
        a. is a normal inhabitant of the mammalian gut.
        b. helps keep harmful bacteria at bay.
        c. has mutant strains causing a deadly foodborne illness.
        d. produces vitamin K.
   *   e. all of these

M 45. *E. coli*
        a. is a normal inhabitant of the mammalian gut.
        b. has some mutant strains that produce toxins and cause disease.
        c. is grown in laboratories around the world.
        d. produces vitamin K.
   *   e. all of these

M 46. *Borrelia burgdorferi* is the cause of
        a. tetanus.
        b. syphilis.
   *   c. Lyme disease.
        d. legionnaires disease.
        e. severe diarrhea.

THE CURIOUSLY CLASSIFIED PROTISTS

E 47. Which of the following does NOT belong to the protists?
   *   a. bacteria
        b. protozoans
        c. radiolarians
        d. dinoflagellates
        e. euglenoids

D 48. All EXCEPT which of the following are members of the same group?
        a. *Amoeba*
   *   b. *Clostridium*
        c. *Euglena*
        d. *Trypanosoma*
        e. *Giardia*

E 49. Most protists are
        a. autotrophic.
        b. heterotrophic.
   *   c. single-celled.
        d. multicellular.
        e. polymorphic.

E 50. The group most similar to the first eukaryotic cells is the _?_
   *   a. protists.
        b. plants.
        c. fungi.
        d. animals.
        e. both a and c

M 51. The term "algae" is used primarily for organisms in which of these groups?
        a. Bacteria
   *   b. Protista
        c. Plantae
        d. Bacteria and Protista only
        e. Bacteria, Protista, and Plantae

M 52. Which of the following is NOT true of *Euglena*?
   *   a. It moves by pseudopodia.
        b. It contains chloroplasts.
        c. It absorbs nutrients such as vitamins from its environment in a heterotrophic manner.
        d. Its cell body is not surrounded by a cell wall.
        e. none of these; all statements are true

E 53. A pellicle is a (an)
        a. defensive organ.
   *   b. covering.
        c. organelle of motion.
        d. storage organ.
        e. component of the nucleus.

M 54. Euglenoids
        a. sometimes reproduce faster than their chloroplasts, so that colorless euglenids are produced.
        b. may become a serious parasitic infection in some small children.
        c. reproduce by conjugation.
   *   d. usually can survive only in light.
        e. are exclusively heterotrophic.

M 55. Certain euglenoids are unique among the protists in that they
        a. possess flagella.
        b. reproduce by longitudinal fission.
   *   c. can be heterotrophic and autotrophic.
        d. are multicellular.
        e. contain DNA.

M 56. Pseudopods are characteristic of which of the following groups of protozoans?
        a. ciliates
        b. flagellates
   *   c. radiolarians
        d. apicomplexans
        e. euglenoids

E 57. *Paramecium* is a representative of the
        a. sporozoans.
        b. amoebas.
        c. flagellates.
        d. euglenoids.
   *   e. ciliates.

D 58. Which of the following specialized structures is NOT correctly paired with its function?
        a. gullet—ingestion
        b. cilia—food gathering
   *   c. contractile vacuole—digestion
        d. two nuclei—daughter cells
        e. ingested food—digestive vesicles

M 59. The least mobile protistans include
        a. euglenoids.
        b. ciliates.
    *   c. apicomplexans.
        d. dinoflagellates.
        e. flagellates.

M 60. The apicomplexan parasite *Plasmodium* infects cells
        of which of the following?
        a. blood only
        b. liver only
        c. brain only
    *   d. both blood and liver
        e. blood, liver, and brain

M 61. "Red tides" and extensive fish kills are caused by
        population "blooms" of
        a. *Euglena.*
    *   b. specific dinoflagellates.
        c. diatoms.
        d. *Plasmodium.*
        e. fish.

M 62. Dinoflagellates
        a. may produce red tides that poison and kill fish.
        b. are parasites of fish and invertebrates.
        c. may undergo a population explosion that turns the
           ocean red or various colors.
        d. are aquatic producers in freshwater or marine
           habitats.
    *   e. all of these

M 63. Dinoflagellates are characterized by all EXCEPT
        which of the following?
        a. They secrete neurotoxins that can kill fish.
        b. They spin like tops as they swim.
        c. They poison shellfish such as clams, oysters,
           scallops, and mussels.
    *   d. They have two shells that fit together like petri
           plates.
        e. They are photosynthetic.

M 64. The failure of the potato crop and the subsequent Irish
        famine was due mainly to a fungus belonging to which
        group?
        a. chytrids
        b. imperfect fungi
        c. club fungi
        d. ascomycetes
    *   e. water molds

M 65. Diatoms are characterized by all EXCEPT which of
        the following?
        a. overlapping shells
        b. live in freshwater and cool seas
        c. silica composition
    *   d. flagella
        e. photosynthetic

M 66. Holdfasts and gas-filled bladders are found in species
        of
        a. red algae.
    *   b. brown algae.
        c. bryophytes.
        d. green algae.
        e. blue-green algae.

M 67. Extracts from which of the following groups are used
        to manufacture ice cream, pudding, jelly beans, tooth
        paste, cosmetics, and other products?
        a. seed plants.
        b. ferns.
    *   c. brown algae.
        d. red algae.
        e. green algae.

E 68. The giant kelps would be included in which of the
        following groups?
    *   a. brown algae
        b. red algae
        c. green algae
        d. blue-green algae
        e. purple algae

M 69. The unicellular alga *Chlamydomonas*
        a. lacks an asexual stage.
        b. lacks a sexual stage.
        c. lacks a haploid and a diploid phase.
    *   d. possesses both a haploid and a diploid phase.
        e. lacks a nucleus.

M 70. Red algae
    *   a. are primarily marine organisms.
        b. are thought to have developed from green algae.
        c. contain xanthophylls as their main accessory
           pigments.
        d. are actually brown.
        e. all of these

D 71. Red algae can live in deeper water because of
    *   a. phycobilin pigments.
        b. holdfasts.
        c. chlorophyll *a.*
        d. stonelike cell walls.
        e. their preference for freshwater habitats.

M 72. Agar is produced by
        a. brown algae.
    *   b. red algae.
        c. phycobilins.
        d. brown and red algae.
        e. red algae and phycobilins.

M 73. Slime molds are classified as
    *   a. protists.
        b. fungi.
        c. protozoans.
        d. protists and protozoans.
        e. protists, fungi, and protozoans.

THE FABULOUS FUNGI

E   74. In the ecological community, fungi are
        a. producers if the sun is shining.
        b. consumers of materials digested by their hosts.
    *   c. decomposers of organic matter.
        d. consumers of materials digested by their hosts and decomposers of organic matter.
        e. producers if the sun is shining, consumers of materials digested by their hosts, and decomposers of organic matter.

M   75. In fungi, food materials are digested
        a. within food vacuoles.
    *   b. outside the body.
        c. intracellularly.
        d. by the mitochondria.
        e. by the host organism.

D   76. The value of fungi in the scheme of nature is described by which of the following statements?
        a. Fungi "fix" nitrogen from the air for use by plants.
        b. Fungi trap sunlight energy in carbohydrates.
    *   c. Fungi release elements from organic matter.
        d. Fungi suppress population explosions by parasitizing overproductive animals.
        e. Fungi can do any of the above, depending on the species and environment.

M   77. Saprobes are
        a. cytoplasmic organelles.
        b. metabolic by-products.
    *   c. organisms that feed on dead material.
        d. parasites of plants.
        e. an evolutionary dead end.

E   78. Fungi
        a. are producers.
    *   b. are generally saprobes.
        c. usually have life cycles in which the diploid phase dominates.
        d. include *Fucus* and liverworts.
        e. are typically marine forms.

M   79. Which fungi rely on extracellular digestion and absorption of energy-rich substances from *living* hosts?
        a. slime molds
        b. saprobic fungi
    *   c. parasitic fungi
        d. plasmodial fungi
        e. autotrophic fungi

E   80. All fungi are
        a. unicellular.
        b. multicellular.
        c. autotrophic.
    *   d. heterotrophic.
        e. photosynthetic.

M   81. All fungi
        a. are saprobes.
    *   b. perform extracellular digestion.
        c. are parasites.
        d. are saprobes and perform extracellular digestion.
        e. are saprobes, perform extracellular digestion, and are parasites.

M   82. Which of the following could NOT be used to describe any fungus?
        a. saprophytic
        b. decomposer
        c. parasitic
    *   d. autotrophic
        e. heterotrophic

M   83. A fungus would be expected to exist as
    *   a. a colorless multicellular organism that absorbs the food from its environment.
        b. a small motile organism that would be nocturnal.
        c. an eukaryotic organism that could carry on both photosynthesis and respiration.
        d. an organism that functions as a decomposer in the dark and a producer in the light.
        e. a symbiont or parasite only.

E   84. Most true fungi send out cellular filaments called
        a. mycelia.
    *   b. hyphae.
        c. mycorrhizae.
        d. asci.
        e. gills.

D   85. All EXCEPT which of the following statements concerning fungal body plans are true?
    *   a. A mesh of hyphae is composed of mycelia.
        b. Branching filaments are called hyphae.
        c. Cytoplasm can flow from one cell to another.
        d. Cell walls are chitin-reinforced.
        e. Some filaments become modified into reproductive structures.

M   86. The walls of fungi contain
        a. cellulose.
        b. lignin.
    *   c. chitin.
        d. pectin.
        e. protein.

M   87. The most reliable way to distinguish edible mushrooms from poisonous ones is to
        a. look for basidiospores.
        b. distinguish their colors.
        c. reject any with a brownish tint.
    *   d. rely on fungi specialists.
        e. use special fungus-sniffing dogs.

M   88. Which of the following is a diploid stage in the life cycle of fungi?
        a. spores
        b. vegetative growth of hyphae
    *   c. zygote
        d. gametes
        e. cells produced by budding or fragmentation

M 89. In what way do fungi reproduce?
   a. asexually, through spores
   b. budding of the parent body
   c. sexually, through gametes
   d. asexually, through spores and budding of the parent body
   * e. asexually, through spores; budding of the parent body; and sexually, through gametes

M 90. Which factor is the most important algal contribution to the fungal component of a lichen?
   a. improved water conservation
   b. mechanical protection from being blown away
   * c. photosynthetically derived food
   d. less overlap between individual algal cells
   e. pigment for camouflage

E 91. A lichen is a composite organism made up of
   a. two different fungi.
   * b. a fungus and an alga.
   c. a fungus and a gymnosperm.
   d. a fungus and a bryophyte.
   e. a fungus and a bacterium.

D 92. In lichens, the more "independent" member is the
   * a. alga.
   b. fungus.
   c. mycorrhiza.
   d. imperfect fungus.
   e. water mold.

E 93. Lichens are unable to grow
   a. on bare rocks.
   b. on tree trunks.
   * c. in polluted areas.
   d. in cold temperatures, such as in the tundra.
   e. none of these

M 94. Despite their tolerance for harsh climates, lichens are particularly intolerant of
   a. drought.
   b. cold.
   c. sunlight.
   * d. air pollution.
   e. shade.

E 95. Mycorrhizae are
   a. roots.
   b. bacteria.
   * c. fungus roots.
   d. isolated plants.
   e. small animals found in agricultural soils.

M 96. Mycorrhizae
   a. increase plant growth.
   b. are mutualists.
   c. allow a plant to absorb more water.
   d. increase the surface area for absorption of water and minerals.
   * e. all of these

M 97. Algae are to lichens as _?_ are to mycorrhizae.
   a. club fungi
   * b. tree roots
   c. water molds
   d. plant leaves
   e. mosses

VIRUSES, VIROIDS, AND PRIONS

E 98. Which statement is INACCURATE?
   a. Viruses are not able to move by themselves.
   b. Viruses are not able to reproduce by themselves.
   * c. Viruses are not structurally organized.
   d. Some biologists consider viruses to be forms of life and other biologists consider them to be nonlife.
   e. Viruses contain instructions to manufacture themselves.

M 99. A virus is characterized by all EXCEPT which one of the following?
   * a. enzymes of respiration
   b. nucleic acid core
   c. noncellular organization
   d. protein coat
   e. glycoproteins

M 100. Most scientists do not consider viruses to be "alive" because
   a. they have no genes.
   * b. a host cell is tricked into making copies of the virus.
   c. they are unable to reproduce.
   d. no definite structural features are seen under the microscope.
   e. all of these

M 101. Which of the following is FALSE?
   * a. The outer coats of all viruses are alike.
   b. The virus uses either DNA or RNA at its core, but not both.
   c. Viruses can be replicated only after they enter a living cell.
   d. Most viruses have a protein coat or covering.
   e. A virus may not kill a host cell but may become inactive for a period of latency.

M 102. Which of the following statements about viruses is TRUE?
   a. They were the first forms of life to evolve.
   b. They do not attack plants.
   c. They are able to reproduce without using other organisms.
   d. They are made of protein only.
   * e. They include some forms that are able to attack bacteria.

D   103.   The lysogenic pathway is characterized by
    *   a. passive replication of viral DNA.
           b. extensive transcription of viral DNA.
           c. destruction of the bacterial host.
           d. passive replication of viral DNA and extensive
               transcription of viral DNA.
           e. passive replication of viral DNA, extensive
               transcription of viral DNA, and destruction of the
               bacterial host.

M   104.   When a virus takes over the machinery of a cell, it
           forces the cell to manufacture
           a. more mitochondria for energy for the virus.
           b. more liposomes to isolate themselves from water.
           c. more food particles.
    *   d. more viral particles.
           e. more Golgi bodies so that the cell will secrete the
               excess viruses.

E   105.   Viroids differ from viruses in that the former lack
           a. nucleic acid.
    *   b. protein coats.
           c. the ability to reproduce.
           d. nucleic acid and protein.
           e. organization.

E   106.   Which of the following defines a prion?
           a. a virus without a protein capsid
           b. naked nucleic acid core
           c. cause of autoimmune deficiency diseases
    *   d. infectious protein
           e. a mutant virus

EVOLUTION AND INFECTIOUS DISEASES

E   107.   Which of the following could be called "pathogens"?
           a. viruses
           b. bacteria
           c. protozoans
           d. viruses and bacteria only, because they are alive
    *   e. viruses, bacteria, and protozoans

E   108.   Which of the following would be of greatest concern
           to an epidemiologist?
           a. sporadic outbreak of disease
           b. endemic
           c. epidemic
    *   d. pandemic
           e. all of equal concern

Matching Questions

D   109.   Matching I. Choose the most appropriate letter.
           1. ___ RNA world
           2. ___ prokaryote
           3. ___ autotroph
           4. ___ pathogen
           5. ___ endospore
           6. ___ extreme halophile
           7. ___ antibiotic

           A. "self feeder"
           B. cell with no membrane-bound nucleus
           C. disease-causing agent
           D. "salt lover"
           E. weapon useful against pathogenic bacteria
           F. resistant stage in bacterial life
           G. RNA preceded DNA as protein template

Answers: 1. G   2. B   3. A   4. C
             5. F   6. D   7. E

D   110.   Matching II. Choose the most appropriate letter for
           each.
           1. ___ amoeboids
           2. ___ apicomplexan
           3. ___ red tide
           4. ___ kelps
           5. ___ green algae
           6. ___ red algae
           7. ___ hypha
           8. ___ mushroom
           9. ___ lichen
           10. ___ bacteriophage
           11. ___ lysis
           12. ___ infection

           A. massive algal bloom
           B. above ground part of club fungus
           C. fungus plus algae
           D. move by pseudopods
           E. share a common ancestor with green plants
           F. filament of fungus
           G. release of viral particles
           H. cause of malaria
           I. invasion by a pathogen
           J. large brown algae
           K. virus that infects bacteria
           L. able to live in deep oceans

Answers: 1. D   2. H   3. A   4. J
             5. E   6. L   7. F   8. B
             9. C   10. K   11. G   12. I

Classification Questions

Answer questions 111–115 using the five groups of prokaryotes listed below.

    a. halophiles
    b. cyanobacteria
    c. thermophiles
    d. bacteria
    e. methanogens

D **111.** These bacteria live in temperatures that are not usually conducive to life.

E **112.** These produce methane.

D **113.** These bacteria can live in water of very high salt concentration.

M **114.** These can form heterocysts for making and sharing nitrogen compounds.

M **115.** These have parasitic members.

Answers: 111. c   112. e   113. a

           114. b   115. d

Answer questions 116–120 using the five groups of protistans listed below.

    a. apicomplexans
    b. amoebas
    c. euglenoids
    d. dinoflagellates
    e. trypanosomes

D **116.** This group of protozoans has no locomotor organelles.

M **117.** Possesses eyespot for detecting light needed for photosynthesis.

D **118.** No cell wall, shell, or constrictive pellicles to prevent a change in shape.

M **119.** Toxin from this group can kill humans.

M **120.** Chagas disease and African sleeping sickness are caused by members of this group.

Answers: 116. a   117. c   118. b
           119. d   120. e

Answer questions 121–124 in reference to the three groups of fungi listed below.

    a. zygomycetes
    b. sac fungi
    c. club fungi

M **121.** The common mushroom bought in the average supermarket is most likely a member of this group.

M **122.** The yeast used in the fermentation of grape juice to produce the wines of the world is a member of this group.

D **123.** The common black bread mold is a member of this group.

M **124.** The delicious truffle is a member of this group.

Answers: 121. c   122. b   123. a

           124. c

Selecting the Exception

M **125.** Four of the five answers listed below are components of the mixture used in Miller's experiment. Select the exception.
    a. hydrogen
  * b. oxygen
    c. methane
    d. ammonia
    e. water

M **126.** Four of the five answers listed below are bacterial structures. Select the exception.
    a. endospore
    b. pili
    c. capsule
  * d. eyespot
    e. heterocyst

D **127.** Four of the five answers listed below are related by a common association. Select the exception.
    a. archaea
    b. methanogens
    c. halophiles
  * d. cyanobacteria
    e. thermophiles

D **128.** Four of the five answers listed below have a common relationship. Select the exception.
    a. protists
    b. plants
    c. animals
    d. fungi
  * e. methanogens

M **129.** Four of the five answers listed below are found in viruses. Select the exception.
    a. coat
  * b. prions
    c. DNA or RNA
    d. tail fibers
    e. envelope

M **130.** Four of the five answers listed below are members of the same group. Select the exception.
  * a. archaea
    b. protozoans
    c. chrysophytes
    d. dinoflagellates
    e. euglenoids

M 131. Four of the five answers listed below are protistan structures. Select the exception.
   a. cell membrane
 * b. pili
   c. mitochondrion
   d. eyespot
   e. food vacuole

D 132. Four of the five answers listed below are related by a similar category. Select the exception.
   a. golden algae
   b. red algae
   c. green algae
 * d. blue-green algae
   e. brown algae

D 133. Four of the five answers listed below are amoeboid protozoans. Select the exception.
   a. amoebae
   b. foraminiferans
   c. heliozoans
   d. radiolarians
 * e. diatoms

D 134. Four of the five answers listed below are related to a common fungal group. Select the exception.
 * a. asci
   b. zygomycetes
   c. *Rhizopus*
   d. zygote
   e. spore former

M 135. Four of the five answers listed below can be used in describing aspects of fungal reproduction. Select the exception.
   a. spores
 * b. pollen
   c. dikaryotic
   d. gametangia
   e. asci

E 136. Four of the five answers listed below can be used to describe fungal life. Select the exception.
   a. heterotrophic
   b. saprobic
   c. parasitic
   d. decomposer
 * e. autotrophic

Labeling

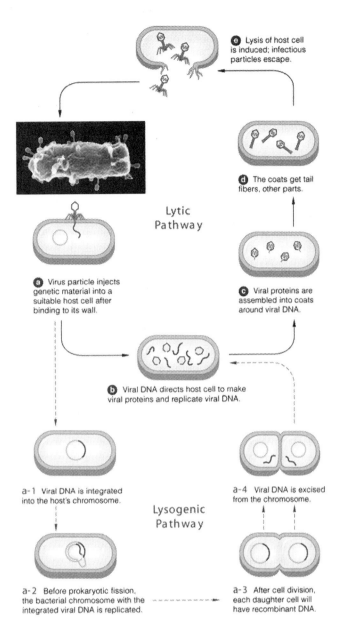

e Lysis of host cell is induced; infectious particles escape.

d The coats get tail fibers, other parts.

Lytic Pathway

c Viral proteins are assembled into coats around viral DNA.

a Virus particle injects genetic material into a suitable host cell after binding to its wall.

b Viral DNA directs host cell to make viral proteins and replicate viral DNA.

a-1 Viral DNA is integrated into the host's chromosome.

a-4 Viral DNA is excised from the chromosome.

Lysogenic Pathway

a-2 Before prokaryotic fission, the bacterial chromosome with the integrated viral DNA is replicated.

a-3 After cell division, each daughter cell will have recombinant DNA.

E **137.** In figure "a," what is being injected into the host cell?
   a. tail fiber
   b. portion of the capsid
   * c. nucleic acid
   d. nutrient material
   e. cytoskeletal elements

M **138.** The upper cycle is named for what is happening in the figure labeled with letter _?_.

E **139.** In the lysogenic pathway, the viral DNA
   a. has been destroyed by host bacterial enzymes.
   * b. is integrated into the bacterial chromosome.
   c. has been copied and changed into bacterial DNA.
   d. is no longer present.
   e. has been transcribed into RNA.

E **140.** Which pathway is *more critical* to the continuing presence of the virus in nature?
   * a. lytic
   b. lysogenic

Answers: 138.   e

CHAPTER 15
PLANT EVOLUTION

Multiple-Choice Questions

PIONEERS IN A NEW WORLD

E   1. Green plants need which of the following?
         a. sunlight energy
         b. water
         c. carbon dioxide
         d. minerals
     *   e. all of these

M   2. Which of the following is TRUE of xylem?
         a. conducts water downward in the plant
         b. transports food upward in the plant
     *   c. transports water and mineral ions throughout the plant
         d. transfers materials from stem to leaf
         e. supports the plant stem

D   3. All EXCEPT which of the following describe trends in plant evolution?
         a. nonvascular to vascular
     *   b. spores of two types to spores of one type
         c. motile gametes
         d. seedless to seeds
         e. haploid to diploid dominance

D   4. Which of the following is NOT a trend evident in plant evolution?
         a. increasing independence from water
         b. development of vascular tissue
     *   c. increasing dominance of the gametophyte generation
         d. evolution from homospory (one type of spore) to heterospory (two types of spores)
         e. development of the importance of the diploid phase of the life cycle

M   5. The cuticle of a plant is primarily for
     *   a. retention of water.
         b. conduction of fluids.
         c. absorption of carbon dioxide.
         d. protection from strong sunlight.
         e. all of these

M   6. In the life cycle of primitive plants, which of the following predominates?
     *   a. haploid stage
         b. diploid stage
         c. large sporophyte body
         d. both diploid stage and large sporophyte body
         e. both haploid stage and large sporophyte body

D   7. By _?_ years ago, plants had begun to invade land.
         a. 2.0 billion
         b. 7.0 billion
     *   c. 500 million
         d. 50 million
         e. 260 million

M   8. Spores within hard capsules are borne by
         a. the sporophyte stage.
         b. diploid organisms.
         c. spores.
     *   d. the sporophyte stage in diploid organisms.
         e. the spores of the sporophyte stage in diploid organisms.

M   9. The first haploid cell in the life cycle of a plant is the
         a. zygote.
         b. gamete.
         c. gametophyte plant.
     *   d. spore.
         e. spore mother cell.

D   10. In the life cycle of vascular plants, meiosis occurs
         a. immediately before fertilization.
         b. during the production of gametes.
         c. as a way of reducing the number of chromosomes in a zygote.
     *   d. in the process of spore formation.
         e. in the gametangia.

M   11. The life cycle of simple plants is dominated by the
         a. haploid phase.
         b. diploid phase.
         c. gametophyte.
     *   d. haploid phase in the gametophyte.
         e. diploid phase in the gametophyte.

M   12. Stomata are responsible for
         a. water escape from the leaves only.
         b. carbon dioxide entry only.
         c. mineral absorption only.
     *   d. regulation of water balance and entry and exit of gases.
         e. water escape from the leaves, carbon dioxide entry, and mineral absorption.

M   13. All EXCEPT which of the following are characteristic of the major trends in terrestrial autotroph evolution?
         a. development of vascular tissue
         b. adaptation to environmental stress
         c. heterospory
         d. fertilization by biotic vectors
     *   e. reduction of the sporophyte phase

M   14.   Gametophytes are
           a. haploid plants that produce spores.
           b. diploid plants that produce spores.
      *   c. haploid plants that produce gametes.
           d. diploid plants that produce gametes.
           e. diploid or haploid plants that produce gametes.

M   15.   In complex land plants, the diploid stage is resistant to
          adverse environmental conditions, such as dwindling
          water supplies and cold weather. The diploid stage
          progresses through which sequence?
           a. gametophyte >>> male and female gametes
           b. spores >>> sporophyte
      *   c. zygote >>> sporophyte
           d. zygote >>> gametophyte
           e. sporophyte >>> zygote

M   16.   The increased complexity among the different
          divisions of land plants is paralleled by increased
          complexity of which of the following?
           a. male gamete
           b. female gamete
           c. gametophyte
      *   d. sporophyte
           e. all of these

M   17.   A gametophyte is
           a. a gamete-producing plant.
           b. haploid.
           c. the plant produced by the fusion of gametes.
           d. the dominant generation in the higher plants.
      *   e. both a gamete-producing plant and haploid.

D   18.   Which of the following is FALSE?
           a. The male gametophyte forms inside the pollen
              grain.
      *   b. Male gametophytes produce sperm.
           c. Pollen grains divide to form microspores.
           d. Microspores are smaller than megaspores.
           e. None of these are false.

D   19.   Which of the following is TRUE concerning seeds?
           a. Present-day ferns produce seeds.
      *   b. Seeds form from the female gametophyte.
           c. Pollen grains mature into seeds.
           d. Most seeds are heterosporous.
           e. All of these are true.

D   20.   The production of two spore types led to the evolution
          of
           a. gymnosperms and angiosperms.
           b. pollen grains and seeds.
           c. male and female plant parts.
           d. pollen grains and seeds in male and female plant
              parts.
      *   e. gymnosperms and angiosperms, which bear pollen
              grains and seeds in male and female plant parts.

THE BRYOPHYTES—NO VASCULAR TISSUES

E   21.   All of the following are bryophytes EXCEPT
           a. mosses
      *   b. ferns
           c. liverworts
           d. hornworts
           e. nonvascular plants

M   22.   Which of the following would NOT be associated with
          vascular plants?
           a. root systems
      *   b. bryophytes
           c. angiosperms
           d. gymnosperms
           e. shoot systems

E   23.   The mosses, liverworts, and hornworts are members of
          which group?
           a. conifers
           b. ferns
           c. gymnosperms
      *   d. bryophytes
           e. angiosperms

D   24.   Which of the following statements is TRUE?
      *   a. Bryophytes have a water-conserving cuticle.
           b. The liverworts and mosses lack true leaves and
              stems but possess true roots.
           c. The sperm and eggs of bryophytes are naked and
              lack any adaptations to keep them from drying out.
           d. Bryophytes do not reproduce sexually except
              under unusual environmental conditions.
           e. Bryophytes produce male and female
              gametophytes that are identical in appearance and
              are identical to sporophytes.

D   25.   Bryophytes differ from all other land plants in that
          they
           a. possess swimming sperm.
      *   b. have independent gametophytes and dependent
              sporophytes.
           c. were the first forms to successfully invade land.
           d. exhibit alternation of generations.
           e. possess gametangia that produce sperm and eggs.

D   26.   Which statement about bryophytes is NOT true?
      *   a. The sporophyte is haploid.
           b. The sporangium produces spores.
           c. The sporophyte is parasitic and attached to the
              gametophyte.
           d. Meiosis precedes spore formation.
           e. Bryophytes require water for sexual reproduction.

E   27.   Mosses are
           a. algae.
      *   b. bryophytes.
           c. vascular plants.
           d. gymnosperms.
           e. extinct.

M 28. Which of the following statements is FALSE?
   a. Mosses do not have xylem and phloem.
   b. Mosses do not have true leaves.
   c. Mosses do not have true stems.
   d. Mosses use rhizoids, not roots, for attachment and absorption.
   * e. Mosses are different from all other plants in that they have an independent sporophyte generation and a dependent gametophyte generation.

SEEDLESS VASCULAR PLANTS

M 29. Ferns are more advanced than mosses because mosses lack which structure found in ferns?
   a. spores
   b. cuticle
   * c. xylem
   d. sporophytes
   e. pollen

M 30. Which of the following produces no seeds?
   a. cycads
   b. conifers
   * c. horsetails
   d. ginkgos
   e. tomato

M 31. In horsetails, lycophytes, and ferns,
   * a. spores give rise to gametophytes.
   b. the main plant body is a gametophyte.
   c. the sporophyte bears sperm- and egg-producing organs.
   d. vascular tissue is absent.
   e. all of these

D 32. Which of the following is NOT true of seedless vascular plants?
   a. Sporophytes are independent of gametophytes.
   * b. Water is not needed for gamete transport.
   c. Sporophytes have vascular tissue.
   d. Seeds are not produced.
   e. Living members still exist.

M 33. Rhizomes in the horsetails serve the same function as _?_ in more advanced land plants.
   a. leaves
   b. stems
   * c. roots
   d. seeds
   e. flowers

M 34. Strobili are
   a. gametangia.
   * b. cone-shaped spore sacs.
   c. homospores.
   d. accessory stems.
   e. horizontal stems.

E 35. The feature of horsetails that was useful before the invention of modern abrasive cleaners was
   a. rhizomes.
   * b. silica in the stems.
   c. photosynthetic cells.
   d. cones at the tips.
   e. its value as a source of stomachache medicine.

D 36. Which of the following statements concerning fertilization in ferns is TRUE?
   a. It occurs within the female structure.
   b. It requires water.
   c. The fertilization product is a seed.
   * d. It occurs within the female structure and it requires water.
   e. It occurs within the female structure, it requires water, and the fertilization product is a seed.

M 37. What is the name given to the "leaves" of a fern?
   a. rhizome
   b. rhizoid
   * c. frond
   d. sorus
   e. bronchus

D 38. Which of the following statements is FALSE?
   a. The ferns differ from other vascular plants because they lack seeds.
   b. The ferns differ from other vascular plants by having an independent sporophyte generation.
   c. The ferns are restricted to wet environments because of the requirements of the gametophytes.
   * d. Ferns have true roots, stems, and leaves.
   e. Ferns possess both xylem and phloem.

M 39. A sorus is
   a. a collection of rust-colored disease spots on a fern.
   b. the fern gametophyte.
   c. an egg-producing structure.
   d. where the sperm are produced.
   * e. a collection of spore chambers.

THE RISE OF SEED-BEARING PLANTS

E 40. Which of the following are seed plants?
   a. cycads
   b. ginkgoes
   c. conifers
   d. angiosperms
   * e. all of these

M 41. Which of the following will eventually produce a mature pollen grain?
   a. megaspore
   b. microsporangium
   * c. microspore
   d. microgamete
   e. all of these

M 42. Microspores mature into
    a. ovules.
    b. seeds.
*   c. pollen grains.
    d. anthers.
    e. plants.

E 43. The seed develops from the
    a. gametophyte.
    b. ovary.
*   c. ovule.
    d. pollen grain.
    e. zygote.

M 44. Which structure will develop into a seed?
    a. archegonium
    b. female gametophyte
*   c. ovule
    d. ovary
    e. pollen grains

GYMNOSPERMS—PLANTS WITH "NAKED" SEEDS

E 45. Which of the following plants are widely planted in cities because of their resistance to insect predators, air pollution, and disease?
    a. lycopods
*   b. ginkgoes
    c. Dutch elms
    d. conifers
    e. grasses

E 46. Which of the following is NOT a conifer?
    a. pine
    b. fir
    c. cedar
*   d. ginkgo
    e. cypress

D 47. Which of the following plants is NOT a gymnosperm?
    a. cycad
    b. spruce
*   c. palm
    d. ginkgo
    e. gnetophyte

M 48. Some gymnosperms
*   a. were the first plants not to have swimming sperm and were therefore freed from the need for water to reproduce.
    b. are divided into two groups, the monocots and eudicots.
    c. were the first plants to develop vascular tissues.
    d. were the first plants to develop flowers to attract insects.
    e. were the first flowering plants.

M 49. Which of these organisms, sometimes called living fossils, is represented by only one species?
    a. *Equisetum,* or horsetails
    b. lycophytes, or club mosses
    c. gnetophyte
*   d. ginkgo
    e. cycad

M 50. The first organisms that did not require water for reproduction were the
    a. ferns.
    b. lycophytes.
    c. cycads.
    d. flowering plants.
*   e. some gymnosperms.

M 51. In pine trees, the immature male gametophyte is
    a. a megaspore.
    b. the embryonic pine seed.
    c. a pollen tube.
*   d. developed within a pollen grain.
    e. all of these

D 52. What occurs within the female cone of a pine tree?
    a. meiosis
    b. mitosis
    c. fertilization
    d. both meiosis and mitosis
*   e. meiosis, mitosis, and fertilization

E 53. A pine tree is
    a. an angiosperm.
    b. a haploid plant body.
*   c. a sporophyte.
    d. a living fossil.
    e. all of these

M 54. A pine seed is composed primarily of
    a. the embryo.
    b. female gametophyte.
    c. seed coats.
    d. the embryo and seed coats.
*   e. the embryo, seed coats, and female gametophyte.

D 55. Which of the following statements about pine cones is correct?
    a. Cones are exclusively female structures.
    b. Cones are the result of pollination.
    c. One type of cone produces microspores.
    d. Seeds are enclosed in cones.
*   e. One type of cone produces microspores and seeds are enclosed in cones.

ANGIOSPERMS—THE FLOWERING PLANTS

M 56. Which of the following do NOT possess vascular tissue?
    a. angiosperms
*   b. bryophytes
    c. conifers
    d. ferns
    e. ginkgoes

E   57.   The first group with flowers was the
          a. algae.
          b. fern allies.
          c. ferns.
     *   d. angiosperms.
          e. gymnosperms.

M   58.   Angiosperms are more advanced than gymnosperms
          because gymnosperms lack which structure found in
          angiosperms?
          a. independent gametophytes
          b. pollen grains
     *   c. fruits
          d. roots
          e. stems

E   59.   The group of seed plants that has the most species is
          the
          a. magnoliids.
          b. ferns.
          c. gymnosperms.
     *   d. eudicots.
          e. monocots.

M   60.   The dominance of flowering plants for the past 100
          million years appears to be related to their coevolution
          with
          a. dinosaurs.
          b. gymnosperms.
     *   c. insect pollinators.
          d. mammals.
          e. birds.

D   61.   Angiosperms
          a. are the most successful of all plants.
          b. are the most diverse of all plants.
          c. are represented by a number of heterotrophic
             plants.
          d. have embryos that are provided with food by an
             endosperm, a unique structure found only within
             the angiosperms.
     *   e. all of these

M   62.   All EXCEPT which of the following are monocots?
          a. lilies
          b. palms
     *   c. roses
          d. grasses
          e. orchids

M   63.   Dependence on animal vectors for fertilization and
          dispersal is characteristic of many species of
          a. ferns.
     *   b. angiosperms.
          c. mosses.
          d. conifers.
          e. pine.

M   64.   The vast majority of plant species are
          a. algae.
          b. bryophytes.
          c. gymnosperms.
     *   d. angiosperms.
          e. extinct.

M   65.   Which is the correct sequence in the evolution of
          plants?
          a. algae, conifers, flowering plants, ferns
          b. ferns, algae, conifers, flowering plants
     *   c. algae, ferns, conifers, flowering plants
          d. ferns, conifers, algae, flowering plants
          e. conifers, ferns, algae, flowering plants

DEFORESTATION IN THE TROPICS

M   66.   Deforestation can produce all of the following
          EXCEPT
          a. reduced rates of evaporation.
          b. disturbed rainfall patterns.
     *   c. increased amounts of usable farmland.
          d. altered carbon dioxide levels.
          e. more absorption of sunlight.

M   67.   Which of the following is NOT associated with
          deforestation?
     *   a. increased soil fertility
          b. slash-and-burn agriculture
          c. tropical forests
          d. greater water runoff rates
          e. decreased carbon dioxide absorption

Matching Questions

D **68.** Matching. Choose the most appropriate answer for each.

1. ___ eudicots
2. ___ conifers
3. ___ club mosses
4. ___ cycads
5. ___ ferns
6. ___ flowering plants
7. ___ ginkgos
8. ___ horsetails
9. ___ mosses, liverworts
10. ___ angiosperm

A. have rhizoids, cuticle, and protected embryo sporophyte

B. "vessel seed"

C. non-seed-bearing, heart-shaped gametophytes; spore-bearing leaves with sori

D. *Lycopodium;* cone-bearing sporophyte; free-living gametophyte

E. only one species left

F. pines and redwood; heterosporous; mostly evergreen

G. confined to tropical or subtropical regions where their seeds are ground into flour

H. most of the herbaceous plants

I. *Equisetum;* homosporous; rhizomes present; aerial stems jointed

J. have coevolved with insect and other pollinators

Answers: 1. H   2. F   3. D   4. G

5. C   6. J   7. E   8. I

9. A   10. B

Classification Questions

Answer questions 69–73 in reference to the vascular plants listed below.

a. horsetails
b. ferns
c. gingkos
d. conifers
e. angiosperms

E **69.** Sori on these plants produce spores on the underside of fronds.

E **70.** These plants have silica deposits in their stems, which makes them good pot scrubbers.

M **71.** Male trees of this group are used as ornamentals but the female trees stink!

M **72.** This group is heterosporous with well-developed seeds and pollen-bearing cones.

M **73.** Seeds of this group are enclosed in an ovary, which, when ripened, may form a fruit.

Answers: 69. b   70. a   71. c   72. d

73. e

Selecting the Exception

D **74.** Four of the five answers listed below are related by the quantity of chromosomes present. Select the exception.
a. spores
* b. sporophyte
c. egg
d. sperm
e. gametophyte

D **75.** Three of the four answers listed below are related by absence of vascular tissue. Select the exception.
* a. ferns
b. liverworts
c. mosses
d. hornworts

D **76.** Four of the five answers listed below are groups in which the sporophyte is dominant. Select the exception.
* a. bryophytes
b. club mosses
c. angiosperms
d. gnetophytes
e. gymnosperms

D **77.** Four of the five answers listed below are heterosporous. Select the exception.
a. angiosperms
b. cycads
c. ginkgo
d. conifers
* e. ferns

E   78. Four of the five answers listed below are
          gymnosperms. Select the exception.
              a. redwoods
              b. cycads
              c. gnetophytes
          *   d. palms
              e. pines

M   79. Four of the five answers listed below are monocots.
          Select the exception.
              a. grass
              b. lily
          *   c. cabbage
              d. orchid
              e. corn

M   80. Four of the five answers listed below are seed
          producers. Select the exception.
          *   a. ferns
              b. conifers
              c. eudicots
              d. ginkgos
              e. monocots

D   81. Four of the five answers listed below are portions of
          the gametophyte generation. Select the exception.
              a. microspore
              b. megaspore
          *   c. ovule
              d. pollen tube
              e. male gametophyte

D   82. Four of the five answers listed below are related by the
          presence of vascular tissue. Select the exception.
              a. ferns
          *   b. mosses
              c. pine trees
              d. flowering plants
              e. horsetails

Labeling

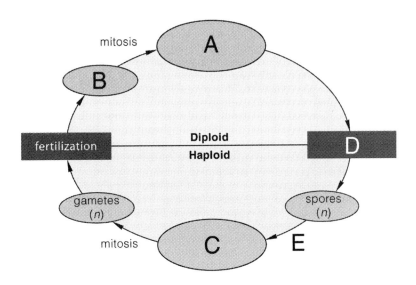

E   **83.** The multicelled sporophyte is represented by letter _?_.

E   **84.** Multicelled gametophytes are represented at letter _?_.

E   **85.** What cell division process is happening at letter "E"?
     a. meiosis
     b. fertilization
     c. cytokinesis
  *   d. mitosis
     e. gamete formation

E   **86.** What cell division process is happening at letter "D"?
  *   a. meiosis
     b. fertilization
     c. cytokinesis
     d. mitosis
     e. gamete formation

E   **87.** What is formed at letter "B"?
     a. sperm
     b. egg
  *   c. zygote
     d. sporophyte
     e. tissue

Answers: 83. A   84. C

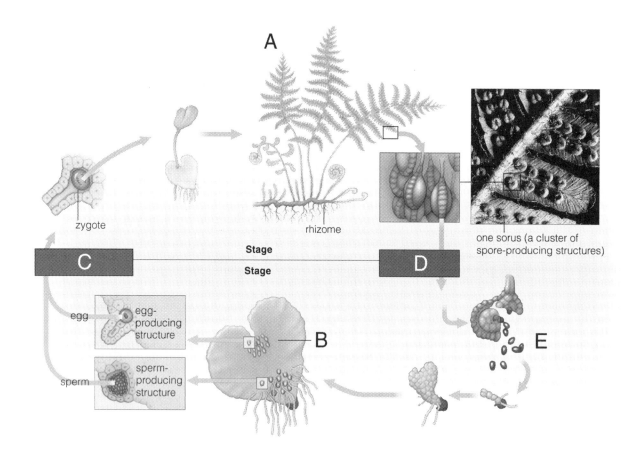

one sorus (a cluster of spore-producing structures)

E   **88.**   The sporophyte stage of the fern is represented by letter _?_.

E   **89.**   The process of fertilization is happening at letter _?_.

M   **90.**   The upper half of the diagram represents the _?_ stage.
         a. haploid
    *   b. diploid

E   **91.**   What is happening at letter "E"?
         a. spore formation
         b. fertilization
         c. cytokinesis
    *   d. spore release
         e. gamete formation

Answers: 88. A   89. C

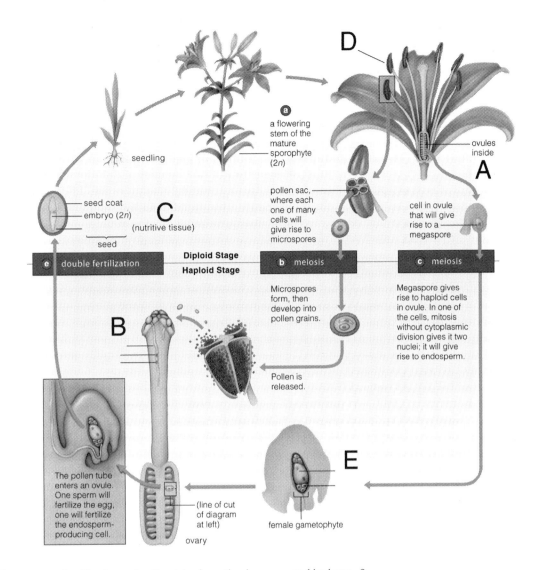

a flowering stem of the mature sporophyte (2n)

seedling

ovules inside

A

D

cell in ovule that will give rise to a megaspore

seed coat
embryo (2n)
C
(nutritive tissue)
seed

pollen sac, where each one of many cells will give rise to microspores

Diploid Stage		
e double fertilization	**b** meiosis	**c** meiosis
Haploid Stage		

Microspores form, then develop into pollen grains.

Megaspore gives rise to haploid cells in ovule. In one of the cells, mitosis without cytoplasmic division gives it two nuclei; it will give rise to endosperm.

B

Pollen is released.

The pollen tube enters an ovule. One sperm will fertilize the egg, one will fertilize the endosperm-producing cell.

(line of cut of diagram at left)

ovary

female gametophyte

E

E **92.** The process of pollination and pollen tube formation is represented by letter _?_.

E **93.** The "nutritive tissue" at letter "C" is properly called
  a. nutrisperm.
 * b. endosperm.
  c. diplosperm.
  d. haplosperm.
  e. megasperm.

E **94.** The male part of the flower is represented by letter _?_.

E **95.** The ovules at letter "A" are located inside the
  a. anther.
  b. pistil.
 * c. ovary.
  d. egg.
  e. petals.

Answers: 92. B 94. D

CHAPTER 16
ANIMAL EVOLUTION

Multiple-Choice Questions

OVERVIEW OF THE ANIMAL KINGDOM

M 1. Which of the following statements is NOT true?
    a. Mammals are vertebrates.
    b. Invertebrates have no backbone.
*   c. There are more vertebrate species than invertebrates.
    d. The phylogenetic tree of animals begins with the sponges.
    e. Arthropods have the most species.

M 2. Which of the following characteristics is NOT true of ALL animal groups?
    a. multicellular
*   b. organ systems
    c. heterotrophic
    d. motile
    e. sexual reproduction

M 3. All animals are multicellular,
*   a. heterotrophic, and are aerobic.
    b. heterotrophic, and lack motility.
    c. autotrophic, and have embryos.
    d. autotrophic, and are motile.
    e. heterotrophic, sexual, and non-embryonic.

M 4. Which of the following cushions and protects internal organs, yet they move independently of the body wall?
*   a. a coelom
    b. mesoderm
    c. a mantle
    d. a water-vascular system
    e. all of these

M 5. A digestive tract is said to be complete if it
    a. possesses specialized regions for different digestive tasks.
    b. produces acids and contains enzymes.
*   c. is a one-way tube with a mouth and an anus.
    d. is surrounded by muscle.
    e. all of these

M 6. Major trends in the evolution of animals include
    a. cephalization, the development of a definite head region.
    b. the development of types of symmetry.
    c. variation in coelomic cavities.
    d. the development of segments.
*   e. all of these

M 7. Which of the following organisms exhibits cephalization?
*   a. flatworms
    b. sea anemone
    c. sea star
    d. sponge
    e. jellyfish

D 8. Which of the following statements is FALSE?
    a. The development of a coelom was necessary before organisms could develop a large size.
    b. Segmentation allows increasing specialization of body parts.
    c. The development of an elongated gut allows specialized regions to carry out different functions.
*   d. Organisms with radial symmetry developed into the ultimate predators.
    e. Bilaterally symmetrical animals also display a head region.

D 9. An animal with bilateral symmetry
    a. has left and right sides.
    b. usually displays cephalization.
    c. produces mirror images regardless of the number of "cuts" through the central axis.
*   d. has left and right sides and usually displays cephalization.
    e. has left and right sides, usually displays cephalization, and produces mirror images regardless of the number of "cuts" through the central axis.

M 10. Which of the following lack a "true" coelom?
    a. flatworms only
    b. annelids only
    c. roundworms only
*   d. flatworms and roundworms
    e. flatworms and annelids

GETTING ALONG WELL WITHOUT ANY ORGANS

M 11. Sponges are
    a. herbivores.
*   b. filter or sieve-feeders.
    c. scavengers.
    d. predators.
    e. carnivores.

D 12. Unlike most other animals, sponges lack
    a. a digestive tract only.
    b. a symmetrical body plan only.
    c. nerve cells only.
    d. a digestive tract and a symmetrical body plan.
*   e. a digestive tract, a symmetrical body plan, and nerve cells.

D 13. Sponge cells obtain nutrients by
    a. absorbing food that diffuses from the central cavity.
    b. capturing food in their microvilli.
*   c. absorbing food distributed by amoeboid cells.
    d. phagocytosing bacteria and other small food items.
    e. engulfing food with pseudopods.

M 14. Which one of the following do sponges display?
    a. definite symmetry
    b. organs
    c. anus
*   d. skeletal elements—spicules
    e. appendages

M 15. Feeding in sponges is dependent on
    a. collar cells only.
    b. pores only.
    c. water flow only.
    d. pores and water flow.
*   e. collar cells, pores, and water flow.

D 16. Which of the following groups does NOT have tissues?
    a. roundworms
*   b. sponges
    c. echinoderms
    d. flatworms
    e. cnidarians

E 17. Mesoglea is found in which of the following groups?
    a. sponges
*   b. cnidarians
    c. roundworms
    d. annelids
    e. mollusks

E 18. Nematocysts are
    a. reproductive cells.
    b. excretory organs.
    c. sets of muscle cells.
    d. circulatory cells.
*   e. defensive cells.

M 19. Nematocysts are found only in
*   a. cnidarians.
    b. roundworms.
    c. crustaceans.
    d. echinoderms.
    e. arthropods.

E 20. "Nerve net" describes the nervous system of
    a. flatworms.
*   b. cnidarians.
    c. annelids.
    d. sponges.
    e. none of these

E 21. The "jelly" inside a jellyfish is
    a. mesoderm.
    b. mesohyl.
    c. mesophyll.
*   d. mesoglea.
    e. mesogel.

M 22. Which of the following groups is characterized by radially symmetrical members?
    a. arthropods
*   b. cnidarians
    c. flatworms
    d. chordates
    e. annelids

D 23. Cnidarians do NOT have
    a. tentacles equipped with nematocysts.
*   b. a brain.
    c. radial symmetry.
    d. a digestive cavity.
    e. medusa stages.

M 24. A planula is
    a. a sedentary, attached, tree-shaped form found in corals.
*   b. a swimming larval form with an outer ciliated epidermis.
    c. a kind of parasitic worm.
    d. a fleshy lobe that extends laterally from the body wall of a marine worm.
    e. a rasplike tongue.

M 25. In the life cycle of a typical cnidarian, which of the following would most likely be free-swimming?
    a. medusa only
    b. polyp only
    c. planula only
*   d. medusa and planula
    e. medusa and polyp

D 26. Members of a colony would be described best by which of the following words?
    a. dependent
    b. independent
*   c. interdependent
    d. nondependent
    e. semidependent

FLATWORMS—INTRODUCING ORGAN SYSTEMS

M 27. Which body plan is characterized by simple gas exchange mechanisms, two-way traffic through a highly branched, saclike gut, and a thin, flat body with all cells fairly close to the gut?
    a. cnidarian
    b. roundworm
    c. echinoderm
*   d. flatworm
    e. sponge

M 28. Bilateral symmetry is characteristic of
    a. cnidarians.
    b. sponges.
    c. jellyfish.
*   d. flatworms.
    e. corals.

M   29.   Animals that are hermaphroditic usually have
          a. only one sex.
       * b. both sexes.
          c. only the male sex.
          d. only the female sex.
          e. neither sex.

D   30.   In the life cycle of the fluke responsible for
          schistomiasis, larvae from fertilized eggs enter
          a. a human.
          b. another fluke.
       * c. a snail.
          d. unknown at this time.
          e. a fish.

M   31.   A common intermediate host for most flukes are
          a. mosquitoes.
       * b. snails.
          c. mice.
          d. flies.
          e. clams.

ANNELIDS–SEGMENTS GALORE

D   32.   Which of the following is an organism that possesses
          setae and nerve cords, plus exhibits coordinated
          movements of circular and longitudinal muscle?
          a. sponge
          b. tapeworm
       * c. earthworm
          d. jellyfish
          e. flatworm

D   33.   Earthworms can perform all EXCEPT which of the
          following?
       * a. chewing of food
          b. respiration
          c. aeration of the soil
          d. movement using setae
          e. excretion of water

D   34.   Polychaetes and oligochaetes are the only annelids
          that possess
          a. a closed circulatory system.
          b. jaws or teeth.
       * c. parapods.
          d. ganglia.
          e. a complete digestive tract.

M   35.   Which of the following is NOT related to the other
          four?
          a. free-living flatworms
       * b. earthworms
          c. flukes
          d. tapeworms
          e. planarians

M   36.   Which of the following has a gut with two openings, a
          mouth, and an anus?
          a. jellyfish
       * b. earthworms
          c. flatworms
          d. sponges
          e. sea anemone

D   37.   An organism that possesses a scolex and proglottids is
          a. free-living.
       * b. a tapeworm.
          c. a cnidarian.
          d. segmented.
          e. a host.

THE EVOLUTIONARILY PLIABLE MOLLUSKS

M   38.   The _?_ are an animal group with more than 110,000
          species.
          a. roundworms
       * b. mollusks
          c. flatworms
          d. echinoderms
          e. cnidarians

E   39.   A mantle is found only among the
          a. arthropods.
          b. annelids.
          c. echinoderms.
       * d. mollusks.
          e. chordates.

D   40.   Which of the following is in the group characterized
          by a mantle and a soft body?
          a. lobster
          b. crayfish
       * c. octopus
          d. sand dollar
          e. insect

M   41.   The smartest mollusks are
          a. chitons.
       * b. cephalopods.
          c. gastropods.
          d. bivalves.
          e. snails.

D   42.   Cephalopods are the only mollusks that possess
          a. a mantle.
          b. gills.
       * c. a closed circulatory system.
          d. shells.
          e. closed circulation and shells.

AMAZINGLY ABUNDANT ROUNDWORMS

M   43.   Molting is
          a. the anterior attachment organ of a tapeworm.
          b. the feeding organ of a fluke.
          c. an appendage of a polychaete.
       * d. the shedding of the outer covering of an organism.
          e. the larva of an aquatic insect.

M   44.   Which of the following have a flexible cuticle,
          complete gut, and a false coelom mostly filled with
          reproductive organs?
       * a. roundworms
          b. cnidarians
          c. flatworms
          d. echinoderms
          e. sponges

M 45. *Trichinella* and *Wuchereria* are
  *   a. roundworms.
       b. flatworms.
       c. annelids.
       d. circular worms.
       e. flukes.

D 46. For roundworms living in the intestine of a vertebrate, the cuticle would most probably serve in what capacity?
       a. water retention
       b. nutrient absorption
  *   c. protection from digestive enzymes
       d. excretion of metabolic wastes
       e. sensory detection

E 47. Which of the following is mismatched?
       a. sponges—spicules
       b. cnidarians—polyp
  *   c. roundworms—segmentation
       d. flatworms—ovaries and testes
       e. tapeworms—scolex

ARTHROPODS–THE MOST SUCCESSFUL ANIMALS

M 48. The most successful of the invertebrate groups with respect to the numbers of species is
       a. annelids.
  *   b. arthropods.
       c. mollusks.
       d. echinoderms.
       e. roundworms.

M 49. The animal group that contains the greatest number of named species is
       a. mollusks.
  *   b. arthropods.
       c. roundworms.
       d. chordates.
       e. annelids.

M 50. Exoskeletons are most characteristic of which of the following?
       a. mollusks
  *   b. arthropods
       c. echinoderms
       d. chordates
       e. annelids

E 51. What are the unique devices used by insects in atmospheric respiration ?
       a. gills
       b. lunglike chambers
  *   c. a system of small tubes
       d. mantles
       e. pedipalps

M 52. The exoskeleton of a butterfly does NOT provide which of the following?
       a. physical protection
       b. physical support
       c. an antidesiccant surface
  *   d. a respiratory surface
       e. a flight surface

E 53. Molting in arthropods involves primarily a change in
       a. body form and maturity.
       b. sex.
  *   c. body size.
       d. eating habits.
       e. sensory structures.

M 54. Which of the following is a disadvantage of an exoskeleton?
  *   a. It must be shed for its owner to grow.
       b. It does not provide as efficient a muscle anchorage as an endoskeleton.
       c. It allows for excess water loss.
       d. It is not flexible enough to allow a full range of movement.
       e. It is not able to absorb pigments for sufficient camouflage.

M 55. The most successful insects are capable of
       a. walking.
  *   b. flight.
       c. feeding.
       d. copulation.
       e. swimming.

E 56. The most successful animals that have ever evolved are the
       a. vertebrates.
  *   b. insects.
       c. humans.
       d. protozoans.
       e. mollusks.

D 57. Which of the following is NOT a chelicerate?
       a. tick
  *   b. mosquito
       c. spider
       d. horseshoe crab
       e. scorpion

E 58. Metamorphosis in arthropods involves primarily a change in
  *   a. embryo and adult forms.
       b. sex.
       c. body size.
       d. eating habits.
       e. sensory structures.

M 59. Which of the following adaptations has contributed to the success of the insects?
       a. specialized sensory organs only
       b. wings only
       c. high reproductive capacity only
       d. specialized sensory organs and wings
  *   e. specialized sensory organs, wings, and high reproductive capacity

D 60. In the course of evolution, the thorax of an insect has become specialized for
         a. digestion.
         b. reproduction.
    *   c. locomotion.
         d. excretion.
         e. sensation.

THE PUZZLING ECHINODERMS

D 61. Which group is strictly marine, with no freshwater or terrestrial forms?
    *   a. echinoderms
         b. flatworms
         c. cnidarians
         d. mollusks
         e. annelids

M 62. A water-vascular system that operates the tube feet is characteristic of the group comprising the
         a. arthropods.
         b. annelids.
         c. chordates.
         d. mollusks.
    *   e. echinoderms.

M 63. The tube feet of sea stars are used primarily for
         a. excretion of excess water.
    *   b. locomotion.
         c. respiration.
         d. circulation.
         e. sensation.

EVOLUTIONARY TRENDS AMONG VERTEBRATES

M 64. Which of the following statements is NOT true?
         a. All chordates have notochords.
         b. All chordates have pharyngeal pouches or slits.
         c. All chordates have dorsal tubular nerve cords.
    *   d. All chordates are vertebrates.
         e. Chordates have tails.

D 65. The notochord is most closely associated with the
         a. nervous system.
         b. spinal cord.
    *   c. skeletal system.
         d. skin system.
         e. brain.

E 66. The chordate feature still present in the human adult is
         a. pharyngeal gill slits.
    *   b. the nerve cord.
         c. the notochord.
         d. the tail.
         e. all of these

D 67. Which of the following statements is FALSE?
    *   a. All vertebrates have a ventral tubular nervous system.
         b. All vertebrates have a tail at some stage in their life cycle.
         c. All vertebrates have a notochord at some stage in their life cycle.
         d. All vertebrates have pharyngeal gill slits at some stage in their life cycle.
         e. All vertebrates have a dorsal nerve cord.

M 68. Which of the following is NOT a feature that is found exclusively among all vertebrates?
         a. notochord
         b. pharyngeal gill slits
    *   c. four legs
         d. post-anal tail
         e. dorsal nerve cord

D 69. In vertebrate evolution, the appearance of the vertebral column led most directly to development of
         a. limbs such as arms and legs.
    *   b. jaws.
         c. sense organs and the nervous system.
         d. more efficient breathing systems.
         e. greater speed of locomotion.

M 70. In fishes ancestral to land vertebrates, two small outpouchings on the gut wall developed into
         a. heart chambers.
         b. the notochord.
         c. lobes of the liver.
    *   d. lungs.
         e. vocal cords.

M 71. The ostracoderms were
         a. an ancient group of spiny, thin echinoderms.
         b. a group of primitive protochordates.
    *   c. primitive fishes without jaws.
         d. one of the first terrestrial vertebrates.
         e. reptiles with a bony skin.

M 72. Ostracoderms lost out in evolutionary competition to animals
         a. with more protective body coverings.
         b. who were filter feeders.
         c. with lungs.
    *   d. that had begun to develop jaws.
         e. with an exoskeleton.

M 73. Placoderms were the earliest fishes to display
    *   a. jaws.
         b. gill openings.
         c. cartilaginous skeletons.
         d. jaws and gill openings.
         e. jaws, gill openings, and cartilaginous skeletons.

M 74. The vertebrate jaw first appeared in
    *   a. ancient fishes.
         b. amphibians.
         c. reptiles.
         d. birds.
         e. mammals.

MAJOR GROUPS OF JAWED FISHES

E **75.** Sharks and rays belong to the
  a. birds.
  b. amphibians.
  * c. cartilaginous fishes.
  d. bony fishes.
  e. reptiles.

M **76.** Sharks differ from most other fish in that they lack
  a. lungs.
  b. scales.
  * c. bone.
  d. paired appendages.
  e. jaws.

E **77.** The vertebrate lung first appeared in which organisms?
  * a. fishes
  b. amphibians
  c. reptiles
  d. birds
  e. mammals

EARLY AMPHIBIOUS TETRAPODS

D **78.** Amphibians most likely evolved from
  * a. fish with lobed fins.
  b. ray-finned fish.
  c. reptiles.
  d. agnathans.
  e. placoderms.

E **79.** Amphibians are completely dependent on an aquatic environment for
  a. respiration.
  b. feeding.
  * c. reproduction.
  d. respiration and reproduction.
  e. respiration, reproduction, and feeding.

D **80.** A water environment provides more of ALL of the following than does air EXCEPT
  a. support.
  b. buoyancy.
  c. constancy of temperature.
  * d. oxygen.
  e. resistance to movement.

THE RISE OF AMNIOTES

M **81.** Vertebrate colonization of terrestrial habitats increased dramatically with the evolution of
  a. lungs.
  b. paired appendages.
  * c. shelled eggs.
  d. the four-chambered heart.
  e. scales.

M **82.** In the Late Carboniferous, reptiles were able to move into new habitats because of
  a. the increase in numbers of insect prey.
  b. internal fertilization.
  c. the amniotic egg.
  d. internal fertilization and the amniotic egg, only.
  * e. well-developed kidneys, fertilization, and the amniotic egg.

M **83.** Amniotes differ from earlier vertebrates by
  a. their large size.
  b. their three-chambered heart.
  * c. internal fertilization and eggs with membranes.
  d. the possession of a slimy skin.
  e. having external scales.

E **84.** The first group to exhibit an amniotic egg belonged to the
  a. birds.
  b. amphibians.
  * c. reptiles.
  d. bony fish.
  e. mammals.

D **85.** Birds and mammals share which of the following characteristics?
  a. ectothermy (body temperature regulated by environment)
  b. body hair
  * c. four-chambered heart
  d. lung design
  e. amniotic egg

M **86.** Adaptations for flight in birds include all EXCEPT which of the following?
  * a. sound production
  b. lightweight bones
  c. feathers
  d. efficient respiration
  e. four-chambered heart

D **87.** Which adaptation(s) is (are) common to insects and mammals?
  * a. jointed appendages
  b. closed circulatory system
  c. lungs
  d. jointed appendages and closed circulatory system
  e. jointed appendages, closed circulatory system, and lungs

FROM EARLY PRIMATES TO HUMANS

E **88.** Which is NOT an anthropoid?
  a. orangutan
  * b. lemur
  c. spider monkey
  d. gorilla
  e. human

M 89. Humans are least closely related to the
    a. chimpanzee.
    b. orangutan.
    c. gorilla.
  * d. tarsier.
    e. gibbon.

M 90. Which group includes all the others?
    a. tarsoids
    b. hominoids
    c. prosimians
    d. anthropoids
  * e. primates

M 91. Humans belong to all but which one of the following?
    a. hominids
    b. hominoids
  * c. prosimians
    d. anthropoids
    e. primates

E 92. Which of the following can be included in the group called "hominids"?
    a. monkeys
  * b. humans
    c. apes
    d. humans and apes, only
    e. monkeys, humans, and apes

E 93. The evolutionary trend of bipedalism refers to the
    a. ability of only humans to ride a bicycle.
  * b. human ability to habitually walk on two feet.
    c. use of two hands to swing through the trees as monkeys do.
    d. development of a prehensile hand.
    e. use of feet as well as hands for grasping.

M 94. Well-developed molars would be most valuable to
    a. cats.
    b. meat eaters.
  * c. cows.
    d. dogs.
    e. birds.

M 95. The study of teeth tells the researcher what about an animal?
    a. its diet
    b. its lifestyle
    c. its intelligence
  * d. its diet and lifestyle
    e. its diet, lifestyle, and intelligence

E 96. All EXCEPT which factor were important evolutionary adaptations in primates?
    a. daytime vision
    b. bipedalism
    c. an opposable thumb
  * d. the development of a restricted or specialized diet
    e. teeth

E 97. The ability to grasp objects by wrapping the hand around them is termed
    a. opposable.
    b. grabbing.
  * c. prehensile.
    d. grappling.
    e. hooking.

E 98. The ability to hold a paintbrush as an artist does is due to the thumb and fingers being
    a. prehensile.
    b. in line with each other.
    c. bendable.
    d. muscular.
  * e. opposable.

M 99. The most recent level of evolution in primates is considered to be in
    a. brain expansion.
  * b. behavior and culture.
    c. dentition.
    d. hand grip.
    e. daytime vision.

M 100. The location of the eyes on the front of the head in later primates was especially important in
    a. seeing color.
    b. detecting light intensity.
    c. predatory behavior.
  * d. better depth perception.
    e. mating.

M 101. In the evolution of the arboreal primates, which of the following features would NOT be an important evolutionary advancement?
    a. opposable thumbs
    b. stereoscopic vision
  * c. elongated snout with well-developed sense of smell
    d. the ability to see in color
    e. a brain that could assess motion, depth, shape, and color

E 102. The primates first arose about how many million years ago?
    a. 75
  * b. 55
    c. 50
    d. 40
    e. 30

M 103. Primitive primates generally live
  * a. in tropical and subtropical forest canopies.
    b. in temperate savanna and grassland habitats.
    c. near rivers, lakes, and streams in the East African Rift Valley.
    d. in caves with abundant supplies of insects.
    e. all of these

M 104. In comparison to the Oligocene, the climate at the start of the Miocene
    a. remained the same.
    b. became wetter and warmer.
    * c. became drier and cooler.
    d. became wetter and cooler.
    e. became drier and warmer.

M 105. Which group is considered most ancient?
    a. *Homo erectus*
    b. *Australopithecus afarensis*
    c. *Australopithecus africanus*
    d. *Homo sapiens*
    * e. *Sahelanthropus*

D 106. The hominids are characterized by
    a. further expansion and elaboration of the brain.
    b. bipedalism.
    c. omnivorous feeding behavior.
    d. further expansion and elaboration of the brain plus bipedalism.
    * e. further expansion and elaboration of the brain plus bipedalism and omnivorous feeding behavior.

M 107. Hominids are characterized as being
    a. insectivores.
    b. herbivores.
    c. carnivores.
    * d. omnivores.
    e. none of these

E 108. The early hominid fossils are found in
    * a. Africa.
    b. Asia.
    c. Australia.
    d. the South Pacific.
    e. Europe.

M 109. The most important feature of the recent evolution of humans has been
    a. increase in size.
    b. habitat changes.
    * c. cultural evolution.
    d. social behavior.
    e. morphological changes.

M 110. Perhaps the greatest asset possessed by early hominids was
    a. their use of many different kinds of foods.
    b. the ability to walk without using the forelimbs.
    c. a heavy, muscular build.
    * d. the ability to reason and learn.
    e. less hair on the body.

M 111. Fossils of the earliest known distinct hominids are _?_ million years old.
    a. more than 20
    b. about 10
    * c. between 4 and 2
    d. less than 0.5
    e. between 30 and 20

M 112. Which of the following is a hominid?
    a. chimpanzee
    * b. *Australopithecus*
    c. baboon
    d. chimpanzee and *Australopithecus*
    e. chimpanzee, *Australopithecus,* and baboon

M 113. It is thought that the earliest tools were used by hominids to
    a. assist in locomotion.
    b. provide protection.
    * c. facilitate the processing of food.
    d. ward off predators.
    e. wage war.

M 114. The first toolmakers were
    a. *Australopithecus africanus.*
    b. *Australopithecus robustus.*
    c. *Australopithecus boisei.*
    * d. *Homo habilis.*
    e. *Homo erectus.*

E 115. The oldest hominid fossils have been found in
    a. North America.
    b. Eurasia.
    * c. Africa.
    d. Australia.
    e. Europe.

M 116. Fossil evidence suggests that the earliest members of the genus *Homo* were
    a. social.
    b. omnivorous.
    c. toolmakers.
    d. social and omnivorous.
    * e. social, omnivorous, and toolmakers.

D 117. Although the phylogenetic lineages for hominids are not definitive, which of the following statements is NOT a possibility?
    * a. *Homo* preceded *Australopithecus.*
    b. *Homo sapiens* is the most recent.
    c. *Australopithecus* is probably more ancient than *Homo.*
    d. *Homo erectus* preceded *Homo sapiens.*
    e. *Homo* and *Australopithecus* may have evolved at the same time.

M 118. The geographical distribution of hominids changed dramatically between 2 million and 500,000 years ago due to the migrations of
    a. *Australopithecus robustus.*
    b. *Australopithecus boisei.*
    * c. *Homo erectus.*
    d. *Homo sapiens.*
    e. *Homo habilis.*

M   119.   About 40,000 years ago, what kind of evolution replaced biological evolution in the shaping of modern humans?
   * a. cultural
   b. behavioral
   c. chemical
   d. psychological
   e. morphological

M   120.   A hominid of Europe and Asia that became extinct nearly 30,000 years ago was
   a. a dryopith.
   b. *Australopithecus.*
   c. *Homo erectus.*
   * d. Neandertals.
   e. *Sahelanthropus.*

D   121.   "Smaller teeth, prominent chin, smaller facial bones, larger brain, and rounder, lighter skull" would be a partial description of
   a. *Australopithecus robustus.*
   b. *Australopithecus boisei.*
   c. *Homo habilis* (early *Homo*).
   d. *Homo erectus.*
   * e. *Homo sapiens.*

Matching Questions

D   122.   Matching I. Choose the most appropriate answer for each.
   1. ___ insects
   2. ___ annelids
   3. ___ arthropods
   4. ___ flukes
   5. ___ cnidarians
   6. ___ echinoderms
   7. ___ flatworms
   8. ___ arachnids
   9. ___ mollusks
   10. ___ roundworms
   11. ___ sponges
      A. body divided into three regions
      B. groups of parasitic flatworms
      C. planarians, flukes, tapeworms
      D. cause of trichinosis
      E. snails, squids, and clams
      F. spiders, scorpions, ticks, and mites
      G. collar cells present
      H. jellyfish and corals
      I. crustaceans, ticks, and insects
      J. polychaetes, earthworms, and leeches
      K. sea urchins and sea stars

Answers: 1. A   2. J   3. I   4. B
   5. H   6. K   7. C   8. F
   9. E   10. D   11. G

D   123.   Matching II. Choose the one most appropriate letter for each blank.
   1. ___ birds
   2. ___ bony fishes
   3. ___ hominid
   4. ___ humans
   5. ___ anthropoids
   6. ___ australopiths
   7. ___ hominoid
   8. ___ ostracoderms
   9. ___ placoderms
   10. ___ Neandertals
   11. ___ Primates
   12. ___ sharks
   13. ___ snakes

   A. cartilaginous skeleton; jaws
   B. jawless fishes; now extinct
   C. placental mammal with greater degree of culture
   D. group excluding apes
   E. bipedal organisms from about 3.8 to 1 million years ago, with essentially human bodies and ape-shaped heads; brains no larger than those of chimpanzees
   F. feathers
   G. limbless reptile
   H. most primitive fishes with jaws
   I. organisms in a suborder that includes New World and Old World monkeys, apes, and humans
   J. a group that includes apes and humans
   K. the order that includes animals with freely swiveling limbs, mobile grasping digits, upright body posture, good depth perception, and exquisite neural control
   L. a population of *Homo sapiens* that lived from at least 100,000 to as recently as 35,000 years ago; tool users and artisans
   M. swim bladder for buoyancy

Answers: 1. F   2. M   3. D   4. C
   5. I   6. E   7. J   8. B
   9. H   10. L   11. K   12. A
   13. G

D 124. Matching III. Choose the one most appropriate
answer for each.

    1. ___ *Australopithecus*

    2. ___ *Homo erectus*

    3. ___ *Homo sapiens*

    4. ___ Neandertals

       A. lived from approximately 100,000 to 30,000
years ago; skilled toolmakers and artisans

       B. first hominid to leave Africa

       C. lived about 30 million years ago near Fayum

       D. humans since 300,000 years ago

       E. Lucy; between 3.8 to 1 million years ago

Answers: 1. E   2. B   3. D   4. A

Classification Questions

Answer questions 125–129 in reference to the five animal groups
listed below.

    a. sponges
    b. cnidarians
    c. flatworms
    d. roundworms
    e. annelids

D 125. Members of this group have a pseudocoelomic (false)
body cavity.

D 126. Members of this group have a brain with nerve cords,
a saclike or branched gut, and they lack a circulatory
system.

M 127. Members of this group have a brain with a ventral
nerve cord, a complete gut, and a circulatory system
that is usually closed.

E 128. This group contains the most primitive species of the
animal kingdom.

M 129. Earthworms are members of this group.

Answers: 125. d   126. c   127. e

             128. a   129. e

Answer questions 130–134 in reference to the five animal groups
listed below.

    a. annelids
    b. arthropods
    c. mollusks
    d. echinoderms
    e. chordates

D 130. Extinct trilobites were members of this group.

M 131. The larval stage in this group has bilateral symmetry,
whereas the adult stage exhibits radial symmetry.

M 132. Although most are enclosed by hardened shells, this
group's name literally means "soft body."

E 133. This group has the greatest number of species.

D 134. A notochord characterizes this group.

Answers: 130. b   131. d   132. c

             133. b   134. e

Answer questions 135–139 in reference to the groups listed below.

    a. jawless fish
    b. cartilage fish
    c. bony fish
    d. amphibians
    e. reptiles

E 135. Members of this class are fully terrestrial except for
reproduction.

M 136. Ostracoderms could qualify for membership in this
class.

M 137. Members of this class have flexible skeletons but also
possess jaws.

M 138. Some species of this class live in water but are not
dependent upon an aquatic environment.

D 139. Members of one unusual class may have been
ancestors of amphibians.

Answers: 135. d   136. a   137. b

             138. e   139. c

Answer questions 140–143 in reference to the four hominids listed
below.

    a. *Homo habilis*
    b. *Homo erectus*
    c. *Homo sapiens*
    d. *Australopithecus afarensis*

M 140. The Neandertals belong to this species.

M 141. Our own species evolved from this species.

M 142. Dispersed from Africa in waves.

D 143. This species was the first definitely known to use
tools.

Answers: 140. c   141. b   142. b   143. a

Selecting the Exception

M 144. Four of the five answers listed below are
characteristics of the majority of animals. Select the
exception.
    a. multicellular
 * b. exhibit alternation of generations
    c. usually motile at least during part of their life
cycle
    d. usually diploid, sexually reproducing forms of life
    e. usually heterotrophic

D 145. Four of the five answers listed below are related.
         Select the exception.
         a. jellyfish
         b. hydra
     *   c. tunicates
         d. corals
         e. sea anemones

D 146. Four of the five answers listed below are related.
         Select the exception.
         a. sea star
     *   b. sea anemone
         c. sea urchin
         d. sea lily
         e. sea cucumber

D 147. Four of the five answers listed below possess some
         type of coelom. Select the exception.
         a. roundworms
         b. annelids
         c. arthropods
         d. mollusks
     *   e. flatworms

M 148. Four of the five answers listed below are features
         found in sponges. Select the exception.
     *   a. mesoglea
         b. spicule
         c. larvae
         d. collar cells
         e. amoeboid cells

M 149. Four of the five answers listed below are
         characteristics of cnidarians. Select the exception.
         a. planula larvae
         b. polyp form
         c. mesoglea
         d. nematocyst
     *   e. pharynx

M 150. Four of the five answers below are living chordates.
         Select the exception.
         a. lampreys
         b. bony fish
         c. reptiles
     *   d. placoderms
         e. sharks

M 151. Four of the five answers listed below are principal
         characteristics of ALL chordates. Select the exception.
         a. tail
     *   b. bony vertebra
         c. notochord
         d. nerve cord
         e. pharyngeal gill slits

M 152. Four of the five answers listed below are breathing
         mechanisms in chordates. Select the exception.
         a. skin
         b. gills
     *   c. a system of small tubes
         d. lungs
         e. lining of pharynx and mouth

D 153. Four of the five answers listed below are related.
         Select the exception.
         a. lancelet
         b. jawed fish
         c. jawless fish
         d. tunicate
     *   e. squid

E 154. Four of the five answers listed below are anthropoids.
         Select the exception.
     *   a. tarsier
         b. Old World monkey
         c. human
         d. ape
         e. gorilla

Labeling

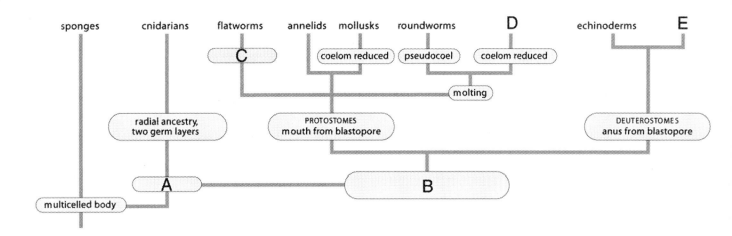

E **155.** Chordates would be placed at letter _?_.

E **156.** Bilateral symmetry would occur at letter _?_.

E **157.** Origination and organization of tissues would occur at letter _?_.

E **158.** Arthropods are placed at letter _?_.

E **159.** Coelom is lost at letter _?_.

Answers: 155. E 156. B 157. A 158. D
159. C

CHAPTER 17
PLANTS AND ANIMALS: COMMON CHALLENGES

Multiple-Choice Questions

LEVELS OF STRUCTURAL ORGANIZATION

E **1.** A collection of particular kinds of cells and intercellular substances that interact in a task or tasks is a(n)
   a. organ.
   b. organ system.
   * c. tissue.
   d. cuticle.
   e. body.

E **2.** Which of the following represents the correct hierarchy of organization in the human body?
   a. cells >>> tissues >>> organ systems >>> organs
   * b. cells >>> tissues >>> organs >>> organ systems
   c. tissues >>> cells >>> organs >>> organ systems
   d. tissues >>> organs >>> cells >>> organ systems
   e. cells >>> organs >>> tissues >>> organ systems

D **3.** The minimum level of organization required for a "division of labor" is the _?_ level.
   a. cellular
   b. organ
   * c. tissue
   d. organ system
   e. body

E **4.** Growth _?_, but development _?_.
   a. is qualitative; is quantitative
   * b. is measured by increased cell numbers; is measured by increased specialization of tissues, organs, and organ systems
   c. occurs only in infants; occurs only in adolescents
   d. continues throughout life; stops at puberty
   e. is by mitosis; is by meiosis

RECURRING CHALLENGES TO SURVIVAL

D **5.** The net direction that an ion or molecule moves is
   a. dependent upon the size of the molecule.
   b. unpredictable because movement is random.
   c. controlled by the temperature of the medium.
   d. controlled by the membranes in the vicinity.
   * e. the result of concentration differences.

M **6.** Movement of a molecule against a concentration gradient is
   a. simple diffusion.
   b. facilitated diffusion.
   c. osmosis.
   * d. active transport.
   e. bulk flow.

D **7.** If the volume of a cell increases, its surface area will
   a. decrease.
   b. remain the same.
   c. increase proportionately.
   d. increase to a greater degree.
   * e. increase to a lesser degree.

D **8.** Volume increases by the _?_ of the diameter, and surface area increases by the _?_.
   a. square; doubling
   b. square; cube
   * c. cube; square
   d. cube; cube
   e. doubling; square

E **9.** The vascular tissues of plants are composed of
   a. epidermis and ground meristem.
   b. ground tissue.
   * c. internal pipelines.
   d. arteries and veins.
   e. sap and water.

HOMEOSTASIS IN ANIMALS

M **10.** Extracellular fluid would NOT include
   a. plasma.
   b. blood.
   c. interstitial fluid.
   * d. cytoplasm.
   e. any of these

D **11.** When nutrients are supplied to a cell, the last fluid through which they must pass before encountering the plasma membrane is the
   a. plasma.
   * b. interstitial fluid.
   c. blood.
   d. intracellular fluid.
   e. cerebrospinal fluid.

M **12.** Which of the following are examples of integrators?
   * a. brain, spinal cord
   b. muscles, glands
   c. sensory cells in eye, tongue, and ear
   d. bones
   e. none of these

E **13.** Which of the following is most directly associated with a stimulus?
   a. integrators
   * b. receptors
   c. effectors
   d. central nervous system
   e. all of these

D   **14.** Which of the following is the correct sequence involved in the regulation of organ systems?
      a. stimulus, receptor, integrator, response, effector
      b. stimulus, response, integrator, receptor, effector
   * c. stimulus, receptor, integrator, effector, response
      d. stimulus, integrator, receptor, effector, response
      e. stimulus, effector, integrator, receptor, response

M   **15.** An effector could be
      a. muscle.
      b. nerve.
      c. gland.
      d. receptor.
   * e. either muscle or gland.

M   **16.** Control of body temperature is an example of which of the following?
      a. homeostatic mechanism only
      b. positive feedback system only
      c. endocrine function only
      d. negative feedback system only
   * e. both homeostatic mechanism and negative feedback system

E   **17.** In feedback systems,
      a. two sets of organs may act in opposition to each other.
      b. a set point may be established.
      c. receptors are required to monitor changing conditions.
      d. changes in environmental conditions (either internal or external) result in a response by the organism.
   * e. all of these

D   **18.** Which of the following involves a positive feedback stimulation?
      a. temperature control
   * b. sexual stimulation
      c. glucose concentration
      d. absorption of toxins
      e. muscle contraction

DOES HOMEOSTASIS OCCUR IN PLANTS?

M   **19.** Which of the following is NOT an example of compartmentalization?
      a. thickened walls around plant wounds
      b. secretion of phenols and other toxic compounds
      c. secretion of resins
      d. response to fungal attack
   * e. circadian rhythms

M   **20.** Rhythmic leaf folding is an example of
      a. adaptation.
      b. division of labor.
   * c. circadian rhythms.
      d. homeostasis.
      e. negative feedback.

HOW CELLS RECEIVE AND RESPOND TO SIGNALS

M   **21.** Cells that can "talk" to each other
      a. are found only in specific endocrine glands.
      b. are equipped with specific receptor molecules.
      c. are muscle cells.
      d. may occur in any part of the body.
   * e. activate a specific receptor by reversible binding of a signaling molecule.

M   **22.** Which of the following statements is TRUE?
   * a. Although signaling molecules are carried to all parts of the body, they produce effects only in cells with proper receptors.
      b. Signaling molecules are limited to steroid compounds.
      c. Signaling molecules are secreted by specialized exocrine glands.
      d. Most signaling molecules are controlled by positive feedback mechanisms involving the pituitary gland.
      e. Signaling molecules are electrical signals to which certain body cells respond.

M   **23.** The important feature of all cells that react to a specific signaling molecule is the
      a. type of blood supply they receive.
      b. proximity of the endocrine gland.
   * c. presence of an appropriate receptor molecule.
      d. characteristics of their plasma membranes.
      e. presence of specific genes responsive to the hormone.

E   **24.** Programmed cell death is
      a. transduction.
      b. compartmentalization.
      c. transcription.
   * d. apoptosis.
      e. none of these

Matching Questions

D   25.   Matching. Choose the one most appropriate answer for each.

1. ___ circadian rhythm
2. ___ effector
3. ___ habitat
4. ___ interstitial fluid
5. ___ apoptosis
6. ___ plasma
7. ___ stimulus
8. ___ tissue

    A.   form of energy that a receptor can detect
    B.   where an organism lives
    C.   muscles and glands are examples
    D.   biological activity repeated in 24-hour cycles
    E.   fluid that bathes all cells
    F.   fluid in the blood
    G.   cell suicide
    H.   groups of cells with a common function

Answers: 1. D   2. C   3. B   4. E
             5. G   6. F   7. A   8. H

Classification Questions

Answer questions 26–31 in reference to the six organization terms listed below.

    a.   cell
    b.   organ system
    c.   growth
    d.   organ
    e.   development
    f.   tissue

M   26.   This term describes the successive stages in the formation of specialized tissues; qualitative.

M   27.   This is a collection of tissues specialized for common function.

M   28.   The vertebrate circulatory system is a good example of this term.

D   29.   Here cells are working together for a specialized function.

D   30.   This is a quantitative term describing an increase in cell numbers.

E   31.   This is the smallest unit of life.

Answers: 26. e   27. d   28. b
             29. f   30 c   31. a

Selecting the Exception

E   32.   Four of the five answers listed below are used to describe participants in the body's division of labor Select the exception.
    a.   tissue
  * b.   growth
    c.   organ
    d.   organ system
    e.   cell

M   33.   Four of the five answers listed below could directly help a plant wall off threats. Select the exception.
  * a.   hormones
    b.   phenols
    c.   resins
    d.   compartmentalization
    e.   chemicals

M   34.   Four of the five answers listed below are true of apoptosis. Select the exception.
    a.   self-destruction
    b.   protease weapons
    c.   cell body shrinks
    d.   phagocytes consume the debris
  * e.   chromosomes are extended throughout the nucleoplasm

CHAPTER 18
PLANT FORM AND FUNCTION

Multiple-Choice Questions

OVERVIEW OF THE PLANT BODY

E 1. Approximately how many species of flowering plants are known?
a. 100,000
b. 180,000
* c. 260,000
d. 360,000
e. 480,000

E 2. Which of the following is NOT part of the plant shoot system?
a. stems
* b. roots
c. flowers
d. leaves
e. all of these are parts of the shoot system

E 3. Most of the plant body is composed of
a. dermal tissue.
b. root tissue.
* c. ground tissue.
d. vascular tissue.
e. cork tissue.

M 4. The tissue systems of the root and shoot system are classified as
a. ground tissue.
b. dermal tissue.
c. vascular tissue.
d. ground and dermal tissues.
* e. ground, dermal, and vascular tissues.

D 5. Which of the following is FALSE?
* a. Periderm is a primary tissue.
b. There is no tissue in animals that corresponds to meristem tissue of plants.
c. Growth from cell division at the tips of stems and roots produces primary growth.
d. Divisions of the lateral meristem increase the diameter of the roots and stems.
e. Lateral meristem produces secondary growth.

M 6. Perpetually young tissues where cells retain the ability to divide are
a. vascular.
* b. meristematic.
c. protective.
d. photosynthetic.
e. all of these

M 7. The division of the lateral meristem
a. results in the production of primary tissue.
b. causes an increase in the length of roots.
c. produces floral tissue.
d. gives rise to the epidermis.
* e. increases the diameter of roots and stems.

M 8. Growth designated as "primary"
a. occurs along the sides of stems.
* b. is dependent upon apical meristem.
c. increases the diameter of older plants.
d. is responsible for additions to woody parts.
e. adds lateral roots.

D 9. Which of the following is mismatched?
a. dermal cells—cutin
b. sclerenchyma—lignin
* c. parenchyma—sclereids
d. xylem—water
e. collenchyma—leaf stalks

M 10. Plant tissue noted for storage, secretion, and regeneration is
a. vascular cambium.
* b. parenchyma.
c. collenchyma.
d. sclerenchyma.
e. none of these

M 11. Parenchyma cells are specialized for and involved in all EXCEPT which of the following activities?
a. photosynthesis
b. wound healing
* c. conduction of food
d. secretion
e. food storage

M 12. The chewy, stringy supporting strands in celery are which cells?
a. xylem
* b. collenchyma
c. phloem
d. sclerenchyma
e. parenchyma

M 13. Sclereids are found in
a. root tips.
* b. seed coats.
c. mesophyll cells that produce food.
d. cortex cells that store food.
e. epidermal cells.

M 14. The gritty stone cells of pears, the hard cells of seed coats, and plant fibers are examples of
        a. xylem.
        b. collenchyma.
        c. phloem.
     * d. sclerenchyma.
        e. parenchyma.

M 15. Which of the following would NOT be considered strengthening or supportive tissue?
        a. collenchyma
        b. xylem
        c. fibers
     * d. parenchyma
        e. sclereids

M 16. If a mutation prevented the formation of lignin, which tissue would be most affected?
        a. vascular cambium
        b. parenchyma
        c. collenchyma
     * d. sclerenchyma
        e. all of these

M 17. Which of these is NOT associated with sclerenchyma?
        a. lignin
     * b. photosynthesis
        c. support
        d. sclereids
        e. fibers

M 18. Lignin is to cellulose strands as _?_ is to epidermal cells.
        a. cuticulin
        b. epidermin
        c. pectin
     * d. cutin
        e. chitin

D 19. If cell walls did not vary in thickness or were not perforated,
     * a. xylem and phloem would not be able to function as vascular tissue.
        b. gas exchange could not occur across the stomata.
        c. water could not enter the epidermal cells of the root.
        d. the terminal bud could not cause the stem to elongate.
        e. all of these

E 20. Cells that are the main water-conducting cells of a plant are
        a. sclereids.
     * b. tracheids and vessel members.
        c. sieve tubes.
        d. parenchyma.
        e. all of these

M 21. The cells that function with the sieve tubes are the
        a. vessels.
     * b. companion cells.
        c. adjunct cells.
        d. sclereids.
        e. periderm.

D 22. Which of the following statements concerning xylem is NOT correct?
     * a. Each xylem vessel is one continuous cell.
        b. The direction of flow is mainly from root upward.
        c. Water and minerals are transported.
        d. Tracheids and vessel members participate.
        e. There are pits in the walls.

D 23. Which of the following cells are alive at maturity?
     * a. sieve tube members
        b. vessel members
        c. tracheids
        d. vessel members and tracheids
        e. sieve tube members and vessel members

M 24. Which of the following cells are alive?
        a. tracheids
        b. cork
        c. sclereids
     * d. parenchyma
        e. vessel members

D 25. A cuticle
        a. resists water loss.
        b. covers epidermal cells.
        c. may contain waxes and cutin.
        d. resists attack by microorganisms.
     * e. all of these

E 26. The cell walls of surface-facing epidermal cells are filled with which of the following to reduce water loss?
     * a. cutin
        b. pectin
        c. lignin
        d. suberin
        e. chitin

E 27. Air and water vapor cross the epidermis via
        a. pits.
        b. perforations.
        c. osmosis.
     * d. stomata.
        e. tracheids.

M 28. The periderm
        a. replaces the epidermis when some plants mature.
        b. is a protective tissue.
        c. is a dermal tissue.
        d. is found on woody plants.
     * e. all of these

M 29. A cotyledon is which of the following?
        a. embryonic root
        b. seed cover
        c. flower part
     * d. a leaflike structure on plant embryos
        e. fruit

D 30. Which of the following is true of monocots?
    a. has two cotyledons
    b. leaf veins usually netlike
    c. pollen grains with three pores
    * d. vascular bundles distributed throughout ground tissue
    e. floral parts in multiples of fours and fives

M 31. Which of the following is a dicot?
    a. corn
    b. ryegrass
    * c. beans
    d. wheat
    e. lily

PRIMARY STRUCTURE OF SHOOTS

D 32. The vascular bundles of dicots separate the ground tissue into two zones. Which of the following correctly describes the arrangement of these zones?
    a. outermost xylem >>> phloem >>> pith >>> cortex
    b. outermost phloem >>> xylem >>> pith >>> cortex
    * c. outermost cortex >>> phloem >>> xylem >>> pith
    d. outermost pith >>> phloem >>> xylem >>> cortex
    e. outermost cortex >>> xylem >>> phloem >>> pith

M 33. Dicots have stems
    a. with scattered vascular bundles.
    * b. with a pith and cortex.
    c. with no vascular cambium.
    d. that develop only primary tissues.
    e. none of these

M 34. Buds are produced
    a. in the axils of leaves.
    b. at the very ends of stems.
    c. at the nodes.
    d. by an apical meristem.
    * e. all of these

M 35. All EXCEPT which of the following are true of buds?
    * a. consist of mature, secondary tissues
    b. may occur at the tip of the twig
    c. some are called lateral
    d. may give rise to leaves
    e. mostly meristematic tissue

D 36. Which of the following statements is FALSE?
    * a. Axillary buds are found at the tip of the stems.
    b. Internodes are the spaces between leaves.
    c. Cotyledons are leaves within a seed.
    d. Ground tissue is the most common type of tissue in a plant.
    e. Dermal tissue covers the body of the plant.

M 37. Leaves arise
    a. as part of the periderm.
    b. as part of secondary growth.
    * c. at the end of a stalk, or petiole.
    d. as a result of differentiation of cambium cells.
    e. from the lateral, not the apical, meristem.

M 38. The stalk that supports the individual dicot leaf is the
    a. vascular bundle.
    * b. petiole.
    c. node.
    d. bundle sheath.
    e. stomata.

E 39. Stomata
    a. are found in the root cells.
    b. may be found scattered anywhere throughout the plant.
    * c. allow the movement of gases into and out of plants.
    d. prevent the loss of water from plants.
    e. remain open at all times.

M 40. Which of the following is mismatched?
    a. cotyledon—seed leaf
    b. petiole—leaf stalk
    * c. deciduous—evergreen
    d. veins—vascular bundles
    e. blade—leaf

E 41. The main photosynthetic area of a leaf is composed of
    * a. mesophyll.
    b. cortex.
    c. xylem.
    d. epidermis.
    e. none of these

M 42. Photosynthesis takes place in the
    a. stomata.
    b. vascular bundles.
    c. cuticle.
    d. lower and upper epidermis.
    * e. mesophyll tissue.

M 43. The veins of leaves are used for
    a. support.
    b. identification.
    * c. transport of water and nutrients.
    d. detachment in the autumn.
    e. regeneration.

PRIMARY STRUCTURE OF ROOTS

M 44. Roots are involved in all EXCEPT which of the following activities?
    a. support
    b. food storage
    * c. food production
    d. anchorage
    e. absorption and conduction

M 45. Mitosis takes place in which region of the root?
    a. zone of maturation
    b. root cap
    c. zone of elongation
    * d. meristem region
    e. region of differentiation

M   46.   If you were to penetrate through the epidermal layer of a root, you would next encounter the
          a. xylem.
          b. endodermis.
        * c. cortex.
          d. phloem.
          e. pericycle.

M   47.   The tissue found in the center of a root is
        * a. xylem.
          b. endodermis.
          c. cortex.
          d. phloem.
          e. pericycle.

M   48.   The layer of cells responsible for branch roots and the development of cork as a root thickens is the
          a. xylem.
          b. endodermis.
          c. cortex.
          d. phloem.
        * e. pericycle.

M   49.   Most monocots have numerous _?_ roots arising from the stem.
        * a. adventitious
          b. primary
          c. fibrous
          d. secondary
          e. tap

M   50.   Which of the following gives rise to lateral roots?
          a. endodermis
          b. cortex
          c. epidermis
        * d. pericycle
          e. pith

D   51.   Which of the following is in contact with the soil into which it is growing?
          a. vascular cylinder
          b. apical meristem
        * c. root cap
          d. pericycle
          e. outer cortex

M   52.   Root hairs are the extensions of the
          a. apical meristem.
        * b. epidermal cells.
          c. pericycle.
          d. vascular bundles.
          e. root cap.

D   53.   Lateral roots are the product of the
        * a. pericycle.
          b. vascular cylinder.
          c. epidermis.
          d. apical meristem.
          e. endodermis.

D   54.   In monocots, adventitious roots are associated with
          a. fibrous root systems.
          b. stems.
          c. taproot systems.
        * d. fibrous root systems and stems, only.
          e. fibrous root systems and taproot systems.

SECONDARY GROWTH—THE WOODY PLANTS

M   55.   Lateral meristems
          a. are groups of dividing cells.
          b. are responsible for increases in the width of a stem or root.
          c. are also called cambium.
          d. produce secondary growth only.
        * e. all of these

D   56.   The cell type that is found only in secondary tissue is
          a. epidermis.
          b. sclereids.
        * c. periderm cork cells.
          d. collenchyma.
          e. cuticle.

M   57.   Which of the following is also a lateral meristem?
        * a. cork cambium
          b. procambium
          c. protoderm
          d. ground meristem
          e. all of these

M   58.   Annual growth rings are formed in woody stems principally through the activities of the
          a. pericycle.
          b. pith.
        * c. vascular cambium.
          d. mesophyll.
          e. endodermis.

M   59.   If a sieve tube in a plant becomes blocked, the plant will experience difficulty in
          a. carrying on transpiration.
          b. the transport of minerals.
        * c. the translocation of food throughout the plant.
          d. completing cell division and experiencing normal growth.
          e. gaining oxygen.

M   60.   Secondary xylem is formed in association with the
          a. pith.
        * b. inner face of vascular cambium.
          c. outer face of vascular cambium.
          d. inner face of cork cambium.
          e. outer face of cork cambium.

M   61.   In an annual tree ring, the wood with large diameter, thin-walled cells is
        * a. produced each spring.
          b. the remnant of the bark produced the year before.
          c. formed from crushed phloem cells.
          d. produced in the winter.
          e. less dense.

D   62.   Which of the following statements is FALSE?
  a. Some perennial plants may consist of primary growth only.
  b. Cork cambium and vascular cambium are cells that form lateral meristems.
  c. Nonwoody plants are herbaceous.
  * d. Phloem is formed on the inside of vascular cambium, whereas xylem is formed on the outside.
  e. Sapwood surrounds heartwood.

PLANT NUTRIENTS AND AVAILABILITY IN SOIL

M   63.   By definition, humus includes all of the following EXCEPT
  a. feces.
  b. dead organisms.
  c. leaf litter.
  * d. weathered rock.
  e. decomposing organic matter.

E   64.   The soil particles that hold dissolved nutrients best are composed of
  a. sand.
  * b. clay.
  c. humus.
  d. silt.
  e. quartzite.

E   65.   Topsoil is designated as horizon
  * a. A.
  b. B.
  c. C.
  d. O.
  e. Z.

D   66.   The oxygen needed by plants is ultimately derived from
  a. aerobic respiration.
  * b. photosynthesis.
  c. anaerobic respiration.
  d. electrolysis.
  e. lightning discharges.

E   67.   Which of the following elements is obtained by plants directly from the atmosphere?
  a. nitrogen
  b. hydrogen
  * c. carbon
  d. iron
  e. sulfur

E   68.   Plants in general require how many essential elements for their growth and survival?
  a. 6
  b. 12
  * c. 16
  d. 22
  e. 28

E   69.   Which of the following elements required by plants does NOT come directly from the soil?
  * a. carbon
  b. nitrogen
  c. magnesium
  d. potassium
  e. iron

D   70.   Which element is found as a component of amino acids, proteins, chlorophyll, nucleic acids, and coenzymes?
  * a. nitrogen
  b. potassium
  c. sulfur
  d. phosphorus
  e. magnesium

D   71.   Which element is a component of nucleic acids and contributes to water-solute balances?
  a. nitrogen
  * b. potassium
  c. sulfur
  d. phosphorus
  e. magnesium

D   72.   Chlorosis and drooped leaves are caused by a deficiency of
  a. nitrogen.
  b. potassium.
  c. sulfur.
  d. phosphorus.
  * e. magnesium.

E   73.   Leaching is caused by
  a. wind and water movements.
  b. wind only.
  * c. water only.
  d. wind, running water, and ice.
  e. none of these

HOW DO ROOTS ABSORB WATER AND MINERAL IONS?

M   74.   The Casparian strip is associated with the
  a. epidermis.
  b. vascular tissue.
  c. cortex.
  d. root hairs.
  * e. endodermis.

M   75.   Which of the following statements is FALSE?
  a. Root hairs are composed of single epidermal cells.
  b. Nodules containing bacteria enable plants to increase their absorption of nitrogen.
  * c. Water moves through the Casparian strip.
  d. Water travels along the cells of the cortex but must move through the cytoplasm of endodermal cells.
  e. In plant cells, ATP is produced by both photosynthesis and respiration.

M   76. Which of the following could NOT be used in a
          description of the Casparian strip?
          a. waxy
          b. endodermis
      *   c. permeable
          d. exodermis
          e. waterproof

D   77. The endodermis in the plant root
      *   a. regulates the movement of water and minerals
              into the vascular cylinder.
          b. prevents water from moving through the
              Casparian strip.
          c. is the outer absorptive surface for water uptake.
          d. forces water to move through the Casparian strip.
          e. controls food transport.

M   78. Water absorption depends primarily on
          a. abscisic acid.
          b. cohesion-tension.
      *   c. the concentration gradient.
          d. active transport.
          e. the potassium pump.

M   79. The water and minerals absorbed by the roots usually
          first enter the
          a. pericycle.
          b. vascular tissue.
          c. cortex.
      *   d. root hairs.
          e. endodermis.

M   80. Nodules found on the roots of leguminous plants are
          involved in supplying which element for the plant?
          a. aluminum
          b. boron
          c. magnesium
      *   d. nitrogen
          e. chlorine

E   81. Plants obtain nitrogen
      *   a. as the product of nitrogen-fixing bacteria.
          b. by absorption of nutrients released from the
              minerals that form the underlying rocks.
          c. directly from the atmosphere through their
              stomata.
          d. only through the application of commercial
              fertilizers.
          e. by the breakdown of proteins in their tissues.

M   82. The nodules found on the roots of plants called
          legumes
          a. are abnormal growths.
          b. house bacteria.
          c. are beneficial to the plant.
          d. are abnormal growths and house bacteria.
      *   e. house bacteria and are beneficial to the plant.

E   83. Mycorrhizae are
          a. roots.
          b. bacteria.
      *   c. fungus roots.
          d. isolated plants.
          e. small animals found in agricultural soils.

M   84. Mycorrhizae
          a. increase plant growth.
          b. are symbionts.
          c. allow a plant to absorb more water.
          d. increase the surface area for absorption of water
              and minerals.
      *   e. all of these

D   85. What would be the effect of the accidental seepage of
          a fungicide into the soil surrounding a plant in a
          mycorrhizal relationship?
          a. The plant would die from lack of nutrients.
      *   b. Water and mineral supply to the plant would slow.
          c. The fungicide would cause the leaves to become
              chlorotic.
          d. The plant would live just as it did before because
              the fungi are not necessary.
          e. none of these

WATER TRANSPORT THROUGH PLANTS

M   86. Water inside all of the xylem cells is being pulled
          upward primarily by
          a. turgor pressure.
      *   b. negative pressures (tensions).
          c. osmotic gradients.
          d. pressure flow forces.
          e. active transport.

M   87. Which of the following causes transpiration?
          a. hydrogen bonding
          b. the drying power of air
          c. cohesion-tension
          d. evaporation
      *   e. all of these

M   88. Which theory of water transport states that hydrogen
          bonding allows water molecules to maintain a
          continuous fluid column as water is pulled from roots
          to leaves?
          a. pressure flow
          b. evaporation
      *   c. cohesion-tension
          d. abscission
          e. fusion

M   89. Water moves through a plant because of
          a. transpirational pull.
          b. the cohesion of water molecules.
          c. the strength of hydrogen bonds holding water
              molecules together.
          d. the replacement of lost water molecules.
      *   e. all of these

M 90. Water tension in a transpiring plant
   a. is exerted on a continuous column of water throughout the plant.
   b. is the result of the polar nature of water molecules.
   c. results in the loss of over 90 percent of the water the plant absorbs.
   d. will exert a pull on water molecules lower down in the plant's vascular system.
   * e. all of these

D 91. If houseplants must be left unattended for any length of time, some people recommend placing plastic bags over them. What is the reasoning behind this procedure?
   a. Water will condense on the inside of the bag and water the soil.
   b. Heat will build up in the bag and keep the plant from freezing.
   c. Photosynthesis will be increased due to the concentration of carbon dioxide in the bag.
   * d. Transpiration will be slowed, and more water will remain in the soil.
   e. The bag will trap carbon dioxide.

HOW DO STEMS AND LEAVES CONSERVE WATER?

D 92. Most of the water moving into a leaf is lost through
   a. osmotic gradients.
   * b. transpiration.
   c. pressure flow forces.
   d. translocation.
   e. all of these

D 93. Most of the water that enters the plant
   a. leaves the plant through the root system.
   * b. is lost through transpiration.
   c. remains in the plant to form the high concentration of water in plant tissue.
   d. remains in the plant to function in translocation.
   e. is used up in cellular metabolism.

E 94. If a cuticle is removed from a leaf, it will
   a. be unable to carry on photosynthesis.
   b. be unable to carry on transpiration.
   * c. lose water and wilt.
   d. stop growing and turn yellow.
   e. bleed to death.

E 95. The waxy covering of the leaf is the
   * a. cuticle.
   b. epidermis.
   c. Casparian strip.
   d. stomata.
   e. none of these

E 96. The openings in leaves that function to exchange gases are called
   a. cuticles.
   * b. stomata.
   c. guard cells.
   d. pits.
   e. pores.

E 97. The cells that surround stomata are
   a. endodermal cells.
   * b. guard cells.
   c. mesophyll cells.
   d. vascular bundle cells.
   e. vessel cells.

D 98. Gas exchange in plants
   a. is not necessary because plants produce their own oxygen.
   * b. cannot occur if there is excess transpiration.
   c. is a one-way process, with carbon dioxide entering the plant and oxygen leaving.
   d. is not required by the roots.
   e. is regulated by nitrogen.

M 99. Which of the following statements is FALSE?
   a. Transpiration creates a tension on water columns in a plant.
   b. Transpiration is the loss of water from a plant in a gaseous form.
   c. Water enters a root because of an osmotic gradient.
   * d. Most of the transpiration in a plant occurs through the cuticle.
   e. Molecules of water exhibit cohesion resulting from hydrogen bonding of water molecules.

M 100. The stomata
   a. open at night.
   * b. are open when the guard cells are turgid.
   c. close when the turgor pressure of the guard cells increases.
   d. are covered by the cuticle to reduce water loss.
   e. all of these

E 101. The cuticle
   a. conserves water.
   b. reduces absorption of carbon dioxide by the plant.
   c. reduces transpiration.
   d. helps prevent wilting.
   * e. all of these

M 102. The stomata are open
   a. during the day.
   b. when the guard cells are turgid.
   c. when the plant is wilted.
   d. during the time that plants are actively photosynthesizing.
   * e. all but "when the plant is wilted."

M 103. Guard cells
 a. surround the stoma.
 b. control the opening to the interior of the leaf.
 c. become turgid when it becomes light if environmental conditions are not too hot or dry.
 d. absorb water from surrounding epidermal cells.
 * e. all of these

D 104. In CAM plants, such as cacti,
 a. the stomata are open both day and night.
 b. the stomata are open during the day even though the plants cannot afford to lose the water.
 c. there are no stomata because the water loss would be too great.
 * d. stomata are open at night.
 e. guard cells are present but operate the reverse of usual plants.

HOW ORGANIC COMPOUNDS MOVE THROUGH PLANTS

D 105. Products of photosynthesis are
 a. used by plant tissues for energy.
 b. stored for use by herbivores.
 c. transported in soluble form to sinks.
 d. interconverted to other forms.
 * e. all of these

M 106. The most common form of sugar transported in phloem is
 a. glucose.
 b. fructose.
 * c. sucrose.
 d. ribose.
 e. starch.

E 107. Carbohydrates are stored in plants in the form of
 a. cellulose.
 b. sucrose.
 * c. starch.
 d. fats.
 e. glucose.

E 108. Movement of soluble organic material through plants is known as
 * a. translocation.
 b. active transport.
 c. passive transport.
 d. transpiration.
 e. none of these

E 109. Sugars are carried throughout the plant in which tissue?
 a. cortex
 b. parenchyma
 c. xylem
 * d. phloem
 e. cambium

M 110. The major food transport substance in plants is
 a. oil.
 b. glucose.
 c. starch.
 d. fructose.
 * e. sucrose.

M 111. The role of companion cells in translocation is to
 a. assist vessel members with movement of organic substances.
 b. supply the potassium ions needed for water absorption.
 * c. load organic compounds into neighboring sieve tubes.
 d. supply the potassium ions needed for water absorption and provide energy to the sieve tube members.
 e. assist vessel members with movement of organic substances, supply the potassium ions needed for water absorption, and provide energy to the sieve tube members.

D 112. Sieve tubes are different from vessel cells because they
 a. carry water, not food.
 b. are not connected to each other.
 * c. are alive, not dead like xylem cells.
 d. conduct minerals.
 e. carry water, not food, and conduct minerals.

E 113. The movement of materials already in the phloem is described as
 a. source-to-sink.
 b. declining pressure flow.
 c. cohesion-tension.
 d. active transport.
 * e. source-to-sink and declining pressure flow.

M 114. The source region in the pressure flow explanation of phloem transport is most often the
 a. root.
 b. flower.
 c. stem.
 * d. leaf.
 e. soil.

M 115. The sink region in the pressure flow explanation of phloem transport could be
 a. growing leaves.
 b. seeds.
 c. fruits.
 d. roots.
 * e. all of these

M 116. Large pressure gradients arise in sieve tube systems by means of
 a. vernalization.
 b. abscission.
 * c. osmosis.
 d. transpiration.
 e. all of these

D 117. Which of the following processes does NOT serve to maintain low pressure at the receiving end of sieve tube pipelines?
 a. Sucrose is converted into cell-wall polysaccharides in the receiving regions.
 b. Sucrose is converted into starch in the receiving regions.
 c. Sucrose is converted to glucose, which is used in cellular respiration at the receiving end.
 * d. High concentrations of dissolved solutes are pumped into the cells of these receiving regions by active transport.
 e. none of these

M 118. The most commonly accepted theory used to explain movement of food in the phloem is
 a. cohesion-tension theory.
 * b. the pressure flow hypothesis.
 c. active transport.
 d. dialysis.
 e. turgor pressure.

M 119. Which of the following statements is TRUE?
 a. There is always a gradient of sucrose concentration from source to sink.
 b. Sucrose is being generated at the source and converted or used at the sink.
 c. Companion cells load organic compounds into neighboring sieve tubes.
 d. Sieve tubes are only passive conduits for translocation.
 * e. all of these

Matching Questions

D 120. Matching I. Choose the one most appropriate answer for each.
 1. ___ companion cells
 2. ___ cork cambium
 3. ___ meristems
 4. ___ palisade mesophyll
 5. ___ pericycle
 6. ___ sclereids
 7. ___ sieve tube member
 8. ___ spongy mesophyll
 9. ___ tracheids
 10. ___ vascular bundles
 11. ___ vessel members

 A. gives rise to periderm
 B. phloem cells that help load the phloem pipelines
 C. dead cells with perforation plates; more efficient at water conduction than other xylem cells
 D. cells that conduct food from photosynthetic source area to storage sink area
 E. a cylinder of parenchyma cells outside the vascular tissue but inside the endodermis
 F. clusters of strands containing xylem and phloem
 G. dead cells without perforation plates; conducting cells of xylem
 H. cells with thick secondary walls impregnated with lignin that are especially abundant in fruits and seeds
 I. the principal photosynthetic region of a leaf
 J. regions that can undergo mitosis
 K. gas exchange and storage plus photosynthesis

Answers: 1. B   2. A   3. J   4. I
 5. E   6. H   7. D   8. K
 9. G   10. F   11. C

D **121.** Matching II. Choose the one most appropriate answer for each.

1. ___ endodermis
2. ___ epidermis
3. ___ parenchyma
4. ___ periderm
5. ___ phloem
6. ___ pith
7. ___ sclerenchyma
8. ___ stomata
9. ___ vascular cambium
10. ___ xylem

   A. outer tissue that is part of the dermal system
   B. leaf's photosynthetic tissues (palisade and spongy) are in this category
   C. transports photosynthetic products away from leaves and stem
   D. cell divisions here produce secondary xylem and phloem
   E. transports water and dissolved nutrients up to the stem and leaves
   F. replaces the epidermis in plants that undergo secondary growth
   G. a single layer of cells that helps control the movement of water and dissolved salts into the xylem pipeline
   H. regulates the movement of carbon dioxide into the leaf and movement of water out of the leaf
   I. generally, dead cells that provide support and strength to all three tissue systems
   J. ground tissue centrally located inside a ring of vascular bundles

Answers: 1. G   2. A   3. B
            4. F   5. C   6. J
            7. I   8. H   9. D
            10. E

D **122.** Matching III. Choose the one most appropriate letter for each.

1. ___ Casparian strip
2. ___ companion cells
3. ___ legumes
4. ___ mycorrhiza
5. ___ nodules
6. ___ sieve tube members
7. ___ root hairs
8. ___ tracheids and vessels
9. ___ translocation
10. ___ transpiration
11. ___ guard cells

   A. responsible for opening and closing of stomata
   B. greatly increase root absorptive surface
   C. pipelines of the xylem
   D. a mutually beneficial association between a fungus and a young root
   E. structures on roots that house nitrogen-fixing bacteria
   F. pipelines of the phloem
   G. evaporation from stems and leaves
   H. actively transport sucrose into sieve tube members
   I. dicot plants that tend to establish symbiotic relationships with nitrogen-fixing bacteria
   J. transport of organic molecules from source region to sink
   K. a waxy band that forces water to diffuse through cells

Answers: 1. K   2. H   3. I
            4. D   5. E   6. F
            7. B   8. C   9. J
            10. G   11. A

Classification Questions

Answer questions 123–127 in reference to the five plant tissues listed below.

    a. parenchyma
    b. collenchyma
    c. sclerenchyma
    d. xylem
    e. phloem

D   **123.** simple tissue of plants, sometimes containing lignin that strengthens the adult plant

E   **124.** vascular tissue that conducts and distributes food to plant cells

E   **125.** vascular tissue that conducts water and dissolved salts throughout a plant

D   **126.** vascular tissue of a plant composed of tracheids and vessel members

D   **127.** plant tissue involved in regeneration following a wound

Answers: 123. c   124. e   125. d

               126. d   127. a

Answer questions 128–132 in reference to the five plant tissues listed below.

    a. protoderm
    b. ground meristem
    c. procambium
    d. vascular cambium
    e. cork cambium

D   **128.** This tissue gives rise to periderm.

D   **129.** This tissue gives rise to primary tissue forming xylem and phloem.

M   **130.** This tissue gives rise to primary vascular tissue.

D   **131.** This tissue gives rise to the protective covering that forms the bark of a tree.

D   **132.** This tissue gives rise to the xylem and phloem of an older tree.

Answers: 128. e   129. c   130. c

               131. e   132. d

Answer questions 133–136 in reference to the four source tissues of plant roots listed below.

    a. primary meristems
    b. secondary tissues
    c. pericycle
    d. vascular cambium

D   **133.** Protoderm and procambium are included in this choice.

D   **134.** This choice includes ground meristem.

M   **135.** This tissue gives rise to lateral roots.

D   **136.** This tissue gives rise to secondary phloem and xylem.

Answers: 133. a   134. a

             135. c   136. d

Selecting the Exception

M   **137.** Four of the five answers listed below are related by a common region of the plant body. Select the exception.
    a. leaf
*   b. root cap
    c. node
    d. axillary bud
    e. stem

M   **138.** Four of the five answers listed below are types of ground tissue. Select the exception.
    a. spongy mesophyll
*   b. xylem
    c. sclerenchyma
    d. parenchyma
    e. collenchyma

D   **139.** Four of the five answers listed below are functions of parenchyma tissue. Select the exception.
*   a. support
    b. heal wounds
    c. store food
    d. conduct photosynthesis
    e. regenerate lost parts

D   **140.** Four of the five answers listed below are characteristic of sclerenchyma cells. Select the exception.
    a. sclereid
    b. found in seed coats
*   c. retain the ability to divide after differentiation
    d. gritty texture of pear cells
    e. used in manufacture of paper, cloth, and rope

D   **141.** Four of the five answers listed below are characteristics of xylem. Select the exception.
    a. is dead at maturity
    b. cell walls are impregnated with lignin
*   c. conducts dissolved food
    d. includes tracheids and vessels
    e. has pits in the walls of the cells

D 142. Four of the five answers listed below are characteristics of phloem. Select the exception.
* a. consists only of cell walls
b. characterized by channels across plant cell walls
c. sieve plates found between some cells
d. includes accessory companion cells
e. transports sugar

D 143. Four of the five answers listed below are characteristics of epidermal cells. Select the exception.
a. have a continuous covering
b. outer walls impregnated with cutin
c. secrete waxes
d. secrete cutin
* e. impregnated with suberin

D 144. Four of the five answers listed below are tissues capable of cell division. Select the exception.
a. cork cambium
b. apical meristem
c. procambium
* d. periderm
e. vascular cambium

M 145. Four of the five answers listed below are parts of tissue found in a cross section of root. Select the exception.
a. cortex
* b. pith
c. pericycle
d. endodermis
e. epidermis

M 146. Four of the five answers listed below are related to vascular tissue. Select the exception.
a. conduction of water and minerals
b. vascular bundle
c. translocation
d. vein
* e. pith

M 147. Four of the five answers listed below are functions of roots. Select the exception.
a. support
* b. synthesis of food
c. absorption of water and minerals
d. conduction of water and solutes
e. anchorage

M 148. Four of the five answers listed below are related by a similar nature. Select the exception.
a. adventitious
b. tap
c. fibrous
d. lateral
* e. insectivorous

M 149. Four of the five answers listed below are types of cells in plants. Select the exception.
a. cork
b. parenchyma
* c. cuticle
d. sieve tube
e. tracheid

D 150. Four of the five answers listed below are parts of a leaf. Select the exception.
a. stoma
b. cuticle
c. mesophyll
* d. node
e. petiole

D 151. Four of the five answers listed below are related by their participation in water movement through plants. Select the exception.
a. hydrogen bonds
b. transpiration
c. cohesion-tension
d. tension in xylem
* e. photosynthesis

D 152. Four of the five answers listed below promote transpiration. Select the exception.
a. potassium ions pumped into guard cells
b. turgor pressure builds up in guard cells
c. photosynthesis occurs in guard cells
d. carbon dioxide enters leaf
* e. presence of cuticle

D 153. Four of the five answers listed below are events that occur when the stomata are open. Select the exception.
a. ATP is used.
b. Carbon dioxide enters.
c. Oxygen diffuses out.
* d. Water is conserved.
e. Guard cells are swelled with water.

D 154. Four of the five answers listed below are events that occur when water is abundant. Select the exception.
a. Leaves absorb more carbon dioxide.
b. Ions are absorbed by the roots.
c. Less oxygen is absorbed by roots.
* d. Stomata are closed.
e. Photosynthesis is not limited by lack of water or carbon dioxide.

D 155. Four of the five answers listed below are sinks for solute deposition. Select the exception.
a. fruits
b. roots
* c. leaves
d. seeds
e. rapidly growing tissue

Labeling

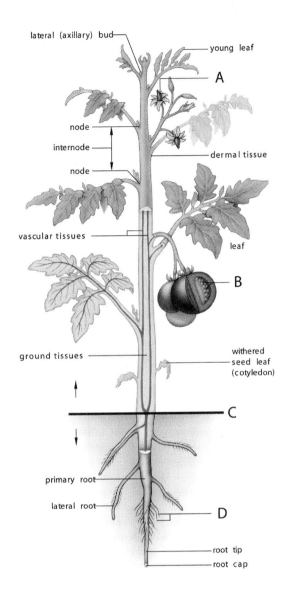

lateral (axillary) bud

young leaf

A

node

internode

node

dermal tissue

vascular tissues

leaf

B

ground tissues

withered seed leaf (cotyledon)

C

primary root

lateral root

D

root tip

root cap

E   **156.**   The absorption of water and minerals would occur at letter _?_.

E   **157.**   The seeds are located inside the structure at letter _?_.

E   **158.**   The plant parts ABOVE the line at "C" represent the
    a. ground tissue only.
    b. root system.
  * c. shoot system.
    d. stalk.
    e. light-independent parts.

E   **159.**   The sexual organs of the plant are contained in the structure at letter _?_.

Answers: 156. D 157. B   159. A

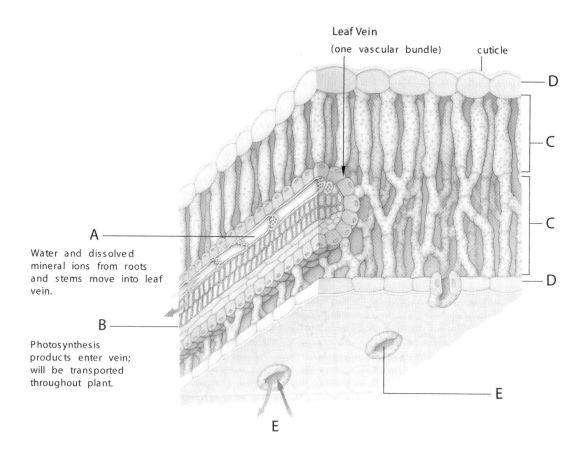

Leaf Vein
(one vascular bundle)   cuticle

— D

C

C

— D

A —

Water and dissolved
mineral ions from roots
and stems move into leaf
vein.

B —

Photosynthesis
products enter vein;
will be transported
throughout plant.

E

E

E   **160.**   Cells rich in chlorophyll and thus the sites of
photosynthesis are in layers represented by the letter
_?_.

E   **161.**   The description of xylem is at letter _?_.

E   **162.**   The description of phloem is at letter _?_.

E   **163.**   The structure at letter "E" is properly called
a. stigma.
b. holes.
c. openings.
d. veins.
*   e. stomata.

Answers: 160. C   161. A   162. B

CHAPTER 19
PLANT REPRODUCTION AND DEVELOPMENT

Multiple-Choice Questions

SEXUAL REPRODUCTION IN FLOWERING PLANTS

M 1. The evolution of flowers and insects is an example of
    a. parallel evolution.
    b. regressive evolution.
*   c. coevolution.
    d. convergent evolution.
    e. divergent evolution.

E 2. Insects are attracted to flowers by
    a. nectaries.
    b. specific colors.
    c. specific color patterns.
    d. floral odors.
*   e. all of these

M 3. Birds and a few insects are able to detect which of the following colors?
    a. yellow
    b. green
    c. blue
*   d. red
    e. violet

E 4. Which color of flowers is most attractive to bees?
    a. white
*   b. blue
    c. red
    d. green
    e. orange

M 5. Foul-smelling flowers may be pollinated by
    a. birds.
*   b. beetles.
    c. bees and bumblebees.
    d. wasps.
    e. bugs and butterflies.

E 6. The function of flowers is to
    a. provide beauty to the environment.
    b. attract insects.
    c. produce sex cells.
    d. enable scientists to classify plants into the proper taxonomic group.
*   e. attract insects and produce gametes.

E 7. Which of the following statements is FALSE?
    a. Flowers are reproductive shoots.
*   b. Trees are gametophytes.
    c. Sporophyte plants can reproduce asexually.
    d. Cells produced by mitosis are clones.
    e. Gametophytes are haploid.

M 8. The sporophyte generation
*   a. is essential for a flowering plant to complete its life cycle.
    b. is the dominant generation in the mosses.
    c. is microscopic in the flowering plants.
    d. produces the sexually reproducing cells—sperm and egg.
    e. is the smallest phase in a tree's life.

M 9. Alternation of generations most likely refers to the
    a. expression of recessive traits.
*   b. presence of a diploid and a haploid generation in the life cycle of plants.
    c. presence of the different sexes in two different plants.
    d. occurrence of a sexually reproducing diploid stage followed by an asexually reproducing haploid stage during the life cycle of higher plants.
    e. rise and fall of life.

M 10. All EXCEPT which of the following are true of angiosperm gametophytes?
    a. produce haploid sex cells
    b. arise from cells within the flowers
*   c. develop independently from the sporophyte
    d. produce eggs or sperm
    e. smaller than sporophyte stage

M 11. The least specialized part of the flower is a
    a. carpel.
    b. stamen.
    c. petal.
*   d. sepal.
    e. ovule.

E 12. A stamen is
    a. composed of a stigma, a style, and an ovary.
    b. the mature male gametophyte.
*   c. the site where microspores are produced.
    d. part of the vegetative phase of an angiosperm.
    e. none of these

E 13. The male part of a flower is the
    a. carpel.
*   b. stamen.
    c. petal.
    d. sepal.
    e. receptacle.

E 14. The male part of a flower includes the
    a. carpel.
    b. stigma.
    c. pollen sacs only.
    d. anther only.
*   e. pollen sacs and anther.

E　15.　The various flower parts are attached to the
　　　　a. style.
　*　b. receptacle.
　　　　c. stigma.
　　　　d. filament.
　　　　e. calyx.

M　16.　The calyx is composed of
　　　　a. petals.
　*　b. sepals.
　　　　c. stigmas.
　　　　d. ovules.
　　　　e. anthers.

E　17.　Stamens contain
　　　　a. petals.
　　　　b. sepals.
　　　　c. stigmas.
　　　　d. ovules.
　*　e. anthers.

M　18.　The corolla is made up of
　　　　a. sepals.
　*　b. petals.
　　　　c. carpels.
　　　　d. pollen grains.
　　　　e. anthers.

M　19.　Which forms the outermost whorl of flower parts?
　*　a. sepals
　　　　b. petals
　　　　c. anthers
　　　　d. carpels
　　　　e. stamens

E　20.　The calyx is composed of
　　　　a. petals.
　*　b. sepals.
　　　　c. anthers.
　　　　d. carpels.
　　　　e. receptacle tissue.

M　21.　Theoretically, a plant should still be able to reproduce sexually even though its _?_ have been removed.
　　　　a. stamens
　*　b. sepals
　　　　c. anthers
　　　　d. ovaries
　　　　e. carpels

D　22.　Which of the following choices represents the correct sequence?
　　　　a. microspores >>> meiosis >>> gametophyte >>> sperm
　*　b. meiosis >>> microspores >>> gametophyte >>> sperm
　　　　c. gametophyte >>> meiosis >>> megaspores >>> eggs
　　　　d. meiosis >>> gametophyte >>> megaspores >>> eggs
　　　　e. meiosis >>> megaspores >>> gametophyte >>> sperm

M　23.　Megaspores produce
　*　a. female gametophytes.
　　　　b. spores.
　　　　c. sporophytes.
　　　　d. embryos.
　　　　e. diploid tissue.

M　24.　What do gametes, spores, and the gametophyte generation have in common?
　　　　a. They are all diploid.
　*　b. They are all haploid.
　　　　c. They are limited to vascular plants.
　　　　d. They have nothing in common.
　　　　e. They are asexual structures.

M　25.　Which of the following is part of the gametophyte generation?
　　　　a. carpel
　　　　b. anther
　*　c. pollen tube nucleus
　　　　d. seed
　　　　e. megaspore

M　26.　Which of the following is FALSE?
　　　　a. Flowers often exhibit coevolution with their pollinators.
　　　　b. Seeds often exhibit coevolution with their disseminators.
　　　　c. The pollen grain is a haploid microspore.
　　　　d. Megaspores are part of the female gametophyte generation.
　*　e. Megaspores and microspores arise through mitosis.

M　27.　The process during which the diploid set of chromosomes becomes haploid is
　　　　a. metastasis.
　　　　b. fertilization.
　　　　c. cleavage.
　*　d. meiosis.
　　　　e. none of these

E　28.　Anthers produce
　　　　a. ovules.
　　　　b. stamens.
　*　c. microspores.
　　　　d. female gametophytes.
　　　　e. none of these

M　29.　Microspores are produced by
　　　　a. carpels.
　　　　b. mitosis.
　*　c. meiosis.
　　　　d. parthenogenesis.
　　　　e. carpels and meiosis.

D　30.　Pollen grains fossilize well because
　*　a. of their strong, resistant walls.
　　　　b. of their small size.
　　　　c. they are haploid.
　　　　d. they are dry.
　　　　e. of the muddy environments into which they fall.

M   31.   Megaspores
           a.   are haploid.
           b.   are found in the embryo sac.
           c.   will develop into gametophytes.
           d.   are female rather than male.
       *   e.   all of these

M   32.   The megaspore usually divides into how many nuclei
          before fertilization?
           a.   2
           b.   4
       *   c.   8
           d.   16
           e.   32

E   33.   The female gametophyte is the
           a.   nucellus.
           b.   ovule.
       *   c.   embryo sac.
           d.   endosperm.
           e.   ovary.

E   34.   The egg is
           a.   diploid.
           b.   tetraploid.
           c.   polyploid.
           d.   triploid.
       *   e.   haploid.

E   35.   Pollination occurs on the
           a.   micropyle.
       *   b.   stigma.
           c.   style.
           d.   anther.
           e.   embryo sac.

E   36.   The place where pollination occurs is the
       *   a.   stigma.
           b.   micropyle.
           c.   anther.
           d.   receptacle.
           e.   style.

E   37.   The pollen tube grows to or through the
           a.   stigma.
           b.   style.
           c.   ovary.
           d.   micropyle.
       *   e.   all of these

E   38.   The endosperm is
           a.   diploid.
           b.   tetraploid.
           c.   polyploid.
       *   d.   triploid.
           e.   haploid.

M   39.   "Double fertilization" in plants is the union of
           a.   two eggs and one sperm.
           b.   two sperm and one egg.
           c.   two sperm and two eggs.
       *   d.   one sperm to one egg and one sperm to the
                endosperm.
           e.   one sperm to the egg and one sperm to the egg
                nucleus.

D   40.   In flowering plants, one sperm nucleus fuses with that
          of an egg, and a zygote forms that develops into an
          embryo. Another sperm nucleus
           a.   fuses with a primary endosperm cell to produce
                three cells, each with one nucleus.
           b.   fuses with a primary endosperm cell to produce
                one cell with one triploid nucleus.
       *   c.   fuses with the diploid endosperm mother cell,
                forming a primary endosperm cell with a single
                triploid nucleus.
           d.   fuses with one of the smaller megaspores to
                produce what will eventually become the seed
                coat.
           e.   none of these

E   41.   The endosperm of a plant
       *   a.   forms the food supply for the new sporophyte
                plant.
           b.   is composed of haploid tissue.
           c.   protects the young embryo within a seed.
           d.   provides a connection between the ovary of a
                flower and a developing seed.
           e.   is produced asexually.

FROM ZYGOTES TO SEEDS PACKAGED IN FRUITS

M   42.   Counting the number of seeds in a fruit will give an
          indication of the number of
           a.   carpels.
           b.   stamens.
           c.   pollen tubes.
       *   d.   ovules.
           e.   flowers.

E   43.   Which of the following is NOT a fruit?
           a.   acorns
           b.   raspberries
       *   c.   potatoes
           d.   pineapple
           e.   pea pods

E   44.   The zygote is
       *   a.   diploid.
           b.   tetraploid.
           c.   polyploid.
           d.   triploid.
           e.   haploid.

Chapter 19 Plant Reproduction and Development   **175**

E 45. The primary function of the endosperm is
   a. protection.
   b. reproduction.
   c. growth.
 * d. food storage.
   e. water absorption.

E 46. Which of the following develops into a seed?
   a. flower
   b. ovary
   c. carpel
 * d. ovule
   e. stamen

E 47. The seed is produced by the development of the
   a. embryo.
 * b. ovule.
   c. ovary.
   d. zygote.
   e. pollen.

E 48. A seed leaf is which of the following?
   a. embryo
   b. coleoptile
   c. endosperm
 * d. cotyledon
   e. suspensor

E 49. A seed does NOT include
   a. endosperm.
   b. seed coats.
   c. cotyledons.
 * d. carpels.
   e. embryo.

D 50. What kind of fruit is formed from fused ovaries of several associated flowers?
   a. aggregate
   b. simple
 * c. multiple
   d. fleshy
   e. dry

M 51. Fruit is produced from the development of the
   a. zygote.
   b. ovule.
   c. flowers.
   d. cotyledon.
 * e. ovary.

M 52. The seeds of fleshy fruits are most likely to be spread by
 * a. animals.
   b. water.
   c. wind.
   d. explosion.
   e. insects.

M 53. Fleshy fruits, such as cherries, are more likely to be dispersed by _?_ than by other means.
   a. wind
   b. adhering to animal fur
 * c. passing through animal guts
   d. falling to the ground and rotting
   e. water currents

ASEXUAL REPRODUCTION OF FLOWERING PLANTS

M 54. All EXCEPT which of the following terms can be used in describing asexual reproduction?
   a. clone
   b. mitosis
   c. identical
 * d. meiosis
   e. parent

M 55. Which is NOT primarily related to asexual reproduction?
   a. adventitious shoots
 * b. pollination
   c. runner formation
   d. cloning
   e. tissue culture

M 56. If a plant is said to reproduce asexually by modes of vegetative growth, this means that
 * a. part of a leaf, a stem, or a root, when torn away from the parent plant and planted under proper conditions, can develop into a new plant.
   b. it cannot reproduce by forming flowers, fruits, and seeds.
   c. the leafy part of the gametophyte can grow into a new plant if planted and grown similar to the way most vegetables are grown.
   d. flowers and fruits from one plant can be grafted onto another closely related plant to produce hybrids.
   e. all of these

E 57. Quaking aspen reproduces vegetatively by
 * a. roots.
   b. corms.
   c. bulbs.
   d. tubers.
   e. rhizomes.

M 58. The term used to describe the cloning of an entire plant from a single cell is
   a. sexual meiosis.
 * b. tissue culture propagation.
   c. reduced integration.
   d. germination mitosis.
   e. phototropism.

PATTERNS OF EARLY GROWTH AND DEVELOPMENT

M 59. All EXCEPT which of the following would likely have an effect on seed germination?
    a. moisture
    b. temperature
  * c. minerals
    d. length of day
    e. oxygen

M 60. Cells that retain the ability to divide are called _?_ cells.
    a. parenchyma
  * b. meristematic
    c. ground
    d. epidermal
    e. mesophyll

M 61. The cells formed by mitosis in a germinating seed are different from one another in all EXCEPT which one of the ways listed below?
    a. amount of cytoplasm
  * b. genetic composition
    c. hormone content
    d. enzymes present
    e. metabolic rate

M 62. In the early growth stages of a seedling, what environmental cue is especially important for plant growth and development?
    a. mitosis
    b. cytoplasmic divisions
    c. hormonal interactions
  * d. water availability
    e. mitosis and cytoplasmic divisions

D 63. Which of the following statements is FALSE?
    a. The movement of water into a seed is known as imbibition.
    b. Water is attracted to hydrophilic proteins in the seed.
  * c. The shoot system is the first part of a cotyledon to grow.
    d. When a seed begins germinating, it starts aerobic respiration.
    e. Germination is completed once the root extends outside the seed.

CELL COMMUNICATION IN PLANT DEVELOPMENT

E 64. Chemicals produced by one group of cells that alters the activity of target cells are called
    a. secretions.
  * b. hormones.
    c. steroids.
    d. polymers.
    e. enzymes.

E 65. The target cells for hormones
  * a. have special receptor (binding) sites.
    b. are located in roots.
    c. are no different from any other cells.
    d. are located in the interior of the plant.
    e. all of these

M 66. Which of the following is NOT accurate in describing a hormone?
  * a. Hormones produced by a particular species affect only that species.
    b. Only those cells that have specific receptors can respond to any one hormone.
    c. Hormones in general are produced by one cell and cause their effects in another cell.
    d. Hormones are a type of signaling molecule.
    e. Hormones are chemicals.

M 67. Synthetic auxins are used as
    a. pesticides.
  * b. herbicides.
    c. fungicides.
    d. insecticides.
    e. all of these

M 68. 2,4-D, a potent dicot weed killer, is a synthetic
  * a. auxin.
    b. gibberellin.
    c. cytokinin.
    d. phytochrome.
    e. none of these

M 69. A widely used synthetic auxin is
    a. 3,7-C.
  * b. 2,4-D.
    c. 1,5-K.
    d. 3,6-T.
    e. 1,4-X.

E 70. The plant hormone thought to be involved with response to gravity and light is
    a. abscisic acid.
  * b. auxin.
    c. gibberellin.
    d. ethylene.
    e. none of these

M 71. Studies on the growth of coleoptiles involve
    a. florigen.
    b. ethylene.
  * c. auxin (IAA).
    d. abscisic acid.
    e. gibberellin.

D 72. Which of the following is mismatched?
    a. cytokinin—retards aging
    b. auxin—promotes cell elongation
  * c. gibberellin—involved in phototropism and gravitropism
    d. abscisic acid—promotes stomatal closure
    e. ethylene—promotes fruit ripening

M 73. Gibberellins have their most dramatic effects
   a. on leaves.
   b. in cell elongation.
   c. in fruit ripening.
 * d. in stem lengthening.
   e. on flowers.

M 74. The plant hormone that promotes cell division is
   a. auxin.
   b. gibberellin.
 * c. cytokinin.
   d. florigen.
   e. ethylene.

M 75. What hormone can be used commercially to prolong the shelf life of fresh vegetables?
   a. abscisic acid
 * b. cytokinins
   c. auxins
   d. IAA
   e. florigen

M 76. The plant hormone that promotes dormancy in plants and seeds is
 * a. abscisic acid.
   b. auxin.
   c. gibberellin.
   d. ethylene.
   e. none of these

M 77. In contrast to most other plant hormones, which hormone is a growth inhibitor?
   a. auxin
   b. gibberellin
   c. cytokinin
 * d. abscisic acid
   e. ethylene

M 78. The only plant hormone that is gaseous is
   a. auxin.
   b. gibberellin.
   c. cytokinin.
   d. florigen.
 * e. ethylene.

M 79. The plant hormone that promotes fruit ripening is
   a. auxin.
   b. gibberellin.
   c. cytokinin.
   d. florigen.
 * e. ethylene.

ADJUSTING RATES AND DIRECTIONS OF GROWTH

D 80. Perhaps a plant's greatest liability is its inability to
   a. produce growth hormones.
   b. use aerobic respiration.
 * c. move when conditions around it deteriorate.
   d. produce its own lipids and proteins.
   e. respond to dwindling supplies of nutrients and water.

E 81. What is the principal substance that causes phototropism in stems or leaves?
 * a. auxin
   b. gibberellin
   c. abscisic acid
   d. ethylene
   e. all of these

M 82. A house plant that has been placed in the window will grow toward the source of light because auxin
   a. becomes more concentrated on the illuminated side of the plant.
 * b. becomes less concentrated on the illuminated side of the plant.
   c. becomes more concentrated in the roots of the plant.
   d. inhibits the growth of cells on the shady side, so the cells on the sunny side grow faster.
   e. is produced only when the sun shines.

M 83. Which color of light is most effective in producing phototropism?
   a. red
 * b. blue
   c. yellow
   d. white
   e. green

M 84. The primary root of a seedling grows down
   a. to avoid light.
   b. in response to gravity.
   c. because the cells on the top of the root grow faster than those on the bottom of the root.
   d. in response to different concentrations of auxin.
 * e. all except "to avoid light."

MEANWHILE, BACK AT THE FLOWER . . .

M 85. The pigment responsible for photoperiodism is
   a. chlorophyll.
   b. xanthophyll.
   c. anthocyanin.
 * d. phytochrome.
   e. photoerythrin.

E 86. The absence of which of the following pigments would prevent a plant from responding to the duration of light and darkness?
   a. chlorophyll
   b. xanthophyll
   c. carotene
 * d. phytochrome
   e. chlorophyll

E 87. Rhythms that are repeated every 24 hours are collectively and specifically known as
   a. sleep movements.
   b. tropisms.
   c. biorhythms.
 * d. circadian rhythms.
   e. the biological clock.

M 88. Phytochrome is converted from the inactive to the active form by being exposed to light of what color?
   a. far red
 * b. red
   c. yellow
   d. white
   e. blue

E 89. In the dark, plants CANNOT
   a. grow.
   b. respire.
   c. move.
 * d. utilize chlorophyll.
   e. form carotenoid pigment.

M 90. All EXCEPT which of the following are hormones?
   a. IAA
   b. abscisic acid
 * c. phytochrome
   d. cytokinin
   e. All are hormones.

E 91. Photoperiodism is the
   a. duration of flowering in a plant.
   b. amount of light needed by a plant to exhibit normal growth.
 * c. biological response of a plant to a change in the length of daylight relative to darkness.
   d. light phase of photosynthesis during which photolysis of water occurs.
   e. time of the day when light shines.

D 92. Which of the following terms refers to the change in relative day length?
   a. photoerythrin
   b. phototropism
   c. photorhythmic
   d. photochrome
 * e. photoperiodism

M 93. Day-neutral plants are
   a. short-day plants.
 * b. able to form flowers when they mature.
   c. night-blooming plants.
   d. triggered to bloom by cold weather.
   e. none of these

M 94. Which of the following statements is FALSE?
   a. Long-day plants bloom in the spring.
 * b. Short-day plants bloom around noon.
   c. Short-day plants bloom in late summer and early fall.
   d. Chrysanthemums, cockleburs, and poinsettias are long-day plants.
   e. Day-neutral plants flower when mature enough to do so.

M 95. Short-day plants
   a. flower in spring.
   b. will not bloom until they have been exposed to a dark period longer than a critical length.
   c. flower in the fall.
   d. will not bloom if their dark period is interrupted by two to five minutes of light.
 * e. all of these

LIFE CYCLES END, AND TURN AGAIN

E 96. _?_ refers to the phase from full maturity until the eventual death of plant parts or the whole plant
   a. dormancy.
   b. vernalization.
   c. abscission.
 * d. senescence.
   e. none of these

E 97. The aging of a plant from the time of full maturity is known as
 * a. senescence.
   b. vernalization.
   c. abscission.
   d. dormancy.
   e. chlorosis.

M 98. Abscission affects
   a. leaves.
   b. fruits.
   c. flowers.
 * d. all of these
   e. none of these

E 99. The requirement of cold weather before a particular plant process occurs (i.e., germination) is known as
   a. the biological clock.
 * b. vernalization.
   c. photoperiodism.
   d. biennial life cycle.
   e. biorhythm.

D 100. If peach trees growing in specific mild climates of the southern United States do not receive about 850 hours of temperatures below 40 degrees, they will not produce flowers in the spring. This is explained by which of the following terms?
   a. photoperiodism
   b. phototropism
   c. senescence
 * d. vernalization
   e. dormancy

M 101. All of the following are cues for plant dormancy EXCEPT
   a. cold temperature.
   b. long nights.
   c. dry soil.
 * d. IAA.
   e. nitrogen and poor soil.

REGARDING THE WORLD'S MOST NUTRITIOUS PLANT

M **102.** Quinoa is a valuable food plant because it
   a. has a high protein content.
   b. is rich in iron.
   c. has calcium.
   d. is resistant to drought.
 * e. is all of these.

E **103.** *Kwashiorkor* is a disease caused by a deficiency in
   a. iron.
   b. calcium.
 * c. protein.
   d. carbohydrates.
   e. vitamins.

Matching Questions

D **104.** Matching I. Choose the one most appropriate answer for each.

1. ____ aggregate fruit
2. ____ anther
3. ____ carpel
4. ____ embryo sac
5. ____ embryo sac cell containing two nuclei
6. ____ megaspores
7. ____ meiosis
8. ____ microspores
9. ____ multiple fruit
10. ____ ovary
11. ____ ovule
12. ____ petal
13. ____ pollen grain
14. ____ sepal
15. ____ stigma

A. haploid cells in the anther
B. reduction of chromosome number by one-half
C. after fertilization, ripens into fruit tissue
D. helps form endosperm
E. cluster of matured ovaries attached to a common receptacle
F. modified leaf with pigments and fragrance-producing cells
G. mature microspore
H. female reproductive organ
I. landing platform for pollen
J. pollen-bearing structure
K. haploid cells in the ovule
L. outermost whorl of leaf parts on a receptacle; generally green, but sometimes pigmented
M. female gametophyte
N. matured ovaries of several flowers fused together into a single mass (for example, pineapple, fig)
O. after fertilization, will form a seed

Answers:

1. E	2. J	3. H	4. M
5. D	6. K	7. B	8. A
9. N	10. C	11. O	12. F
13. G	14. L	15. I	

D   105.   Matching II. Choose the one most appropriate answer for each. Some letters may not be used.

1. ___ abscisic acid
2. ___ ABA
3. ___ biological clock
4. ___ coleoptile
5. ___ ethylene
6. ___ germination
7. ___ gibberellin
8. ___ auxin
9. ___ phytochrome
10. ___ circadian
11. ___ short-day plant
12. ___ target cell
13. ___ long-day plant
14. ___ toxin
15. ___ vernalization

A. flower each successive year or after several years of vegetative growth
B. promotes cell elongation in stems
C. has receptor sites for a particular hormonal message
D. a structure surrounding the growing tip of corn
E. blue-green pigment that absorbs light energy
F. low-temperature stimulation of flowering
G. stimulates stomata closure and might be involved in root geotropism
H. stimulates fruit ripening
I. reproduces in spring
J. internal mechanism for recurring changes
K. occurring on a 24-hour cycle
L. flowers in autumn
M. resumption of growth after a period of dormancy as with a seed
N. a growth inhibitor
O. promotes stem elongation in dwarf plants
P. chemical that harms different species

Answers: 1. G   2. N   3. J   4. D
5. H   6. M   7. O   8. B
9. E   10. K   11. L   12. C
13. I   14. P   15. F

Classification Questions

Answer questions 106–110 in reference to the five flower parts listed below.

a. anther
b. stigma
c. ovule
d. ovary
e. stamen

E   106.   During fertilization of a flowering plant, the male gamete first adheres to this structure.

M   107.   A pollen tube ultimately grows into this structure.

M   108.   Fertilization of a flowering plant occurs inside of this structure.

M   109.   This structure produces pollen.

M   110.   Male meiosis occurs in this structure.

Answers: 106. b   107. c   108. c
109. a   110. a

Answer questions 111–115 in reference to the five flower parts listed below.

a. megaspore
b. microspore
c. ovule
d. ovary
e. seed

D   111.   This structure gives rise to the female gametophyte.

D   112.   This structure is female and haploid.

M   113.   This matures to form a haploid pollen grain.

D   114.   The egg is ultimately derived from this structure.

D   115.   During early development, the plant embryo is most intimately associated with this structure.

Answers: 111. a   112. a   113. b
114. a   115. c

Answer questions 116–120 in reference to the five plant hormones listed below.

a. auxins
b. gibberellins
c. cytokinins
d. abscisic acid
e. ethylene

M   116.   These hormones are most closely associated with cell division.

M   117.   These hormones are involved in stem elongation and closely related chemically to certain weed killers like 2,4–D.

D   118.   This hormone controls rate of transpiration.

E   119.   This hormone is a gas that promotes ripening.

M   120.   This hormone promotes bud and seed dormancy.

Answers: 116. c   117. a   118. d
119. e   120. d

Selecting the Exception

M 121. Four of the five answers listed below are related by gender. Select the exception.
   a. carpel
   b. ovary
   * c. stamen
   d. style
   e. stigma

M 122. Four of the five answers listed below are whorls of floral organs. Select the exception.
   * a. receptacle
   b. stamen
   c. carpel
   d. petal
   e. sepal

M 123. Four of the five answers listed below are haploid. Select the exception.
   a. gametophyte
   * b. zygote
   c. sperm
   d. meiospore
   e. gamete

E 124. Four of the five answers listed below are nonreproductive parts of a flower. Select the exception.
   a. calyx
   * b. anther
   c. corolla
   d. petal
   e. sepal

M 125. Four of the five answers listed below are related by a common gender. Select the exception.
   a. carpel
   b. integument
   c. embryo sac
   * d. microspore
   e. egg

E 126. Four of the five answers listed below are the results of fertilization. Select the exception.
   a. fruit
   b. seed
   c. embryo
   * d. pollen
   e. endosperm

E 127. Four of the five answers listed below are useful to flowers as means of attracting vectors. Select the exception.
   a. nectar
   b. flower color
   c. color patterns
   d. pollen
   * e. wind

M 128. Four of the five answers listed below are parts of a germinating seed. Select the exception.
   * a. ovary
   b. cotyledon
   c. embryo
   d. coat
   e. endosperm

M 129. Four of the five answers listed below are adaptations to aid in dispersal of fruit. Select the exception.
   a. hooks
   b. spines
   * c. smooth surface
   d. hairs
   e. sticky substances

M 130. Four of the five answers listed below are associated with auxin. Select the exception.
   a. used as herbicide
   * b. promotes cell division
   c. promotes cell elongation
   d. functions in phototropism
   e. indoleacetic acid

D 131. Four of the five answers listed below are true for gibberellin. Select the exception.
   a. helps seeds germinate
   b. found in fungi
   c. causes stem elongation
   * d. triggers flower production
   e. is a growth hormone

D 132. Four of the five answers listed below are functions of abscisic acid. Select the exception.
   a. may be involved in the maturation of embryos
   b. promotes stomata closure
   c. promotes seed dormancy
   d. confers resistance to water stress
   * e. stimulates cell elongation

D 133. Four of the five answers listed below are characteristics of ethylene. Select the exception.
   a. brightens citrus rinds
   b. promotes fruit ripening
   * c. triggers cells division
   d. is a gas
   e. controls growth of most tissues

D 134. Four of the five answers listed below are plant activities affected by phytochrome. Select the exception.
   * a. tropism
   b. stem elongation
   c. seed germination
   d. leaf expansion
   e. formation of flowers, fruits, and seeds

Labeling

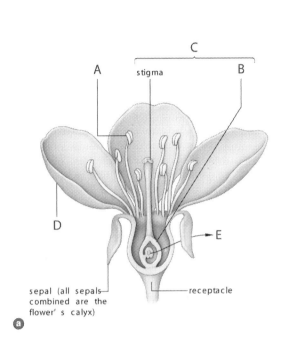

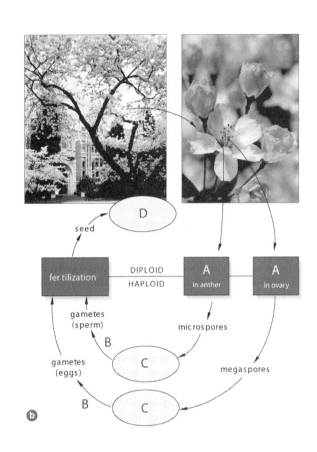

Questions 135–139 pertain to figure "a."

E **135.** The pollen are produced in the structure at letter _?_.

E **136.** The carpel is indicated by letter _?_.

E **137.** The seeds will form in the structure at letter _?_.

E **138.** The ovary, which will develop into fruit is at letter _?_.

E **139.** The highly colored portion of the flower is at letter _?_.

Questions 140 and 141 pertain to figure "b."

E **140.** Does meiosis occur at letter "A" or "B"?

E **141.** Is the sporophyte at letter "C" or "D"?

Answers: 135. A   136. C   137. E

138. B   139. D   140. A

141. D

CHAPTER 20
ANIMAL TISSUES AND ORGAN SYSTEMS

Multiple-Choice Questions

ORGANIZATION AND CONTROL IN ANIMAL BODIES

E **1.** Homeostasis provides what kind of environment?
   a. positive
 * b. constant
   c. limiting
   d. changing
   e. chemical and physical

M **2.** Which of the following phrases would most likely be used in a discussion of homeostasis?
   a. respond to environmental stimuli
 * b. tolerable limits
   c. rapid energy turnover
   d. cycle of elements
   e. structural and functional units of life

E **3.** Each cell is able to maintain a constant internal environment. This is called
   a. metabolism.
 * b. homeostasis.
   c. physiology.
   d. adaptation.
   e. evolution.

E **4.** Chemical and structural bridges link groups or layers of like cells, uniting them in structure and function as a cohesive
   a. organ.
   b. organ system.
 * c. tissue.
   d. cuticle.
   e. homeostasis.

M **5.** Which of the following represents the correct hierarchy of organization in the human body?
   a. cells >>> tissues >>> organ systems >>> organs
 * b. cells >>> tissues >>> organs >>> organ systems
   c. tissues >>> cells >>> organs >>> organ systems
   d. tissues >>> organs >>> cells >>> organ systems
   e. organs >>> tissues >>> cells >>> organ systems

M **6.** The minimum level of organization required for a "division of labor" is the _?_ level.
   a. cellular
   b. organ
 * c. tissue
   d. organ system
   e. body

FOUR BASIC TYPES OF TISSUES

E **7.** The tissue that lines all internal surfaces is
 * a. epithelium.
   b. loose connective.
   c. supportive connective.
   d. fibrous.
   e. adipose.

D **8.** Adhering and gap junctions are found at the
   a. endoplasmic reticulum.
   b. nuclear membrane.
 * c. plasma membrane.
   d. Golgi apparatus.
   e. ribosomes.

D **9.** Cells with gap junctions are typical of tissues
   a. that suffer wear, abrasion, and mechanical insults.
   b. such as bone and cartilage that must withstand external forces.
 * c. that require rapid signal flow.
   d. that secrete enzymes or hormones.
   e. all of these

M **10.** Which of the following junctions influences the passage of ions and small molecules between cells?
 * a. gap
   b. adhering
   c. loose
   d. tight
   e. plasma

D **11.** Epithelial cells are specialized for all EXCEPT which of the following functions?
   a. secretion
   b. protection
   c. filtration
 * d. contraction
   e. absorption

E **12.** The secretion of tears, milk, sweat, and oil is a function of what tissue?
 * a. epithelial
   b. loose connective
   c. lymphoid
   d. nervous
   e. adipose

E **13.** Exocrine glands secrete
   a. saliva.
   b. sweat.
   c. milk.
   d. mucus.
 * e. all of these

M 14. Which of the following is TRUE of the basement membrane?
  a. It overlies the epithelium at its free surface.
  b. It is composed partially of epithelial cells and partially of connective tissue.
  c. It is mostly lipid and embedded celluloid fibers.
* d. It lies between the epithelium above and connective tissue below.
  e. It cements the layers of stratified epithelium together.

M 15. If you microscopically examined a slide and observed a single layer of closely packed cells with microvilli on the free or open side and a basement membrane underlying the sheet of cells, you would expect this to be a slide of
  a. adipose tissue.
  b. dense regular connective tissue.
* c. epithelial tissue.
  d. muscle tissue.
  e. cartilage.

M 16. Which of the following is NOT defined as connective tissue?
  a. bone
* b. skeletal muscle
  c. cartilage
  d. collagen
  e. blood

E 17. What type of tissue is blood?
  a. epithelial
  b. muscular
* c. connective
  d. adipose
  e. noncellular fluid

M 18. An extracellular matrix, or "ground substance," is characteristic of
  a. muscle tissue.
  b. epithelial tissue.
* c. connective tissue.
  d. nervous tissue.
  e. embryonic tissue.

M 19. Which of these is NOT connective tissue?
  a. cartilage
  b. blood
  c. bone
  d. fat
* e. outer layer of skin

E 20. Dense fibrous tissues that connect muscle to bone are called
  a. muscles.
  b. cartilage.
  c. ligaments.
* d. tendons.
  e. all of these

M 21. Bones are linked together at skeletal joints by
  a. tendons.
  b. intercellular junctions.
* c. ligaments.
  d. cartilage.
  e. collagen.

M 22. Collagen fibers are characteristic of which tissue?
  a. muscle
  b. epithelial
* c. connective
  d. nervous
  e. embryonic

M 23. Tendons connect
  a. bones to bones.
  b. bones to ligaments.
* c. muscles to bones.
  d. bones to cartilage.
  e. all of these

D 24. Collagen fibers supply
  a. strength.
  b. elasticity.
  c. energy.
  d. rigidity.
* e. all except "energy"

E 25. Cartilage is found
  a. in the nose.
  b. between limb bones.
  c. in the outer ear.
  d. between vertebrae.
* e. all of these

E 26. Which element is found with ground substances in bone?
  a. potassium
  b. fluorine
* c. calcium
  d. iron
  e. phosphorus

E 27. Adipose tissue cells are filled with
  a. minerals.
* b. fat.
  c. cartilage.
  d. fibers.
  e. muscles.

D 28. Which of the following correctly matches connective tissue with its deposits?
  a. blood—fats
  b. adipose—polysaccharide
* c. bone—minerals
  d. cartilage—calcium
  e. All of these are matched correctly.

M   29. Which of the following tissues would be associated
         with the following terms: collagen, matrix,
         hemoglobin, minerals?
         a. epithelial
         b. nervous
     *   c. connective
         d. muscle
         e. reproductive

M   30. If its cells are striated and connected by gap junctions
         so that the cells contract as a unit, the tissue is
         a. smooth muscle.
         b. dense fibrous connective.
         c. supportive connective.
     *   d. cardiac muscle.
         e. skeletal muscle.

E   31. Muscle that is NOT striped and is involuntary is
         a. cardiac.
         b. skeletal.
         c. striated.
     *   d. smooth.
         e. cardiac and smooth.

E   32. Cardiac muscle cells are
         a. involuntary.
         b. voluntary.
         c. striated.
         d. slow contracting.
     *   e. involuntary and striated.

M   33. Smooth muscles are
         a. striated and voluntary.
         b. isolated, spindle-shaped cells.
         c. found in the walls of hollow structures such as the
             stomach, bladder, and uterus.
         d. involuntary and nonstriated.
     *   e. all except "striated and voluntary"

E   34. Rapid communication throughout the body is
         accomplished by
     *   a. neurons.
         b. blood.
         c. hormones.
         d. muscles.
         e. connective tissue.

ORGAN SYSTEMS MADE FROM TISSUES

D   35. A fish embryo was accidentally stabbed by a graduate
         student in a developmental biology laboratory. Later,
         the embryo developed into a creature that could not
         move and had no supportive or circulatory systems.
         Which embryonic tissue had suffered the damage?
         a. ectoderm
         b. endoderm
     *   c. mesoderm
         d. protoderm
         e. both ectoderm and protoderm

D   36. A student attempting to learn more about the process
         of embryological development manipulated an embryo
         early in the developmental process. The creature that
         developed was normal in almost every aspect, except
         for some of the organs lining the digestive tract. The
         tissue that was disturbed was the
         a. ectoderm.
     *   b. endoderm.
         c. gastroderm.
         d. mesoderm.
         e. both ectoderm and gastroderm.

E   37. Muscle cells are produced by
         a. the ectoderm.
         b. the endoderm.
     *   c. the mesoderm.
         d. the ectoderm and endoderm.
         e. all of the germ layers.

E   38. The lining of the digestive tract is produced by
         a. the ectoderm.
     *   b. the endoderm.
         c. the mesoderm.
         d. the endoderm and mesoderm.
         e. all of the germ layers.

E   39. The nervous system is produced by
     *   a. the ectoderm.
         b. the endoderm.
         c. the mesoderm.
         d. the endoderm and ectoderm.
         e. all of the germ layers.

E   40. The external covering of the body is produced by
     *   a. the ectoderm.
         b. the endoderm.
         c. the mesoderm.
         d. the ectoderm and mesoderm.
         e. all of the germ layers.

E   41. The skeletal and circulatory systems are produced by
         a. the ectoderm.
         b. the endoderm.
     *   c. the mesoderm.
         d. two of the germ layers.
         e. all of the germ layers.

E   42. The lining of the gut and the stomach, liver, and
         pancreas are produced by
         a. the ectoderm.
     *   b. the endoderm.
         c. the mesoderm.
         d. two of the germ layers.
         e. all of the germ layers.

M   43. Somatic cells can form all but which of the following?
     *   a. gametes
         b. epithelia
         c. muscles
         d. digestive organs
         e. Somatic cells form all of these.

M 44. The endocrine system functions in
       a. conduction.
       b. contraction.
    * c. hormonal control of body functioning.
       d. protection against disease.
       e. cell production.

M 45. Excreting excess fluids and filtering wastes from the
       blood is the direct responsibility of which system?
       a. integumentary
       b. immune
       c. digestive
    * d. urinary
       e. circulatory

E 46. Which system is involved with generating heat?
       a. endocrine system
       b. nervous system
    * c. muscular system
       d. respiratory system
       e. skeletal system

M 47. Integration of body functions is controlled by
       a. the respiratory system.
       b. the nervous system.
       c. the endocrine system.
       d. the defense system.
    * e. both the nervous system and endocrine system.

D 48. Organs of which of the following systems are the most
       diffuse and the least likely to be physically connected?
       a. integumentary system
    * b. endocrine system
       c. skeletal system
       d. muscular system
       e. digestive system

E 49. Which system produces red blood cells?
       a. endocrine
    * b. skeletal
       c. muscular
       d. defense
       e. integumentary

M 50. Which of the following terms means the structure is
       located away from the central part of the body?
       a. dorsal
       b. inferior
       c. superior
       d. proximal
    * e. distal

D 51. Of the following organs, which is NOT in the
       abdominal cavity?
       a. stomach
       b. liver
    * c. heart
       d. intestine
       e. pancreas

E 52. What we usually call the "back" of the human body is
       really the
       a. anterior.
    * b. posterior.
       c. inferior.
       d. superior.
       e. laterior.

SKIN—EXAMPLE OF AN ORGAN SYSTEM

E 53. The integumentary system is responsible for all
       EXCEPT which of the following?
       a. protection against bacterial attack
       b. repair small cuts and burns
       c. synthesis of vitamin D
    * d. blood cell formation
       e. cool the body on hot days

E 54. The largest organ of the vertebrate body is which of
       the following?
       a. lungs
       b. liver
       c. stomach
    * d. skin
       e. small intestines

M 55. All EXCEPT which of the following are functions of
       the skin?
       a. protection from bacterial invasion
       b. regulation of body temperature
    * c. production of tanning hormones
       d. sensing of the external world
       e. production of vitamin D

M 56. Which of the following is NOT found in the
       epidermis?
       a. stratified epithelium
    * b. blood vessels
       c. tight cell junctions
       d. keratin
       e. melanin

D 57. Which of the following is NOT characteristic of the
       epidermis?
       a. stratified epithelium
    * b. adipose tissue to insulate and cushion
       c. keratinocytes
       d. cell junctions
       e. melanin pigments

E 58. Melanin protects the skin from
       a. desiccation.
       b. abrasion.
    * c. ultraviolet radiation.
       d. infrared damage.
       e. invasion by bacteria.

M 59. Which of the following statements is FALSE concerning the outermost layer of the epidermis?
  a. It is the first to feel any abrasion.
  b. Keratin provides waterproofing.
  c. Millions of cells are worn off daily.
 * d. Its cells are undergoing rapid cell division.
  e. It is very thin.

M 60. Which of the following components of the dermis is INCORRECTLY matched with its usual function?
  a. blood vessels—nutrient supply
 * b. sweat glands—hormone secretion
  c. oil glands—lubrication of hair and skin
  d. hairs—insulation
  e. receptors—pain

Matching Questions

D 61. Matching I. Choose the one most appropriate answer for each.
  1. ___ adipose tissue
  2. ___ blood
  3. ___ dense connective tissue
  4. ___ glandular epithelium
  5. ___ loose connective tissue
  6. ___ plasma
  7. ___ neuron
  8. ___ epidermis

  A. ligaments and tendons are made of this
  B. found beneath the skin and in areas between organs
  C. receives, conducts, and initiates signals in response to environmental changes
  D. stores fatty reserves
  E. offers resistance to mechanical injury and loss of internal fluids; also a barrier against microorganisms
  F. secretes extracellular products such as sweat, mucus, tears, and saliva
  G. plasma plus free cells; involved in transport
  H. fluid portion of blood

Answers: 1. D   2. G   3. A   4. F
          5. B   6. H   7. C   8. E

D 62. Matching II. Choose the one most appropriate answer for each.
  1. ___ muscle cells
  2. ___ lining of the intestine
  3. ___ nervous system
  4. ___ external body covering
  5. ___ skeletal system
  6. ___ circulatory system
  7. ___ stomach, liver, and pancreas (excluding the muscles and nerves)

  A. develop(s) from ectoderm in embryo
  B. develop(s) from endoderm in embryo
  C. develop(s) from mesoderm in embryo

Answers: 1. C   2. B   3. A   4. A
          5. C   6. C   7. B

Classification Questions

Answer questions 63–67 in reference to the five types of connective tissue listed below.
  a. loose tissue
  b. dense tissue
  c. adipose tissue
  d. cartilage
  e. blood

E 63. Tendons are composed of this.

E 64. Often attaches an epithelium to the wall of an organ.

M 65. This tissue forms the external portions of the nose and the external ear.

E 66. This tissue provides nourishment to each of the other connective tissues.

M 67. In some animals, one type helps warm the body by heat production.

Answers: 63. b   64. a   65. d
             66. e   67. c

Answer questions 68–72 in reference to the five organ systems listed below.

    a. circulatory
    b. lymphatic
    c. digestive
    d. endocrine
    e. respiratory

M **68.** Breaks food down into component molecules and absorbs them.

E **69.** Defends the body against infections and tissue damage.

M **70.** Rapidly delivers oxygen to tissue fluid that bathes all cells.

M **71.** Helps stabilize internal pH and temperature.

M **72.** Hormonally controls body functioning.

Answers: 68. c   69. b   70. e

            71. a   72. d

Selecting the Exception

M **73.** Three of the four answers listed below are germ layers. Select the exception.
    a. ectoderm
    b. mesoderm
*   c. blastoderm
    d. endoderm
    e. All of these are germ layers.

D **74.** Four of the five answers listed below are derived from the same germ layer. Select the exception.
    a. kidney
*   b. brain
    c. muscle
    d. respiratory system
    e. skeleton

D **75.** Four of the five answers listed below are derived from the same germ layer. Select the exception.
    a. lining of intestinal tract
*   b. circulatory system
    c. liver
    d. pancreas
    e. stomach

M **76.** Four of the five answers listed below are secreted by an exocrine gland. Select the exception.
    a. wax
    b. saliva
*   c. hormone
    d. milk
    e. mucus

D **77.** Four of the five answers listed below are related by a common tissue type. Select the exception.
    a. adipose
    b. bone
    c. cartilage
    d. blood
*   e. epithelium

D **78.** Four of the five answers listed below are sites where cartilage is found. Select the exception.
    a. embryonic skeleton
    b. vertebral discs
    c. external ear
    d. end of long bones in skeleton
*   e. tips of the fingers

D **79.** Four of the five answers listed below are functions of the skeleton. Select the exception.
*   a. control of body temperature
    b. production of blood cells
    c. protection
    d. calcium and phosphorus storage
    e. muscle attachment

Labeling

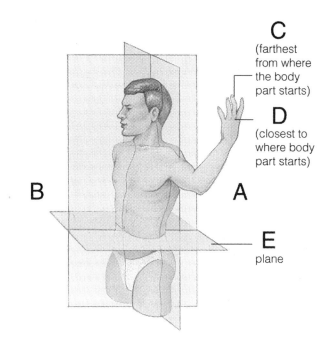

C
(farthest from where the body part starts)

D
(closest to where body part starts)

B

A

E
plane

E   **80.**   The anterior direction is indicated by letter _?_.

E   **81.**   The posterior direction is indicated by letter _?_.

E   **82.**   Distal is indicated by letter _?_.

E   **83.**   Proximal is indicated by letter _?_.

E   **84.**   Letter "E" is the _?_ plane.
      *   a. transverse
            b. frontal
            c. abdominal
            d. midsagittal
            e. dorsal

Answers: 80. B   81. A   82. C

            83. D

CHAPTER 21
HOW ANIMALS MOVE

Multiple-Choice Questions

SO WHAT IS A SKELETON?

M   1.   Organisms with external skeletons are exemplified by
     a. octopuses and earthworms.
     b. mollusks.
     c. sea anemones.
*   d. insects and crabs.
     e. vertebrates.

E   2.   Which organisms have a hydrostatic skeleton with a soft body wall?
*   a. earthworms
     b. spiders
     c. sponges
     d. crabs
     e. vertebrates

E   3.   In which of the following types is the skeletal substance NOT technically a part of the animal?
     a. exoskeleton
     b. endoskeleton
     c. musculoskeleton
     d. articuloskeleton
*   e. hydrostatic

M   4.   For an arthropod, an exoskeleton has which serious disadvantage?
*   a. inability to grow
     b. too much weight for flying
     c. poor placement of muscles for leverage
     d. lack of flexible appendages
     e. poor water retention

E   5.   Which organisms have a somewhat rigid internal skeleton and many muscles?
     a. octopuses
     b. earthworms
     c. sea anemones
     d. insects
*   e. vertebrates

M   6.   Bone cells lie in a _?_-hardened, collagen-rich organic matrix
     a. phosphorus.
     b. iron.
     c. magnesium.
*   d. calcium.
     e. sulfur.

M   7.   The human axial skeleton includes all EXCEPT which of the following?
     a. skull
     b. ribs
*   c. pectoral girdle
     d. sternum
     e. vertebral column

E   8.   Which of the following is NOT part of the appendicular skeleton?
     a. clavicle
     b. scapula
     c. fibula
*   d. ribs
     e. patella

E   9.   The bone in the upper arm is the
     a. radius.
     b. ulna.
     c. tibia.
*   d. humerus.
     e. femur.

E   10.   Bones in fingers or toes are called
     a. hyoid.
     b. patella.
     c. scapula.
     d. clavicle.
*   e. phalanges.

E   11.   The knee bone or kneecap is the
     a. hyoid.
*   b. patella.
     c. scapula.
     d. clavicle.
     e. phalanx.

E   12.   The collarbone is the
     a. hyoid.
     b. patella.
     c. scapula.
*   d. clavicle.
     e. phalanx.

E   13.   The shoulder blade is the
     a. hyoid.
     b. patella.
*   c. scapula.
     d. clavicle.
     e. phalanx.

M   14.   Which of the following joins two bones?
     a. fontanels
*   b. ligaments
     c. keratinocytes
     d. tendons
     e. sarcomeres

E　15. In spongy bone tissue, the spaces are filled with
　　　a. air.
　　　b. blood.
　　　c. cartilage.
　*　d. marrow.
　　　e. lymph.

M　16. Which tissue has Haversian canals?
　　　a. adipose
　*　b. bone
　　　c. cartilage
　　　d. epithelial
　　　e. muscular

D　17. If some bleached bones found lying in the desert were carefully examined, which of the following would NOT be present?
　*　a. osteocytes
　　　b. Haversian canals
　　　c. calcium
　　　d. marrow cavity
　　　e. compact bone tissue

D　18. All EXCEPT which of the following are associated with bone formation?
　　　a. osteoblasts
　　　b. cartilage
　*　c. osteoporosis
　　　d. marrow cavity formation
　　　e. calcium

M　19. The vertebral discs with small amounts of movement are examples of what kind of joints?
　　　a. synovial
　　　b. fibrous
　*　c. cartilaginous
　　　d. hinge
　　　e. none of these

HOW DO BONES AND MUSCLES INTERACT?

M　20. Smooth muscle is
　*　a. mainly a component of the stomach, bladder, and other internal organs.
　　　b. responsible for movement of the skeleton.
　　　c. involved in contraction of the heart.
　　　d. connected to bones by tendons.
　　　e. involuntary and nonstriated; plus it is involved in contraction of the heart.

D　21. The ability to extend a leg originates from
　　　a. contraction of ligaments and tendons.
　*　b. contraction of a muscle.
　　　c. lengthening of a muscle.
　　　d. combination of push and pull by antagonistic muscle pairs.
　　　e. muscle recoil.

E　22. Muscles are attached to bones by means of
　　　a. sarcomeres.
　　　b. ligaments.
　　　c. cross-bridges.
　　　d. cuticle.
　*　e. tendons.

M　23. The biceps muscle is located
　*　a. in the forelimb.
　　　b. on the back.
　　　c. in the hip area.
　　　d. in the lower leg.
　　　e. in the neck.

HOW DOES SKELETAL MUSCLE CONTRACT?

E　24. Each muscle fiber is also called a
　　　a. muscle.
　*　b. muscle cell.
　　　c. myofibril.
　　　d. sarcomere.
　　　e. all of these

D　25. Which of the following includes all the others?
　　　a. actin
　　　b. myofibril
　　　c. myosin
　　　d. myofilament
　*　e. muscle fiber

D　26. By the sliding-filament model, when a sarcomere shortens,
　　　a. the actin filaments shorten.
　　　b. the myosin filaments shorten.
　　　c. both actin and myosin shorten.
　*　d. neither actin nor myosin shortens.
　　　e. actin and myosin act independently.

D　27. During muscle contractions,
　　　a. Z bands move closer to one another.
　　　b. the actin and myosin filaments slide over each other.
　　　c. the filaments move toward the middle of the sarcomere during contraction and away on relaxation.
　　　d. the muscle fibers thicken.
　*　e. all of these

D　28. During contraction,
　　　a. cross-bridges of muscle filaments are broken and reformed.
　　　b. ATP is used to form cross-bridges.
　　　c. muscle cells use glycogen as their energy source.
　　　d. if there is a poor supply of oxygen, glycogen depletion by glycolysis will lead to fatigue.
　*　e. all of these

D　29. In their action, muscles could best be compared to
　*　a. ropes.
　　　b. levers.
　　　c. push rods.
　　　d. screws.
　　　e. hammers.

M   30. The element specifically associated with muscle contraction is
   a. phosphorus.
   b. potassium.
 * c. calcium.
   d. sodium.
   e. chlorine.

M   31. The most immediate, but necessarily limited, source of energy for reformation of ATP in muscle cells is
   a. aerobic respiration.
   b. mitochondrial pathways.
   c. electron transport phosphorylation.
 * d. creatine phosphate.
   e. anaerobic fermentation.

M   32. Which of these occurs as a result of rigorous muscular exercise?
   a. ATP accumulation
   b. actin depletion
 * c. lack of oxygen
   d. glycogen buildup
   e. sarcomere formation

PROPERTIES OF WHOLE MUSCLES

D   33. An active, nonfatiguing muscle would be expected to have
   a. aerobic respiration.
   b. numerous mitochondria.
   c. moderate rates of contraction.
   d. aerobic respiration and moderate rates of contraction.
 * e. aerobic respiration, moderate rates of contraction, and numerous mitochondria.

E   34. Muscle fatigue is a result of
 * a. accumulation of lactic acid.
   b. exhaustion of available ATP.
   c. reduction in lactic acid and oxygen debt.
   d. failure of calcium channels to open after prolonged use.
   e. lack of creatine.

M   35. A motor neuron and all the muscle fibers under its control is called what kind of unit?
   a. end
   b. movement
   c. muscle
 * d. motor
   e. coordination

M   36. The mechanical force that resists gravity in the lifting of an object is
   a. muscle fatigue.
   b. a motor unit.
 * c. muscle tension.
   d. a muscle twitch.
   e. tetanus.

M   37. A sustained contraction is called
   a. a twitch.
 * b. tetanus.
   c. isotension.
   d. fatigue.
   e. dystrophy.

M   38. Which of the following is NOT true of aerobic exercise?
 * a. More myofibrils develop.
   b. It is of long duration.
   c. There is an increase of mitochondria quantities.
   d. The number of blood capillaries is increased.
   e. Oxygen consumption goes up.

Classification Questions

Answer questions 39–43 in reference to the five bones listed below.
   a. clavicle
   b. lumbar vertebra
   c. tibia
   d. tarsal
   e. metacarpal

E   39. This bone is not part of the appendicular skeleton.

M   40. This bone is commonly called the collarbone.

M   41. If one had a slipped disk, that disk might be next to this bone.

D   42. This bone is in the ankle.

M   43. This bone connects to the lower end of the femur.

Answers: 39. b   40. a   41. b
         42. d   43. c

Selecting the Exception

D   44. Four of the five answers listed below are found in bone. Select the exception.
   a. lacunae
 * b. muscle fibers
   c. Haversian system
   d. blood capillaries
   e. osteocyte

E   45. Four of the five answers listed below possess the same type of skeleton. Select the exception.
 * a. beetle
   b. snake
   c. bird
   d. human
   e. frog

M   46.   Four of the five answers listed below possess the same
          type of skeleton. Select the exception.
          a. butterfly
          b. fly
     *   c. earthworm
          d. crab
          e. grasshopper

M   47.   Four of the five answers listed below are parts of the
          same anatomical area. Select the exception.
          a. humerus
     *   b. fibula
          c. radius
          d. clavicle
          e. scapula

M   48.   Four of the five answers listed below are parts of the
          same skeletal division. Select the exception.
          a. cranium
          b. ribs
          c. sternum
          d. vertebrae
     *   e. phalanges

D   49.   Four of the five answers listed below are substances
          that participate in muscle contraction. Select the
          exception.
     *   a. iron
          b. calcium
          c. ATP
          d. actin
          e. myosin

Labeling

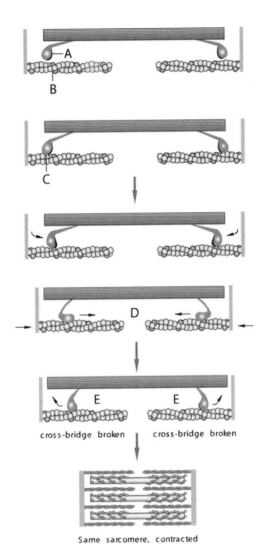

cross-bridge broken   cross-bridge broken

Same sarcomere, contracted

E **50.** The figure depicts various stages in contraction according to the _?_ model.
*   a. sliding filament
    b. shortening myosin
    c. lengthening action
    d. crumbling fiber
    e. contracting fibril

E **51.** Myosin is represented by the letter _?_.

E **52.** Actin is represented by the letter _?_.

E **53.** The interaction of filaments at letter "C" is called a
    a. synapse.
*   b. cross-bridge.
    c. crossover.
    d. bond.
    e. suture.

E **54.** At "D" the filaments are
    a. contracted.
    b. expanded.
    c. shorter.
    d. longer.
*   e. closer together.

E **55.** The energy source at "E" is
    a. lactate.
    b. pyruvate.
    c. NADH.
*   d. ATP.
    e. glucose.

Answers: 51. A   52. B

CHAPTER 22
CIRCULATION AND RESPIRATION

Multiple-Choice Questions

THE NATURE OF BLOOD CIRCULATION

M   1.   The interstitial fluid is
    a.   what helps keep conditions tolerable for enzymes and other molecules.
    b.   an extracellular fluid.
    c.   what fills the tissue spaces.
    d.   part of the body's internal environment.
  * e.   all of these

M   2.   Extracellular fluid contains all EXCEPT which of the following?
  * a.   red blood cells
    b.   ions
    c.   certain soluble proteins
    d.   lymph
    e.   water

D   3.   Which of the following is usually NOT present in an open circulation system?
  * a.   veins
    b.   the heart
    c.   arteries
    d.   blood
    e.   arterioles

E   4.   Which animal has a closed circulatory system?
    a.   clam
  * b.   human
    c.   spider
    d.   snail
    e.   insect

M   5.   Which of the following statements is FALSE?
    a.   The systemic circuit carries oxygenated blood.
  * b.   Humans have an open circulatory system.
    c.   The function of the heart is to generate pressure to make the blood flow through the circulatory system.
    d.   The rate of blood flow varies throughout the circulatory system.
    e.   The interstitial fluid is returned to the circulatory system in the lymphatic system.

M   6.   Which of the following statements is FALSE?
  * a.   Blood circulates faster through a fish than through a human.
    b.   Fish have only one heart pump, but humans have a heart divided into two pumps.
    c.   Humans have one major capillary bed, whereas fish have two capillary beds.
    d.   Blood pressure is lower in the capillary beds than in the major blood vessels.
    e.   The circulation of blood in humans is more efficient than in fish.

M   7.   The pulmonary circuit
    a.   involves the hepatic portal vein.
    b.   moves oxygen-rich blood to the lungs.
    c.   includes the coronary arteries.
  * d.   leads to, through, and from the lungs.
    e.   all of these

M   8.   In the human systemic circuit, blood will pass through all EXCEPT which of the following?
    a.   liver
    b.   limbs
  * c.   lungs
    d.   digestive organs
    e.   brain

CHARACTERISTICS OF HUMAN BLOOD

E   9.   All EXCEPT which of the following can occur in the blood?
  * a.   digestion of nutrients
    b.   binding of oxygen with hemoglobin
    c.   transport of phagocytic cells
    d.   proteins that transport lipids and fat-soluble vitamins
    e.   transport of dissolved gases

D   10. Which cell does NOT belong with the others?
  * a.   red blood cells
    b.   neutrophils
    c.   lymphocytes
    d.   basophils
    e.   macrophages

D   11. Which white blood cells are most abundant?
  * a.   neutrophils
    b.   lymphocytes
    c.   macrophages
    d.   eosinophils
    e.   basophils

D   12. Which cell is NOT involved with the defense response?
  * a.   erythrocytes
    b.   neutrophils
    c.   lymphocytes
    d.   basophils
    e.   macrophages

D   13. Which cell is the most abundant in the human body?
    a.   lymphocytes
    b.   basophils
  * c.   erythrocytes
    d.   neutrophils
    e.   platelets

M   14.   Which cell releases substances that initiate clotting?
          a. lymphocytes
          b. basophils
          c. erythrocytes
          d. neutrophils
     *   e. platelets

M   15.   In humans, which cell does NOT have a nucleus?
     *   a. erythrocytes
          b. lymphocytes
          c. neutrophils
          d. basophils
          e. macrophages

M   16.   Human red blood cells
     *   a. have no nucleus.
          b. are the primary carriers of carbon dioxide in the blood.
          c. are phagocytes.
          d. release clotting factors when they are ruptured.
          e. are produced in lymphoid organs.

M   17.   Most of the oxygen in the blood is transported by
          a. plasma.
          b. serum.
          c. platelets.
     *   d. hemoglobin.
          e. leukocytes.

E   18.   Red blood cells originate from stem cells in the
          a. liver.
          b. spleen.
          c. yellow bone marrow.
     *   d. red bone marrow.
          e. thymus gland.

M   19.   Stem cells
     *   a. retain the ability to divide and give rise to groups of cells.
          b. are phagocytic.
          c. are the most common type of blood cells.
          d. transport oxygen and carbon dioxide.
          e. are more numerous in women than in men.

D   20.   A normal red blood cell count would be in the range of _?_ per microliter.
          a. 3,000–6,750
          b. 250,000–300,000
     *   c. 4.8–5.4 million
          d. 1.6–3.2 million
          e. 20,000–100,000

M   21.   How long does the average red blood cell live?
          a. 4 days
          b. 4 weeks
     *   c. 4 months
          d. 1 year
          e. 4 years

D   22.   Stem cells for blood cell formation are found in the
          a. arteries.
     *   b. bone marrow.
          c. liver.
          d. spleen.
          e. pancreas.

D   23.   Stem cells give rise to
          a. red blood cells.
          b. megakaryocytes.
          c. macrophages.
          d. lymphocytes.
     *   e. all of these

E   24.   About how many quarts of blood does a normal, 150-pound human male have?
          a. 2 to 3
          b. 3 to 4
     *   c. 4 to 5
          d. 5 to 6
          e. 6 to 7

E   25.   What percent of the total blood volume does plasma normally amount to?
          a. 15 to 25
          b. 33 to 40
     *   c. 50 to 60
          d. 66 to 75
          e. about 80

M   26.   Proteins constitute what percentage of the human plasma?
          a. 1–2
          b. 91–92
          c. 12–15
     *   d. 7–8
          e. 50–60

E   27.   Which of the following makes up the greatest percentage of human plasma?
          a. albumin
          b. red blood cells
          c. white blood cells
     *   d. water
          e. dissolved ions, sugars, hormones, etc.

E   28.   Hemoglobin binds with which important element?
          a. chlorine
          b. sodium
     *   c. iron
          d. copper
          e. magnesium

E   29.   Megakaryocytes fragment to produce
          a. red blood cells.
          b. lymphocytes.
     *   c. platelets.
          d. basophils.
          e. neutrophils.

E 30. Megakaryocytes
   *   a. produce platelets by fragmentation.
        b. produce leukocytes.
        c. are wandering phagocytes.
        d. are disc-shaped cells that transport gases.
        e. produce antibodies.

M 31. Blood rich in oxygen is what color?
        a. yellow
        b. pink
   *   c. bright red
        d. blue
        e. purple

M 32. If a test tube of whole blood is subjected to
        centrifugation, the cells will be packed in the bottom
        of the tube and the fluid above it will be designated
        a. water.
        b. serum.
        c. lymph.
        d. interstitial fluid.
   *   e. plasma.

M 33. When they are mature and circulating in the blood,
        which of these blood components have no nuclei?
        a. platelets only
        b. leukocytes only
        c. erythrocytes only
   *   d. platelets and erythrocytes
        e. leukocytes and erythrocytes

HUMAN CARDIOVASCULAR SYSTEM

M 34. In its travel through the human body, blood usually
        continues on from capillaries to enter
        a. arterioles.
   *   b. venules.
        c. arteries.
        d. veins.
        e. other capillaries.

D 35. Which of the following statements is TRUE?
        a. Arteries carry only oxygenated blood.
   *   b. The systemic circuit leaves the heart from the left
           ventricle.
        c. Blood passes through only one capillary bed on its
           trip through the systemic circuit.
        d. Platelets survive a longer time than erythrocytes.
        e. The heart is able to pick up the oxygen it needs as
           the blood flows through it.

M 36. Blood in arteries
   *   a. always travels away from the heart.
        b. travels away from the heart only if it is oxygen
           rich.
        c. always travels toward the heart.
        d. travels from the lungs.
        e. is always oxygen-rich.

M 37. The blood receiving zone of a vertebrate heart is
        a. a plaque.
        b. the aorta.
   *   c. an atrium.
        d. a capillary bed.
        e. all of these

M 38. Atria differ from ventricles in that they
        a. are larger.
        b. have thicker walls with more muscles.
   *   c. receive blood from veins.
        d. have a higher blood pressure.
        e. empty through the semilunar valves.

E 39. The aorta leaves the
        a. left atrium.
        b. right atrium.
   *   c. left ventricle.
        d. right ventricle.

E 40. The pulmonary artery carries blood away from the
        a. aorta.
        b. right atrium.
   *   c. right ventricle.
        d. left atrium.
        e. left ventricle.

E 41. Blood from the body is first received by the heart in
        the
        a. coronary vein.
        b. left atrium.
        c. right ventricle.
   *   d. right atrium.
        e. left ventricle.

D 42. The human heart
   *   a. will contract as a result of stimuli from the
           sinoatrial node.
        b. contracts only as a result of nerve stimulation
           from the central nervous system.
        c. is activated primarily through the autonomic
           nervous system.
        d. pulse is primarily under the control of the
           atrioventricular node.
        e. is independent of all nervous control.

M 43. The pacemaker is which of the following nodes?
   *   a. sinoatrial
        b. semilunar
        c. atrioventricular
        d. inferior vena cava
        e. superior vena cava

M 44. Heart excitation originates in the
        a. atrioventricular node.
        b. intercalated disk.
   *   c. sinoatrial node.
        d. pericardium.
        e. all of these

D 45. If a physician hears two "lub" sounds instead of one, then which of the following conditions is TRUE?
   a. The semilunar valves are not closing simultaneously.
   b. The atrial blood is flowing backward and causing the extra sound.
 * c. The atrioventricular valves are not closing at the same time.
   d. The AV and semilunar valves are not closing at the same time.
   e. No such double sound has ever been heard.

D 46. An artificial pacemaker supplements the actions of
   a. sympathetic nerves.
   b. the atrioventricular node.
   c. the medulla oblongata.
 * d. the sinoatrial node.
   e. the heart muscle itself.

D 47. Which of the following statements is FALSE?
 * a. A heart will stop beating when the nerves to the heart are severed.
   b. Some cardiac muscle cells are self-excitatory.
   c. The pacemaker of the heart is the sinoatrial node.
   d. Cardiac muscles join end to end to allow rapid communication.
   e. Cardiac muscles contract essentially in unison.

STRUCTURE AND FUNCTION OF BLOOD VESSELS

E 48. Which of the following has the highest blood pressure?
   a. right ventricle
   b. right atrium
 * c. left ventricle
   d. left atrium
   e. pulmonary circulation

M 49. What occurs during systole?
   a. Oxygen-rich blood is pumped to the lungs.
 * b. The heart muscle tissues contract.
   c. The atrioventricular valves suddenly open.
   d. Oxygen-poor blood from all body regions except the lungs flows into the right atrium.
   e. all of these

E 50. Blood pressure is highest in the
 * a. aorta.
   b. pulmonary artery.
   c. capillary bed.
   d. subclavian vein.
   e. inferior vena cava.

M 51. The diastolic pressure for a normal young adult would be
   a. 60 mm Hg.
 * b. 80 mm Hg.
   c. 100 mm Hg.
   d. 120 mm Hg.
   e. 140 mm Hg.

D 52. Which of the following statements is TRUE?
   a. The systolic pressure is determined when the first sound is heard after pumping up the pressure cuff.
   b. The diastolic pressure is the smaller of the two pressure values.
   c. The difference between the systolic and diastolic pressure is the pulse pressure.
   d. Diastole is at the end of the cardiac cycle.
 * e. All of these are true.

M 53. Reabsorption
   a. is the movement of materials through capillaries.
   b. is the movement of components of the interstitial fluid into a capillary bed.
   c. occurs at the beginning of the capillary bed.
   d. occurs at the end of the capillary bed.
 * e. is movement of water by osmosis from the interstitial fluid into the protein-rich plasma.

M 54. By controlling their musculature, which of the following can vary the resistance to blood flow?
   a. arteries
   b. veins
   c. capillaries
 * d. arterioles
   e. all of these

M 55. Because of their great elasticity, which of the following can function as blood volume reservoirs during times of low metabolic output?
 * a. veins and venules
   b. arteries
   c. arterioles
   d. capillaries
   e. all of these

D 56. Which of the following controls the distribution of blood?
   a. arteries
 * b. arterioles
   c. capillaries
   d. venules
   e. veins

E 57. Which of the following are pressure reservoirs that smooth out pulsations in pressure generated by each cardiac cycle?
 * a. arteries
   b. arterioles
   c. capillaries
   d. venules
   e. veins

E	58.	Which of the following are highly distensible reservoirs for blood volume?
a.	arteries
b.	arterioles
c.	capillaries
d.	venules
*	e.	veins

M	59.	The greatest volume of blood is found in the
a.	aorta and arteries.
b.	capillaries.
*	c.	veins.
d.	lungs.
e.	heart.

CARDIOVASCULAR DISORDERS

D	60.	The coronary vessels
*	a.	supply and drain the heart's muscular wall.
b.	bypass the heart ventricles.
c.	send blood directly to the lungs.
d.	are not really necessary because the heart can get its blood supply from the "inside."
e.	lead directly from the atria to the ventricles.

D	61.	Hemostasis in vertebrates includes all EXCEPT which of the following?
a.	blood clot formation
b.	smooth muscle in the damaged vessel wall contents
*	c.	release of iron to aid in the clumping of platelets
d.	spasm
e.	platelets clump together

M	62.	The most common vascular disease affecting a quarter of American adults is
a.	phlebitis.
*	b.	hypertension.
c.	leukemia.
d.	sickle-cell anemia.
e.	a stroke.

D	63.	Which of the following statements is FALSE?
a.	LDL levels are elevated in atherosclerotic plaque.
b.	Hemostasis is a process to control bleeding.
c.	Hypertension is called the silent killer.
d.	In atherosclerosis, the diameter of the lumen of a blood vessel narrows.
*	e.	If a blood clot becomes dislodged and travels in the bloodstream, it is called a thrombus.

M	64.	Arteries thicken and lose elasticity in
a.	atheriosclerosis.
b.	hemostasis.
c.	hypertension.
d.	an embolism.
*	e.	arteriosclerosis

M	65.	In atherosclerosis,
a.	smooth muscle proliferates.
b.	plaque forms.
c.	lipids accumulate in the arterial wall and narrow the inside diameter.
d.	fibrous connective tissue is laid down.
*	e.	all of these

M	66.	Cholesterol is believed to be carried by
a.	albumin.
b.	high-density lipoproteins only.
c.	low-density lipoproteins only.
d.	triglycerides.
*	e.	both high-density and low-density lipoproteins.

THE NATURE OF RESPIRATION

M	67.	Which vertebrate body system is most closely associated functionally with respiration?
a.	urinary
b.	digestive
c.	endocrine
*	d.	circulatory
e.	integumentary

M	68.	The movement of both oxygen and carbon dioxide in the body is accomplished mostly by
a.	exocytosis and endocytosis.
b.	bulk flow.
c.	osmosis.
*	d.	diffusion.
e.	facilitated diffusion.

D	69.	As an animal grows larger, the surface area increases by the _?_ of its dimensions.
a.	cube
*	b.	square
c.	square root
d.	doubling
e.	quotient

M	70.	Which of the following is FALSE?
a.	All respiratory surfaces must be kept moist.
b.	The amount of gas diffusing across a respiratory membrane is dependent upon the surface area and the partial pressure of each gas.
*	c.	The surface area of an expanding balloon increases at the same rate as its volume.
d.	The movement of the flap over a fish's gill is a participant in ventilation.
e.	A hemoglobin molecule binds to four oxygen molecules.

M 71. Ventilation could be defined as
    a. cilia moving over the gills.
    b. movement of water past cells by using flagella.
    c. muscle action moving air in and out of the lungs.
    d. tracheal exchanges.
  * e. all of these

M 72. For a respiratory surface to function in the exchange of gases within an animal, it must
    a. be thin and soft.
    b. have a high number of blood vessels.
    c. have mucus or a moist covering.
    d. be extensive.
  * e. all of these

D 73. Countercurrent exchange, in conjunction with respiratory systems, is a mechanism that explains how
  * a. a fish can extract more oxygen from water than it could using a one-way flow.
    b. ventilation occurs.
    c. sounds originating in the vocal cords of the larynx are formed.
    d. intrapleural pressure is established.
    e. all of these

D 74. The group of animals with the most efficient respiratory system is the
    a. amphibians.
  * b. birds.
    c. mammals.
    d. reptiles.
    e. fish.

M 75. Birds
    a. exchange gases through air sacs.
    b. exchange gases with their lungs as they breathe in or out.
    c. have exceptionally large and flexible lungs.
    d. have four air sacs for each lung that behave like bellows.
  * e. exchange gases with their lungs as they breathe in or out and have four air sacs for each lung that behave like bellows.

HUMAN RESPIRATORY SYSTEM

M 76. What is the proper sequence in the flow of air in mammals?
    a. nasal cavities, larynx, pharynx, bronchi, trachea
    b. nasal cavities, pharynx, bronchi, larynx, trachea
  * c. nasal cavities, pharynx, larynx, trachea, bronchi
    d. nasal cavities, larynx, pharynx, trachea, bronchi
    e. nasal cavities, bronchi, larynx, trachea, pharynx

M 77. The last mammalian structure that air moves through before the alveoli is the
    a. larynx.
    b. glottis.
  * c. bronchioles.
    d. trachea.
    e. pharynx.

D 78. When humans breathe using only the mouth, which of the following is most diminished?
  * a. filtering
    b. warming
    c. moisturizing
    d. texturizing
    e. flowing

D 79. Food and drink are prevented from entering the respiratory passageways during swallowing by means of the
    a. glottis.
    b. pharynx.
  * c. epiglottis.
    d. larynx.
    e. trachea.

M 80. When you swallow, the epiglottis covers the opening to the
    a. pharynx.
    b. esophagus.
  * c. larynx.
    d. bronchus.
    e. alveoli.

M 81. In pleurisy,
    a. some of the alveoli fill with fluid.
  * b. the pleural membrane becomes inflamed and swollen and causes painful breathing.
    c. the diaphragm develops muscular cramps.
    d. the vagus nerve is irritated.
    e. the intercostal muscles become inflamed and cause pain during deep breathing.

E 82. Actual exchange of gases in the lungs occurs in the
    a. bronchi.
  * b. alveoli.
    c. bronchioles.
    d. tracheas.
    e. glottis.

M 83. Which of the following is NOT found in lung tissue?
    a. blood capillaries
    b. alveolar sacs
    c. interstitial fluid
    d. connective tissue
  * e. muscle

E 84. The human vocal cords are located in the
    a. glottis.
    b. pharynx.
    c. trachea.
  * d. larynx.
    e. bronchus.

MOVING AIR AND TRANSPORTING GASES

M 85. During inhalation,
    a. the pressure in the thoracic cavity is greater than the pressure within the lungs.
*   b. the pressure in the thoracic cavity is less than the pressure within the lungs.
    c. the diaphragm moves upward and becomes more curved.
    d. the chest cavity volume decreases.
    e. all of these

M 86. Which of the following would NOT occur during exhalation?
    a. diaphragm moves upward
    b. air moves out
    c. chest muscles relax
*   d. pressure in chest cavity decreases
    e. ribs move down and in

M 87. Oxygen moves from alveoli to the bloodstream
*   a. because the concentration of oxygen is greater in alveoli than in the blood.
    b. mainly due to the activity of carbonic anhydrase in the red blood cells.
    c. by using the assistance of carbaminohemoglobin.
    d. through active transport.
    e. all of these

M 88. Hemoglobin
    a. tends to give up oxygen in regions where partial pressure of oxygen exceeds that in the lungs.
    b. tends to hold onto oxygen when the pH of the blood drops.
    c. tends to release oxygen where the temperature is lower.
*   d. is where blood is warmer and carbon dioxide's partial pressure is high.
    e. all of these

M 89. Oxyhemoglobin gives up O_2 when
*   a. carbon dioxide concentrations are high.
    b. body temperature is lowered.
    c. pH values are high.
    d. CO_2 concentrations are low.
    e. all of these

D 90. Hemoglobin
    a. tends to release oxygen under warmer temperatures.
    b. picks up more oxygen the higher its partial pressure.
    c. picks up more oxygen when it is saturated.
    d. will give up oxygen when the partial pressure of oxygen is higher than it is in the lungs.
*   e. tends to release oxygen under warmer temperatures and picks up more oxygen the higher its partial pressure.

M 91. Most of the carbon dioxide produced by the body is transported to the lungs in
    a. a gaseous form.
    b. blood plasma.
    c. carbaminohemoglobin.
*   d. bicarbonate ions.
    e. carbonic acid.

WHEN THE LUNGS BREAK DOWN

E 92. Carbon monoxide
    a. has a very low affinity or attraction to hemoglobin.
    b. is unlikely to be transported by the circulatory system.
    c. is not the cause of death of people who breathe excessive amounts of automobile exhaust.
*   d. can arise from cigarette smoke.
    e. is not the cause of death of people who breathe excessive amounts of automobile exhaust and can arise from cigarette smoke.

E 93. A chronic inability to get sufficient oxygen across damaged alveolar tissues is called
    a. apnea
*   b. emphysema
    c. SIDS
    d. bronchitis
    e. pleurisy

E 94. Smoking has been shown to cause
    a. bronchitis.
    b. emphysema.
    c. lung cancer.
    d. coronary heart disease.
*   e. all of these

Matching Questions

D **95.** Matching. Choose the one most appropriate answer for each.

1. ___ alveoli
2. ___ bronchi
3. ___ diaphragm
4. ___ epiglottis
5. ___ rib muscles
6. ___ larynx
7. ___ nasal cavity
8. ___ oxyhemoglobin
9. ___ pharynx
10. ___ pleural sac
11. ___ trachea
12. ___ ventilation

A. flexible windpipe reinforced with cartilage
B. surrounds each lung
C. oxygen-rich form of respiratory protein
D. contains two true vocal cords
E. alter chest cavity volume
F. where air is filtered, warmed, and moisturized
G. throat cavity behind the mouth
H. inhalation and exhalation
I. connect trachea to lungs
J. flaplike structure that points upward and allows air to enter trachea; closed during swallowing
K. contraction moves it downward
L. microscopically small pockets lined with moist epithelium

Answers: 1. L   2. I   3. K   4. J

5. E   6. D   7. F   8. C

9. G   10. B   11. A   12. H

Classification Questions

Answer questions 96–100 in reference to the five components of mammalian blood listed below.

a. red blood cells
b. basophils
c. platelets
d. proteins
e. hemoglobin

M **96.** These blood components play a central role in clotting blood following an injury.

M **97.** These blood components contain hemoglobin.

M **98.** These blood components are a type of phagocyte.

M **99.** These blood components are the second most abundant dissolved in the plasma.

M **100.** Oxygen is transported throughout the body by this blood component.

Answers: 96. c   97. a   98. b

99. d   100. e

Answer questions 101–105 in reference to the four structures of the heart listed below.

a. right atrium
b. left atrium
c. left ventricle
d. right ventricle

M **101.** Blood from the superior and inferior venae cavae enters the heart via this structure.

M **102.** Blood passes to the lungs from this structure.

M **103.** Deoxygenated blood exits the heart from this structure.

M **104.** Oxygenated blood enters the heart via this structure.

M **105.** Blood is pumped to the majority of the body by this structure.

Answers: 101. a   102. d   103. d

104. b   105. c

Answer questions 106–110 in reference to the five components of respiratory systems listed below:

    a. pharynx
    b. larynx
    c. trachea
    d. bronchiole
    e. alveolus

E **106.** The voice box is located here.

M **107.** Air "dead ends" in this component.

M **108.** Gas exchange between the air in the lungs and their blood supply occurs here.

E **109.** Air moves from the nasal cavity into this component.

M **110.** Spent air moves from the bronchial tubes back to this component.

Answers: 106. b   107. e   108. e

                109. a   110. c

Selecting the Exception

D **111.** Four of the five answers listed below designate organisms with open circulation. Select the exception.
    a. insects
    b. snails
    c. spiders
    d. clams
  * e. frogs

M **112.** Four of the five answers listed below are related by a common property. Select the exception.
    a. neutrophil
  * b. erythrocyte
    c. lymphocytes
    d. macrophage
    e. basophil

M **113.** Four of the five answers listed below are characteristics of most veins. Select the exception.
    a. blood volume reservoirs
    b. contain valves
    c. low wall resistance
  * d. transport oxygen
    e. low blood pressure

M **114.** Four of the five answers listed below are components of the human respiratory system. Select the exception.
    a. thoracic cavity
    b. pleural sac
    c. diaphragm
  * d. spiracle
    e. larynx

D **115.** Four of the five answers listed below are related by the same function. Select the exception.
    a. blood plasma
    b. carbaminohemoglobin
  * c. oxyhemoglobin
    d. carbonic acid
    e. bicarbonate ions

Labeling

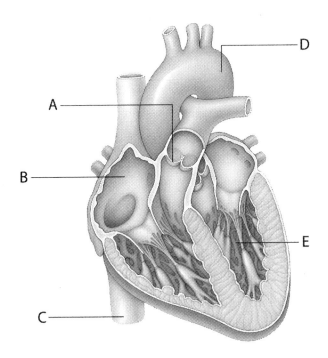

E **116.** The vessel returning blood from the lower regions of the human body is indicated by the letter _?_.

E **117.** The right atrium at letter _?_ receives oxygen-poor blood.

E **118.** The vessel at letter _?_ will eventually branch to smaller vessels that will carry blood to all parts of the body.

E **119.** The valve at "A" controls flow of blood
    a. to the head.
  *   b. to the lungs.
    c. from the body.
    d. from the lungs.
    e. to the body.

E **120.** The left ventricle is at letter _?_.

Answers: 116. C   117. B   118. D   120. E

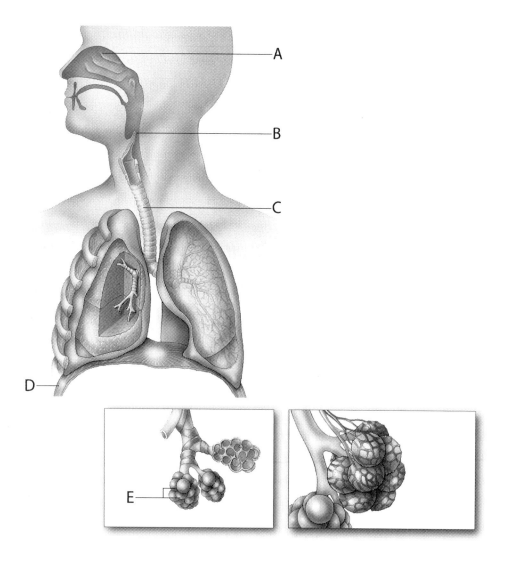

E   **121.** The structure that "powers" breathing is located at the letter _?_.

E   **122.** The structure at "C" is the
     a. esophagus.
     b. gullet.
     c. epiglottis.
     d. pharynx.
     * e. trachea.

M **123.** The structure at "B" is the _?_, which _?_.
     a. tongue; produces speech.
     * b. epiglottis; closes the windpipe.
     c. larynx; produces sound.
     d. epiglottis; closes the esophagus.
     e. pharynx; holds the trachea open.

Answers: 121. D

CHAPTER 23
IMMUNITY

Multiple-Choice Questions

INTEGRATED RESPONSES TO THREATS

M 1. All EXCEPT which of the following can be called a pathogen?
    a. virus
    b. bacterium
    c. fungus
  * d. cancer
    e. parasitic worms

E 2. Which cells are divided into two groups: T cells and B cells?
    a. macrophages
  * b. lymphocytes
    c. complement cells
    d. platelets
    e. all of these

E 3. In "adaptive immunity"
    a. nonspecific responses dominate.
    b. there is little specificity.
    c. phagocytes ingest any pathogen they encounter.
    d. the body is defenseless until age two.
  * e. lymphocytes are defensive against specific pathogens.

M 4. Which system involves plasma proteins activated when they contact a bacterial cell?
    a. infection
  * b. complement
    c. bodyguard
    d. enhancer
    e. defender

M 5. Which of the following is NOT active in defending the body against pathogens?
    a. monocytes
  * b. erythrocytes
    c. neutrophils
    d. eosinophils
    e. macrophages

M 6. Phagocytes perform their services in
    a. the blood only.
    b. tissue spaces only.
    c. the lymph system only.
    d. the blood and tissue spaces, only.
  * e. the blood, tissue spaces, and lymph system.

M 7. Phagocytes are derived from stem cells in the
    a. spleen.
    b. thymus.
  * c. bone marrow.
    d. blood.
    e. liver.

D 8. Interleukins
    a. are secreted by macrophages.
    b. trigger any B cell that has become sensitive to the specific antigen (the one inducing interleukin production) to divide.
    c. are the chemical triggers that cause tissue to release antihistamine.
    d. are effective only on pathogens that have invaded body cells.
  * e. cause T and B cells to undergo division and differentiation.

E 9. All of the cells involved in the immune response are
    a. complements.
    b. erythrocytes.
    c. markers.
  * d. leukocytes, also called white blood cells.
    e. erythrocytes, also called white blood cells.

SURFACE BARRIERS

M 10. Lysozyme
    a. is secreted by endocrine glands in the skin.
  * b. destroys the cell wall of invading bacteria.
    c. is produced in the lymph nodes and actively disables bacteria.
    d. has proved to be a very effective defense against viruses.
    e. is active within the circulatory system.

M 11. The barrier to invasion by microbes involves
    a. urine.
    b. established resident microbes.
    c. ciliated mucous membranes.
    d. lysozyme and other enzymes.
  * e. all of these

E 12. All EXCEPT which of the following are good barriers to invasion by microbes?
    a. mucous membranes
    b. eye secretions
  * c. broken skin
    d. urine
    e. gut bacteria

D 13. Normal bacterial inhabitants of the human body
    a. are naturally resistant to antibiotics.
  * b. are able to outcompete some invading pathogens and thus are one of the body's defense mechanisms.
    c. can be transformed into pathogenic forms if a person's resistance to disease is low.
    d. are unable to survive the human body's defense mechanisms.
    e. none of these

THE INNATE IMMUNE RESPONSE

D   14.   Which of the following would NOT be the result of the action of the complement system?
- a. lysis of a pathogen's membrane
- *b. trapping of pathogens in tangled protein threads
- c. marking of pathogens for destruction by macrophages
- d. attraction of phagocytes to the scene of pathogen invasion
- e. promotion of the inflammatory response

M   15.   The complement system
- a. includes a group of about 20 plasma proteins.
- b. induces a cascade of proteins that counteract invasion by coating the invading cells.
- c. attracts phagocytic leukocytes to attack invading cells.
- d. causes the lysis of the plasma membranes of invading cells.
- *e. all of these

M   16.   Histamine causes
- a. blood vessels to contract.
- b. capillaries to lose their permeability.
- *c. small blood vessels to "leak."
- d. a destruction of mast cells.
- e. an opening of the area of infection through which the body's defense system can enter.

E   17.   The swelling at the site of a wound is the result of the secretion of
- a. kinins.
- *b. histamines.
- c. neutrophils.
- d. interferons.
- e. leukocytes.

D   18.   Which event does NOT occur in the inflammatory response?
- a. Tissue swells because of outflow from capillary beds.
- *b. Blocking antibodies inactivate the resident mast cells.
- c. White blood cells are attracted to the area by chemotaxis.
- d. Complement proteins help identify invading material.
- e. The foreign invaders are engulfed and destroyed by phagocytosis.

M   19.   Inflammation
- *a. leads to the release of histamine, which causes capillaries to become "leaky."
- b. is increased by use of antihistamine drugs.
- c. does not occur during allergic reactions.
- d. is initiated by the buildup of dead cells and bacteria.
- e. is not affected by the action of the complement system.

TAILORING RESPONSES TO SPECIFIC ANTIGENS

D   20.   Terms that describe the adaptive immune response include all EXCEPT which of the following?
- a. specific
- b. diverse
- c. memory
- *d. general
- e. self versus nonself

M   21.   Which cells produce and secrete antibodies that set up bacterial invaders for subsequent destruction by macrophages?
- a. phagocytes
- b. macrophages
- *c. B cells
- d. T cells
- e. all of these

D   22.   Which cells are held in reserve to be used for a rapid response to subsequent intruders of the same type?
- a. helper T
- b. natural killer cells
- c. cytotoxic T
- *d. memory
- e. B

M   23.   Which cells are the longest lasting in the body?
- a. helper T
- b. natural killer cells
- c. cytotoxic T
- *d. memory
- e. B

M   24.   Body cells have self-markers located
- a. in their nuclei.
- b. in the endoplasmic reticulum.
- c. in the mitochondria.
- *d. on the plasma membrane.
- e. inside the Golgi bodies.

D   25.   Which of the following would be ignored in most instances by lymphocytes?
- a. cells coated with complement proteins
- b. cells with antigens on their surface
- *c. "self" cells with MHC markers
- d. cells with both antigen and self-MHC markers
- e. cells with damaged or mutant self-MHC markers

M   26.   The markers for each cell in a body are referred to by the letters
- *a. MHC.
- b. HTC.
- c. ADS.
- d. RSW.
- e. AKA.

E   27.   The markers that identify "self" are actually
- a. genes.
- *b. proteins.
- c. lipids.
- d. small surface bumps.
- e. three letters of the alphabet.

ANTIBODIES AND OTHER ANTIGEN RECEPTORS

E   **28.** Antibodies are shaped like the letter
    a. C.
    b. E.
    c. H.
    d. K.
  * e. Y.

E   **29.** The antibody molecule consists of how many polypeptide chains, including light and heavy chains?
    a. 2
    b. 3
  * c. 4
    d. 5
    e. 6

E   **30.** Antibodies are
  * a. proteins.
    b. steroids.
    c. polysaccharides.
    d. lipoproteins.
    e. all of these

E   **31.** Antibodies belong to a group of compounds known as
    a. self-recognizing compounds.
  * b. immunoglobulins.
    c. histosaccharides.
    d. antisteroids.
    e. virulent bases.

M   **32.** The antigen binds to the _?_ region of an antibody.
    a. constant
    b. curved
  * c. variable
    d. Z
    e. Q

D   **33.** An antibody
    a. can activate the complement system.
    b. can be split into new sites that bind antigens.
    c. may bind to receptors on phagocytic cells.
    d. may break off and form the basis for immune memory.
  * e. can also prevent pathogen binding to host cells.

D   **34.** Which statement is NOT true?
    a. When an invading bacterium is destroyed by a macrophage, its antigens are preserved.
  * b. Acting alone, antibodies attack and destroy invading antigens.
    c. Helper T cells recognize the major histocompatibility complex and antigens on the surface of macrophages.
    d. Self cells have major histocompatibility complex markers or antigens.
    e. Helper T cells secrete interleukins, which help the cells of the immune system communicate with each other.

M   **35.** Which immunoglobulin is able to pass the placenta to protect the fetus from pathogens?
  * a. IgG
    b. IgA
    c. IgD
    d. IgM
    e. IgE

M   **36.** Which immunoglobulinm is the first to be secreted in an immune response?
    a. IgG
    b. IgA
    c. IgD
  * d. IgM
    e. IgE

D   **37.** The infinite variety of antibodies that can be generated by B cells is due to
    a. the infinite variety of genes in these cells.
  * b. the shuffling of genes to produce an infinite variety of proteins.
    c. the recombination of genes due to crossing over.
    d. the infinite variety of genes in these cells and the recombination of genes due to crossing over.
    e. the infinite variety of genes in these cells, the recombination of genes due to crossing over, and the shuffling of genes to produce an infinite variety of proteins.

ANTIBODY-MEDIATED IMMUNE RESPONSE

D   **38.** In the primary immune response,
    a. a clone of sensitive lymphocytes is ready for any subsequent invasion of the same antigen.
    b. some of the clone cells will remain alive for decades.
    c. clone cells may be modified to attack new invaders.
    d. clone cells are continually reproduced to confer immunity against subsequent invasion.
  * e. effector cells function immediately against this initial exposure to an antigen.

D   **39.** Clones of B or T cells are
    a. being produced continually.
    b. interchangeable.
  * c. produced only when their surface proteins recognize specific protein antigens.
    d. known as memory cells.
    e. produced and mature in the bone marrow.

D   **40.** The primary immune response
    a. is shorter in duration than a secondary response.
    b. is quicker than a secondary response.
    c. depends on random construction of appropriate antibodies.
    d. is the result of a reproduction of an appropriate lymphocyte resulting in a sensitive clone.
  * e. includes a secretion of IgG, IgA, or IgE that recognizes the same antigen as the original B cell receptor.

D 41. Which of the following statements is FALSE?
   a. Only B cells and their progeny make antibodies.
 * b. The primary immune response is faster and more complete than a secondary immune response.
   c. Virgin B cells already have antibodies but have not yet encountered an antigen.
   d. Macrophages will digest invading bacterial cells but do not destroy the antigens that eventually become mounted on the surface of the macrophages.
   e. Some B cell progeny differentiate into memory cells.

M 42. Which cells produce antibodies?
   a. helper T
   b. natural killer cells
   c. cytotoxic T
   d. memory
 * e. B

D 43. Which cell begins to secrete several interleukins recognized by B cells as a signal to divide and differentiate?
 * a. helper T
   b. natural killer cells
   c. cytotoxic T
   d. memory
   e. B

D 44. Which of the following statements is FALSE?
   a. Cytotoxic T cells kill cancer cells only if the cause is viral.
   b. MHC markers of grafted cells are identified as foreign in organ transplants unless the donor is a twin.
 * c. The function of helper T cells is to phagocytize invading organisms.
   d. Each pathogen has its own unique antigen.
   e. The clonal selection theory holds that an activated B cell or T cell divides rapidly to produce a clone of immunologically identical cells that are specific for the antigen that selected them.

THE CELL-MEDIATED IMMUNE RESPONSE

M 45. Which of the following is NOT a lymphoid organ?
   a. tonsils
   b. nodules
 * c. thyroid
   d. spleen
   e. thymus

M 46. Which of the following is most likely to happen in a lymph node?
   a. oxygenation of the interstitial fluid
   b. production of B and T lymphocytes
 * c. macrophages engulfing organisms foreign to the body
   d. attachment of MHC markers to self cells
   e. destruction of red blood cells and recycling of their contents

M 47. Which of the following are NOT generally targets of T cells?
   a. transplants of foreign tissue
   b. cancer
   c. infections caused by viruses
 * d. bacteria outside body cells
   e. all of these

M 48. Which cells are the primary weapon against infected body cells and tumors?
   a. helper T
   b. natural killer cells
 * c. cytotoxic T
   d. memory
   e. B

M 49. Mutant and cancerous cells are destroyed by which cells?
   a. helper T
   b. natural killer cells
 * c. cytotoxic T
   d. memory
   e. B

D 50. Which of the following statements is FALSE?
   a. Cytotoxic T cells kill body cells that have been invaded by pathogens.
 * b. The cell-mediated response is ineffective against a pathogen that has already entered the cytoplasm of a body cell.
   c. Cytotoxic T cells are produced by the bone marrow but mature in the thymus gland.
   d. Cytotoxic T cells are unable to destroy free-floating viruses they encounter in the bloodstream.
   e. Cytotoxic T cells secrete perforins that are able to punch holes in infected cells.

D 51. Effector cells
   a. are fully differentiated lymphocytes.
   b. manufacture and secrete antibodies.
   c. can develop from either T or B cells.
   d. secrete antibodies or interleukins depending on their origin.
 * e. all of these

M 52. Cell-mediated response
 * a. involves helper T cells.
   b. involves the action of antibodies to destroy invaders.
   c. acts only on extracellular clues.
   d. results in the production of clones of plasma cells.
   e. all of these

M 53. Most organ transplants fail because
   a. of poor vascular connection between host and donor tissue.
   b. the migrating leukocytes attack the tissue adjacent to the transplant.
 * c. cytotoxic T cells enter the transplant through the connecting blood vessels and kill the individual transplant tissue.
   d. introduced tissues produce antibodies that cause a massive reaction.
   e. all of these

D 54. What is the cell that destroys cells if an infection or malignant transformation alters its MHC markers?
   a. cytotoxic T cells
 * b. natural killer cells
   c. helper T cells
   d. macrophages
   e. MHC-guided cells

DEFENSES ENHANCED OR COMPROMISED

M 55. A vaccine contains
   a. killed pathogen.
   b. weakened pathogen.
   c. noninfective fragments of a pathogen.
   d. full-strength pathogen.
 * e. All except "full-strength pathogen" may be used.

M 56. Passive immunity can be obtained by
   a. having the disease.
   b. receiving a vaccination against the disease.
   c. receiving antibodies by injection.
   d. receiving antibodies from the mother at birth.
 * e. receiving an injection of antibody purification from the blood of someone who already has fought the disease.

D 57. The purpose of a second immunization of vaccine is to
   a. produce a mild case of the disease.
   b. stimulate the immune response.
   c. cause memory cells to be formed.
   d. stimulate the immune response and cause memory cells to be formed.
 * e. elicit a secondary immune response in which memory cells form.

M 58. Whenever the body is re-exposed to a sensitizing agent, the IgE antibodies cause the
 * a. production of cytokines.
   b. release of antihistamines.
   c. suppression of the inflammatory response.
   d. production of clonal cells.
   e. all of these

M 59. Which of the following statements is FALSE?
   a. Individuals are injected with antibodies in passive immunity.
   b. A genetically engineered virus is not as potentially dangerous as a weakened but intact pathogen.
   c. Allergies occur when the body makes a secondary immune response to a normally harmless substance.
 * d. Allergies are a nuisance but are never dangerous or life-threatening.
   e. Allergies cause the secretion of mucus, prostaglandins, and histamines.

M 60. A person sensitive to bee stings may die minutes after a sting due to
   a. a collapse of the immune system.
   b. a clogging of the capillaries.
 * c. a release of excessive fluids from the permeable capillary beds and a plummeting of blood pressure.
   d. respiratory distress caused by excessive mucus.
   e. the extremely sharp rise in blood pressure.

M 61. When the body's defenses turn against its own cells, the disorder is called
 * a. an autoimmune response.
   b. anaphylactic shock.
   c. acquired immune deficiency syndrome.
   d. passive immunity.
   e. an inflammatory response.

AIDS: IMMUNITY LOST

E 62. The reason AIDS is so serious is that
   a. the excessive immune reaction leads to death.
   b. it is so highly contagious.
 * c. there is no cure for those already infected.
   d. it is caused by a retrovirus.
   e. many natural reservoirs may spread the disease at any time.

E 63. Kaposi's sarcoma is a cancer characteristic of people who have
 * a. AIDS.
   b. allergic reactions.
   c. a hypersensitive immune system.
   d. ancestors who come from Cyprus.
   e. herpes.

M 64. Which of the following statements is FALSE?
   a. The virus that causes AIDS is the human immunodeficiency virus.
   b. The AIDS virus is a retrovirus.
   c. The AIDS virus attacks macrophages and helper T cells.
   d. Even though the AIDS virus does not have its own DNA, it causes the host to produce DNA that will become part of host chromosomes.
 * e. HIV produces a typical innate response.

E 65. Of the following, AIDS is usually transferred by
         a. casual contact.
         b. food.
         c. water.
       * d. sexual intercourse.
         e. insect bites.

E 66. The human immunodeficiency virus (HIV-1) primarily destroys which cells?
         a. B
         b. M
         c. T1
       * d. helper T cells
         e. natural killer cells

M 67. Interferon is a chemical produced by
         a. helper T cells.
         b. plasma cells.
         c. B cells.
         d. macrophages.
       * e. cells that have been invaded by a virus.

E 68. Which of the following statements is FALSE?
         a. There is evidence that antibodies do not neutralize the HIV virus.
         b. HIV has the highest mutation rate of any known virus.
       * c. The HIV virus can be transferred by means of saliva, breast milk, tears, vaginal secretions, semen, blood, amniotic fluid, cerebrospinal fluid, and urine.
         d. It will be very difficult to form a vaccine against all the mutated forms of HIV.
         e. Currently, prevention of the spread of HIV depends upon implementing behavioral controls through education.

Matching Questions

D 69. Matching. Include the most appropriate letter in each blank at the left.
         1. ___ antigens
         2. ___ B lymphocytes
         3. ___ perforin
         4. ___ clone
         5. ___ complement proteins
         6. ___ cytotoxic T lymphocytes
         7. ___ interleukins
         8. ___ macrophages
         9. ___ memory cells
        10. ___ innate immunity
        11. ___ retroviruses
        12. ___ stem cells
        13. ___ natural killer cells
        14. ___ vaccine

A. fast, preset responses to a fixed set of nonself cues

B. cells that directly destroy body cells already infected by viral or fungal parasites, as well as mutant and cancerous cells

C. lymphocytes that are held in reserve, circulate in the bloodstream, and enable a rapid response to subsequent encounters with the same invader

D. binding antigen activates it in cascading reactions

E. the only cells that make antibodies

F. cytotoxic lymphocytes active in adaptive immune responses

G. stimulate bone marrow stem cells, attract phagocytes, activate natural killer cells

H. "big eaters" that alert other lymphocytes to the invasion of specific antigens; participate in both innate and adaptive immune responses

I. self-perpetuating, undifferentiated animal cells

J. a group of cells that are all produced asexually from one original parent cell

K. surface patterns of nonself molecules or particles

L. proteins released by cytotoxic T cells to destroy target cell membranes

M. preparation injected into the body to elicit a primary immune response

N. one of this group has been identified as the causative agent of AIDS

Answers:
1. K 2. E 3. L 4. J
5. D 6. B 7. G 8. H
9. C 10. A 11. N 12. I
13. F 14. M

Classification Questions

Answer questions 70–74 in reference to the five types of white cells listed below.

      a. macrophages
      b. helper T cells
      c. B cells
      d. cytotoxic T cells
      e. natural killer cells

D   **70.** These cells kill tumor cells but are not B or T lymphocytes.

M   **71.** These cells scavenge dead cells and attack bacteria directly.

D   **72.** These cells destroy cells infected by viruses.

D   **73.** These cells recognize cell surface antigens and initiate the proliferation of lymphocytes.

M   **74.** Antibody production occurs in these cells.

Answers: 70. e   71. a   72. d

              73. b   74. c

Answer questions 75–79 in reference to the five items listed below.

      a. antigens
      b. antibodies
      c. helper T cells
      d. cytotoxic T cells
      e. memory B cells

E   **75.** These bind, as in a lock-and-key mechanism, to foreign proteins.

D   **76.** These produce immunoglobulins in response to the reinvasion by a virus.

D   **77.** These are implicated in rejection of tissue and organ transplants.

M   **78.** An Rh+ molecule in the body of an Rh woman is an example of these.

D   **79.** These implement a faster, secondary response.

Answers: 75. b   76. e   77. d

              78. a   79. e

Selecting the Exception

M   **80.** Four of the five answers listed below are barriers to invasion. Select the exception.
      a. intact skin
      b. mucous membrane
      c. urine
  *   d. blood plasma
      e. lysozyme

D   **81.** Four of the five answers listed below are characteristic reactions of the complement system to invaders. Select the exception.
      a. causes an amplifying cascade of reactions to invaders
  *   b. triggers the secretion of histamines
      c. causes invading cells to lyse
      d. enhances the recognition of invaders by phagocytes
      e. creates gradients that attract phagocytes

D   **82.** Four of the five answers listed below are events of the inflammatory response. Select the exception.
      a. increase in capillary permeability
      b. release of histamine
      c. dilation of blood vessels
  *   d. decrease in temperature of the affected areas
      e. migration of phagocytes toward the affected area

M   **83.** Four of the five answers listed below are targets of the immune system. Select the exception.
      a. viruses
  *   b. normal cells
      c. cancer cells
      d. bacteria
      e. debris and dead cells

CHAPTER 24
DIGESTION, NUTRITION, AND EXCRETION

Multiple-Choice Questions

THE NATURE OF DIGESTIVE SYSTEMS

D 1. The respiratory system interacts with the digestive
       system in the role of
       a. supplying oxygen for metabolism of nutrients.
       b. carrying away carbon dioxide.
       c. providing nitrogen for protein synthesis.
   *   d. supplying oxygen for metabolism of nutrients and
           carrying away carbon dioxide.
       e. supplying oxygen for metabolism of nutrients,
           carrying away carbon dioxide, and providing
           nitrogen for protein synthesis.

M 2. Which of the following possess an incomplete
       digestive system?
       a. annelids
   *   b. flatworms
       c. mollusks
       d. arthropods
       e. echinoderms

E 3. Ruminants need multiple stomach chambers to digest
       a. starch.
       b. proteins.
   *   c. cellulose.
       d. lignin.
       e. catin.

M 4. Which of the following statements about pronghorn
       antelopes is FALSE?
       a. They are ruminant animals.
       b. Their eye sockets are positioned far back in their
           skulls.
   *   c. They do not require as much food as predators.
       d. They spend more of their time eating than
           predators.
       e. Their cheek teeth (molars) have much larger
           crowns than human teeth.

D 5. Which of the following statements about digestion is
       FALSE?
       a. Ruminant animals have symbiotic bacteria to aid
           in the digestion of their food.
       b. It takes longer to digest plant material than meat.
       c. Chewing results in mechanically breaking down
           food and exposing more cellulose to digestive
           enzymes.
       d. Humans have a greater range of foods in their diet
           than most other species.
   *   e. Pronghorn antelopes and other herbivores are
           characterized by a single but disproportionately
           large stomach.

E 6. In a bird, the muscular digestive organ in which food
       is crushed into small bits is the
       a. lumen.
   *   b. gizzard.
       c. crop.
       d. stomach.
       e. cloaca.

M 7. Chewing
       a. breaks food down into smaller pieces.
       b. physically and mechanically breaks up the food.
       c. increases the surface area of food exposed to
           digestive enzymes.
       d. actually mixes some enzymes with the food.
   *   e. all of these

M 8. The process that moves nutrients into the blood or
       lymph is
   *   a. absorption.
       b. assimilation.
       c. digestion.
       d. ingestion.
       e. all of these

M 9. Animals without teeth, such as birds, have an organ
       that accomplishes the same action as teeth. What is it?
       a. beak
       b. pharynx
   *   c. gizzard
       d. cloaca
       e. dentine

E 10. Birds have a crop that is modified for
        a. digestion of cellulose.
    *   b. food storage.
        c. mechanical breakdown of food.
        d. digestion of fats.
        e. storage and elimination of undigested food.

HUMAN DIGESTIVE SYSTEM

D 11. Which of the following is a rather passive participant
        in the digestive process?
        a. small intestine
    *   b. esophagus
        c. pancreas
        d. mouth
        e. liver

M 12. Which of the following organs of the digestive system is different from the other four because it does NOT produce any secretions that aid in the digestive process?
   a. stomach
   b. liver
*   c. esophagus
   d. pancreas
   e. salivary gland

E 13. Sphincters
   a. are formed by circular muscles.
   b. prevent backflow.
   c. can malfunction and cause problems.
   d. open and close.
*   e. all of these

M 14. Sphincters are
   a. areas of the gastrointestinal tract where food is stored.
*   b rings of circular muscles that subdivide the gut.
   c. outpouchings of the gut that provide fluids for solubilizing food.
   d. specialized glands that secrete digestive juices.
   e. a double layer of muscles that envelop digestive organs such as the stomach or small intestine.

E 15. The digestion of which class of foods begins in the mouth?
*   a. carbohydrates
   b. proteins
   c. lipids
   d. amino acids
   e. nucleic acids

M 16. During the process of swallowing, the
   a. esophagus is temporarily closed by the glottis.
*   b. epiglottis closes the trachea leading to the lungs.
   c. pharynx restricts food entry to the esophagus.
   d. epiglottis seals the esophagus.
   e. none of these

M 17. High stomach acidity
   a. creates ideal conditions for carbohydrate digestion.
   b. promotes emulsification of fats.
*   c. enhances protein digestion.
   d. blocks the release of histamine, thereby favoring production of peptic ulcers.
   e. converts lipases into their active forms.

M 18. Stomach motility
   a. decreases following a heavy meal.
*   b. mixes ingested food.
   c. is unaffected by emotional state or external environmental factors.
   d. may be retarded when stretch receptors on the stomach wall are activated.
   e. is increased by hormones released in response to high stomach acidity.

E 19. Chyme is formed in the
   a. mouth.
   b. esophagus.
*   c. stomach.
   d. small intestine.
   e. large intestine.

E 20. The digestion of proteins begins in the
*   a. stomach.
   b. pancreas.
   c. small intestine.
   d. large intestine.
   e. esophagus.

D 21. Which of the following components of a hamburger would leave the stomach with no digestion having begun?
   a. protein
   b. starch
   c. sugar (in the catsup)
   d. lipid
*   e. both sugar (in the catsup) and lipid

E 22. The acid released in the stomach is
   a. carbonic acid.
*   b. hydrochloric acid.
   c. nitric acid.
   d. sulfuric acid.
   e. phosphoric acid.

E 23. The first part of the small intestine is the
*   a. duodenum.
   b. ileum.
   c. colon.
   d. cecum.
   e. jejunum.

M 24. Ducts from the pancreas and liver enter the
   a. stomach.
   b. colon.
*   c. duodenum.
   d. jejunum.
   e. ileum.

M 25. Bile
   a. has no effect on digestion.
*   b. helps in the digestion of fats.
   c. helps in the digestion of carbohydrates.
   d. helps in the digestion of proteins.
   e. helps in the digestion of both carbohydrates and proteins.

M 26. Bile
   a. is produced by the liver and is stored in the gallbladder.
   b. contains cholesterol and lecithin.
   c. has no digestive enzymes.
   d. emulsifies fats to increase the surface contact between fat and lipases.
*   e. all of these

M   27.   Which of the following factors adversely affects digestion?
*   a. anxiety and fear
          b. stimulation of sensory receptors in the stomach wall following a large meal
          c. reduced fat or acid content of chyme in the duodenum
          d. elation and relaxation
          e. all of these

E   28.   Protein digestion begins in the
          a. esophagus.
*   b. stomach.
          c. mouth.
          d. small intestine.
          e. large intestine.

M   29.   Concerning the role of the pancreas in digestion,
*   a. no digestion occurs in the pancreas.
          b. endocrine cells secrete bicarbonate, which helps neutralize highly acidic chyme.
          c. endocrine cells release enzymes that break down carbohydrates, fats, proteins, and nucleic acids in the small intestine.
          d. exocrine tissue produces insulin and glucagon that help regulate the metabolism of sugar.
          e. all of these

D   30.   Which of the following is NOT a hormone?
          a. gastrin
          b. secretin
*   c. mucin
          d. cholecystokinin
          e. All of these are hormones.

D   31.   Which of the following chemicals is the first hormone secreted by the intestinal tract in response to the presence of food?
          a. salivary amylase
          b. cholecystokinin
          c. glucose insulinotropic peptide (GIP)
*   d. gastrin
          e. secretin

M   32.   Which of the following acts enzymatically rather than hormonally?
          a. cholecystokinin
*   b. trypsin
          c. secretin
          d. gastrin
          e. all of these

M   33.   Which of the following stimulates the gallbladder to contract?
          a. salivary amylase
*   b. cholecystokinin
          c. ghrelin
          d. gastrin
          e. secretin

M   34.   Which of the following layers lies next to the lumen of the intestinal tract?
          a. longitudinal muscles
          b. circular muscle layer
          c. submucosa
*   d. mucus-coated epithelium
          e. serosa

M   35.   The digestion of fats mostly occurs in the
          a. stomach.
          b. pancreas.
*   c. small intestine.
          d. lymph vascular system.
          e. liver.

M   36.   Of the following, the greatest amount of nutrient absorption takes place in the
          a. stomach.
*   b. small intestine.
          c. colon.
          d. pancreas.
          e. esophagus.

M   37.   Movement of glucose through the membranes of the small intestine is primarily by
          a. osmosis.
          b. bulk flow.
*   c. transport proteins.
          d. diffusion.
          e. all of these

D   38.   Which of the following are tiny projections of the mucosal wall?
          a. microvilli
          b. mucins
*   c. villi
          d. submucosa
          e. jejunum

E   39.   The organ that produces bile is the
          a. pancreas.
          b. small intestine.
*   c. liver.
          d. spleen.
          e. gallbladder.

E   40.   The primary function of the large intestine is
          a. storage of feces.
          b. retention of water.
          c. manufacture of vitamin K.
          d. digestion of fats.
*   e. absorption of water.

D   41.   What structure extends from the first part of the colon, or cecum?
*   a. appendix
          b. rectum
          c. anus
          d. villus
          e. pharynx

M 42. A diet high in fiber
   a. increases the length of time material is in the colon.
   b. increases the chance of cancer.
 * c. prevents appendicitis and speeds movements of materials through the colon.
   d. may increase the incidence of appendicitis in the people who eat too much bulk.
   e. is characteristic of people in urban areas.

HUMAN NUTRITIONAL REQUIREMENTS

M 43. The surgeon general recommends reducing all EXCEPT which of the following components of our diet?
   a. saturated fat
   b. cholesterol
 * c. whole grains
   d. salt
   e. sugar

E 44. The ideal diet consists of all EXCEPT which of the following?
   a. bulk
 * b. refined grains
   c. little salt and sugar
   d. little red meat
   e. fish, poultry, and legumes

M 45. Which of the following should be present in the human diet in the highest percentage?
   a. protein
 * b. carbohydrate
   c. lipid
   d. vitamins
   e. minerals

M 46. Lipids can serve in all EXCEPT which of the following capacities?
 * a. enzymes
   b. energy reserves
   c. membrane structure
   d. insulation
   e. They can serve in all of these capacities.

E 47. Of the 20 amino acids, how many are considered to be essential in that the human body cannot synthesize them?
   a. 2
   b. 5
 * c. 8
   d. 10
   e. 12

D 48. Eating plant-based foods alone requires combining _?_ so that missing ones are present
   a. vitamins.
   b. minerals.
   c. carbohydrates.
 * d. amino acids.
   e. fatty acids.

M 49. Which of the following is found in fish liver oils?
 * a. D
   b. B_1 (thiamine)
   c. C (ascorbic acid)
   d. B_2 (riboflavin)
   e. niacin

M 50. A deficiency of which vitamin produces rickets in children and osteomalacia in adults?
   a. A
   b. B
   c. C
 * d. D
   e. E

M 51. Which vitamin functions in forming a blood clot?
   a. A
   b. E
 * c. K
   d. B
   e. all of these

M 52. A deficiency of vitamin C may give rise to
   a. beriberi.
 * b. scurvy.
   c. pellagra.
   d. hypothyroidism.
   e. all of these

M 53. Pellagra is a deficiency disease related to which of the following vitamins?
   a. A
   b. B_1 (thiamine)
   c. C (ascorbic acid)
   d. B_2 (riboflavin)
 * e. niacin

M 54. Scurvy is a deficiency disease related to which of the following vitamins?
   a. A
   b. B_1 (thiamine)
 * c. C (ascorbic acid)
   d. B_2 (riboflavin)
   e. niacin

D 55. Which of the following statements is NOT true concerning mineral metabolism?
   a. Potassium is needed for the body's acid-base balance.
 * b. Zinc is important in building strong bones and teeth.
   c. Sodium and potassium are needed for muscle and nerve functioning.
   d. Iron is needed for formation of cytochromes and hemoglobin.
   e. All of these statements are true.

M 56. Lack of which element can lead to goiter?
   a. iron
 * b. iodine
   c. calcium
   d. zinc
   e. magnesium

M   57. The element needed for blood clotting, nerve and muscle action, and bone and tooth formation is
     a. iron.
     b. iodine.
  * c. calcium.
     d. zinc.
     e. magnesium.

M   58. The constituent of hemoglobin whose absence leads to anemia is
  * a. iron.
     b. iodine.
     c. calcium.
     d. zinc.
     e. magnesium.

WEIGHTY QUESTIONS, TANTALIZING ANSWERS

M   59. Obese people have a greater risk of
     a. type 2 diabetes.
     b. breast and colon cancers.
     c. osteoarthritis.
     d. heart disease.
  * e. all of these

M   60. If caloric intake is balanced with energy output, body
     a. weight gain will occur.
     b. weight loss will occur.
  * c. weight will remain stable.
     d. fat content will increase.
     e. protein will decrease.

URINARY SYSTEM OF MAMMALS

E   61. Shifts in water-solute balance are managed primarily by
     a. respiration.
     b. caloric intake.
  * c. the urinary system.
     d. endocrine adjustments.
     e. the circulatory system.

E   62. Extracellular fluid includes
     a. interstitial fluid.
     b. blood.
     c. lymph.
     d. blood and lymph, only.
  * e. interstitial fluid, blood, and lymph.

M   63. All EXCEPT which of the following are significant routes for water loss from the body?
     a. excretion in urine
  * b. sneezing
     c. sweating
     d. elimination in feces
     e. evaporation from respiratory surfaces

E   64. The process that normally exerts the greatest control over the water balance of an individual is
     a. sweating.
     b. elimination in feces.
  * c. kidney function.
     d. evaporation through the skin.
     e. respiratory loss.

D   65. Which of the following does NOT dispose of a type of waste directly to the environment?
     a. digestive system
     b. respiratory system
     c. integumentary system
  * d. circulatory system
     e. urinary system

E   66. The most abundant waste product of metabolism is
  * a. carbon dioxide.
     b. ammonia.
     c. urea.
     d. uric acid.
     e. water.

E   67. The tube leading from each kidney to the bladder is the
     a. glomerulus.
  * b. ureter.
     c. urethra.
     d. bladder.
     e. rectum.

E   68. Which of the following is the last structure that urine passes through?
     a. distal tubule
  * b. urethra
     c. urinary bladder
     d. ureter
     e. loop of Henle

M   69. Which of the following processes is under voluntary control?
     a. filtration
     b. reabsorption
  * c. urination
     d. secretion
     e. excretion

HOW THE KIDNEYS MAKE URINE

E   70. The subunit of a kidney that purifies blood and restores solute and water balance is called a
     a. glomerulus.
     b. loop of Henle.
  * c. nephron.
     d. ureter.
     e. all of these

E   71. The functional unit of the kidney is the
     a. Bowman's capsule.
  * b. nephron.
     c. glomerulus.
     d. urinary bladder.
     e. urethra.

M   72.   Filtration occurs in which section of mammalian nephrons?
    *   a.   glomerulus
         b.   loop of Henle
         c.   proximal tubules
         d.   distal tubules
         e.   peritubular capillaries

E   73.   Filtrate that is removed from the blood is collected by the
         a.   loop of Henle.
         b.   glomerulus.
         c.   distal tubule.
         d.   proximal tubule.
    *   e.   Bowman's capsule.

D   74.   After the blood leaves the glomerular capillaries, it next goes to the
         a.   renal vein.
         b.   renal artery.
    *   c.   peritubular capillaries.
         d.   vena cava.
         e.   heart.

E   75.   About what percent of the fluid removed from the blood is eventually returned to the blood?
         a.   59
         b.   90
    *   c.   99
         d.   0.9
         e.   9

M   76.   The movement of excess H^+ and K^+ ions from peritubular capillaries to the nephron tubules is called
         a.   reabsorption.
    *   b.   tubular secretion.
         c.   excretion.
         d.   filtration.
         e.   osmosis.

M   77.   What is the name given to the fluid removed from the blood but not yet processed by the nephron tubules?
         a.   urine
         b.   water
         c.   urethral fluid
    *   d.   filtrate
         e.   renal plasma

M   78.   The process during which potassium and hydrogen ions and some toxic substances are put into urine is called
    *   a.   tubular secretion.
         b.   reabsorption.
         c.   filtration.
         d.   countercurrent multiplication.
         e.   collection.

M   79.   Which of the following substances is NOT filtered from the bloodstream?
         a.   water
    *   b.   most proteins
         c.   urea
         d.   glucose
         e.   sodium

M   80.   Reabsorption is the movement of water and solutes from the _?_ to the _?_.
         a.   interstitial fluid; tubules
         b.   glomerular capillaries; Bowman's capsule
         c.   Bowman's capsule; nephron tubules
    *   d.   nephron tubules; capillaries
         e.   glomerular capillaries; peritubular capillaries

M   81.   In reabsorption,
         a.   plasma proteins are returned to the blood.
         b.   excess hydrogen ions are removed from the blood.
         c.   excess water is passed on to the urine.
    *   d.   nutrients and salts are selectively returned to the blood by osmotic gradients.
         e.   drugs and foreign substances are passed into the urine.

M   82.   Which of the following are most permeable to water and small molecules?
    *   a.   glomerular capillaries.
         b.   peritubular capillaries.
         c.   proximal tubules.
         d.   ureters.
         e.   collecting ducts.

D   83.   The process of filtration in the glomerulus is driven by
         a.   active transport.
    *   b.   hydrostatic pressure of the blood.
         c.   osmosis.
         d.   dialysis.
         e.   sodium-potassium pumps.

D   84.   Reabsorption of solutes and water begins in the
         a.   glomerulus.
    *   b.   proximal tubule.
         c.   distal tubule.
         d.   loop of Henle.
         e.   collecting duct.

M   85.   The hormone that influences sodium reabsorption in the kidney is
         a.   antidiuretic hormone.
         b.   cortisone.
    *   c.   aldosterone.
         d.   corticotropic hormone.
         e.   adrenalin.

D   86.   The antidiuretic hormone
         a.   promotes processes that lead to an increase in the volume of urine.
    *   b.   promotes processes that lead to a decrease in the volume of urine.
         c.   acts on the proximal tubules of nephrons in the kidney.
         d.   is produced by the adrenal cortex.
         e.   all of these

M   87.   Which of the following is actively transported out of the proximal tubules of the kidney?
         a.   bicarbonate ions
    *   b.   sodium ions
         c.   chloride ions
         d.   water
         e.   potassium

E   88.   The hormone that controls the concentration of urine
is
a. insulin.
b. glucagon.
*   c. the antidiuretic hormone.
d. thyroxine.
e. epinephrine.

M   89.   The hormonal control over excretion occurs in the
a. Bowman's capsule.
b. proximal tubule.
*   c. distal tubule.
d. loop of Henle.
e. urinary bladder.

D   90.   Ethanol (drinking alcohol) is an inhibitor of ADH.
Therefore, a person consuming a couple of mixed
drinks should excrete
a. less water because ADH promotes reabsorption.
b. the alcohol because ADH cannot degrade it.
c. ketone bodies formed from the alcohol.
*   d. more water because ADH normally promotes
reabsorption.
e. more water plus the alcohol due to the ADH
inhibition.

WHEN KIDNEYS BREAK DOWN

M   91.   Kidney health is described in terms of
a. the number of kidney stones.
*   b. rate of filtration.
c. water retention.
d. blood clots.
e. hemodialysis.

E   92.   A kidney machine removes solutes from the blood by
means of
a. osmosis.
b. diffusion.
*   c. dialysis.
d. active transport.
e. bulk flow.

Matching Questions

D   93.   Matching I. Choose the one most appropriate answer
for each.
1. ___ bile salts
2. ___ gastrin
3. ___ cholecystokinin
4. ___ chyme
5. ___ ghrelin
6. ___ mucosa
7. ___ ruminants
8. ___ secretin
9. ___ CCK
10. ___ appendix

A. calls for gallbladder contractions and
secretion of pancreatic enzymes
B. stimulates pancreatic bicarbonate secretion
C. no digestive function
D. stimulates hydrochloric acid secretion
E. emulsify fat globules and hydrate lipid
particles
F. have multiple stomachlike chambers, some
of which store populations of
microorganisms
G. innermost layer of the gut; contains diverse
secretory cells
H. enhances appetite
I. stimulates gallbladder and stomach
emptying as well as pancreatic enzyme
secretions
J. a mixture of food particles with the texture
of a puree

Answers: 1. E   2. D   3. I   4. J

5. H   6. G   7. F   8. B

9. A   10. C

D   94.   Matching II. Choose the one most appropriate answer for each.

1. ___ nephron
2. ___ aldosterone
3. ___ secretion
4. ___ ADH
5. ___ ureter
6. ___ peritubular capillaries
7. ___ loop of Henle
8. ___ glomerular filtration
9. ___ hemodialysis
10. ___ tubular reabsorption

A. secreted by adrenal glands; influences sodium reabsorption

B. passive transport of water; active and passive transport of solutes out of the nephron into peritubular capillaries

C. bulk flow of protein-free plasma from capillaries into Bowman's capsule

D. tube from kidney to bladder

E. released from the posterior lobe of the pituitary to regulate urine output

F. movement of ions from blood in peritubular capillaries into accumulating filtrate

G. toxic substances are extracted from blood circulating in cellophane tubes suspended in a warm-water bath

H. tiny blood vessels active in reabsorption

I. connects proximal tubules to distal tubules

J. the working unit of the vertebrate kidney that forms urine

Answers: 1. J   2. A   3. F   4. E

5. D   6. H   7. I   8. C

9. G   10. B

Classification Questions

Answer questions 95–99 in reference to the five components of the gastrointestinal tract listed below.

a. stomach
b. gallbladder
c. small intestine
d. appendix
e. large intestine

D   95.   Full of white blood cells that participate in body defenses.

M   96.   This organ absorbs about 95 percent of the water that enters the human body, either as fluids or as part of food being eaten.

M   97.   Enzymatic digestion of proteins occurs primarily in this organ.

E   98.   Bile salts, bile pigments, cholesterol, and lecithin are stored by this organ.

E   99.   The digestion of cellulose occurs in this part of the digestive system of the cow.

Answers: 95. d   96. e   97. a

98. b   99. a

Answer questions 100–104 in reference to the four glands or structures of the mammalian gastrointestinal tract listed below.

a. salivary glands
b. stomach mucosa
c. intestinal mucosa
d. pancreas

M   100.   Enzymes for digesting proteins are produced there.

M   101.   The enzyme chymotrypsin is produced there.

D   102.   Bicarbonate is produced there.

D   103.   Gastric fluid is produced there.

M   104.   The protein-digesting enzyme, trypsin, is produced there.

Answers: 100. b   101. d   102. d

103. b   104. d

Answer questions 105–109 in reference to the four regions of a nephron listed below.

a. Bowman's capsule
b. proximal tubule
c. descending portion of loop of Henle
d. distal tubule

M 105. Sodium ions are actively transported out of the nephron from this region.

E 106. Filtration of the blood occurs in association with this structure.

D 107. Aldosterone acts on cells here to increase sodium reabsorption.

M 108. Permeability to water is regulated by antidiuretic hormone in this structure.

E 109. The glomerular capillaries are intimately associated with this structure.

Answers: 105. b   106. a   107. d

               108. d   109. a

Selecting the Exception

E 110. Four of the five answers listed below are structures through which ingested foodstuffs travel. Select the exception.
a. crop
* b. liver
c. gizzard
d. large intestine
e. small intestine

E 111. Four of the five answers listed below possess a complete digestive system. Select the exception.
a. human
b. bird
c. earthworm
* d. flatworm
e. fish

M 112. Four of the five answers listed below are layers of the digestive tract. Select the exception.
* a. peritoneum
b. mucosa
c. serosa
d. submucosa
e. muscle layer

M 113. Four of the five answers listed below produce secretions that assist digestion. Select the exception.
a. salivary gland
* b. esophagus
c. pancreas
d. gallbladder
e. liver

D 114. Four of the five answers listed below are hormones associated with digestion. Select the exception.
* a. bile
b. gastrin
c. secretin
d. cholecystokinin
e. leptin

D 115. Four of the five answers listed below are end products of digestion ready for intestinal absorption. Select the exception.
a. monoglycerides
b. nucleotides
* c. disaccharides
d. amino acids
e. fatty acids

M 116. Four of the five answers listed below are conditions related to diet. Select the exception.
a. colon cancer
b. kidney stones
c. cardiovascular disorders
d. obesity
* e. Alzheimer's disease

D 117. Four of the five answers listed below are potentially toxic waste products of metabolism. Select the exception.
a. urea
* b. water
c. uric acid
d. carbon dioxide
e. ammonia

M 118. Four of the five answers listed below are parts of the same structure. Select the exception.
a. distal tubule
b. loop of Henle
* c. ureter
d. proximal tubule
e. Bowman's capsule

M 119. Four of the five answers listed below are functions of the nephron. Select the exception.
a. filtration
* b. dilution
c. excretion
d. reabsorption
e. secretion

D 120. Four of the five answers listed below are the result of ADH (antidiuretic hormone) secretion. Select the exception.
a. Water is reabsorbed in the distal tubule.
b. Fluid volume of blood increases.
* c. Solute concentration in blood rises.
d. Distal tubule and collecting duct becomes more permeable to water.
e. Sodium concentration declines.

Labeling

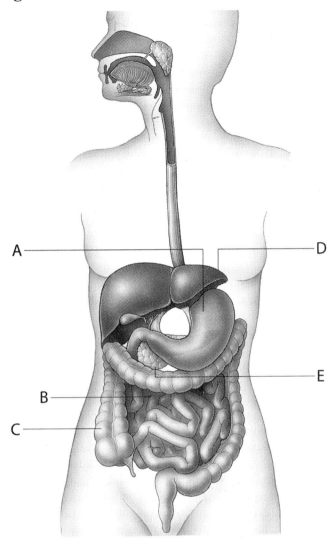

A

D

B

C

E

E   **121.** The organ at letter "E" secretes
- a. digestive enzymes only.
- b. insulin only.
- c. bile only.
- * d. digestive enzymes and insulin.
- e. insulin, digestive enzymes, and bile.

E   **122.** The liver is indicated by the letter _?_.

E   **123.** The majority of the food is digested and absorbed by the organ at letter _?_.

E   **124.** The organ at letter _?_ stores food prior to digestion.

E   **125.** The colon is depicted at the letter _?_.

Answers: 122. D   123. B   124. A   125. C

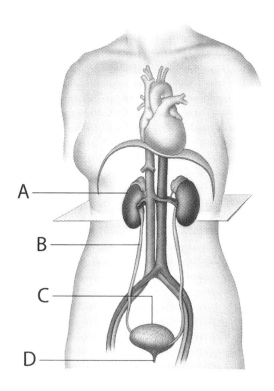

A —

B —

C —

D —

E **126.** Which of the following is NOT true of the organ at
           letter "A"?
           a. Filters water from the blood.
           b. Reclaims solutes.
    *   c. Produces adrenalin.
           d. Excretes urine.
           e. Has connections to the circulatory system.

E **127.** The urethra is located at letter _?_.

E **128.** The flow of urine may be partially blocked by kidney
           stones lodged in the structures located at letter _?_.

Answers: 127. D   128. B

CHAPTER 25
NEURAL CONTROL AND THE SENSES

Multiple-Choice Questions

NEURONS—THE GREAT COMMUNICATORS

E **1.** The basic unit of the nervous system is
*   a. the neuron.
    b. neuroglia.
    c. the brain.
    d. a nerve.
    e. a nerve impulse.

M **2.** Which of the following is NOT true concerning sensory neurons?
    a. They have receptor regions for detection of stimuli.
*   b. They lie in the pathway between the interneurons and motor neurons.
    c. They relay information to the spinal cord.
    d. They are part of a reflex arc.
    e. They are one of three types of neurons.

E **3.** Which of the following sequences is correct?
    a. receptors >>> sensory neurons >>> motor neurons >>> interneurons
    b. sensory neurons >>> receptors >>> motor neurons
    c. motor neurons >>> integrators >>> sensory neurons >>> receptors
    d. receptors >>> motor neurons >>> interneurons >>> sensory neurons
*   e. receptors >>> sensory neurons >>> interneurons >>> motor neurons

M **4.** Neuroglial cells
    a. metabolically support other neurons.
    b. insulate neurons.
    c. outnumber neurons in the brain by ten to one.
    d. hold neurons in place.
*   e. all of these

E **5.** The single, long process that extends from a typical motor nerve cell is the
*   a. axon.
    b. neuron.
    c. synapse.
    d. dendrite.
    e. cell body.

E **6.** The input zone of a neuron is the
    a. axon.
    b. axonal terminals.
    c. cell body.
    d. dendrite.
*   e. cell body and dendrite.

D **7.** Within a single neuron, the direction an impulse follows is
    a. dendrite >>> axon >>> cell body.
    b. axon >>> dendrite >>> cell body.
*   c. dendrite >>> cell body >>> axon.
    d. cell body >>> dendrite >>> axon.
    e. cell body >>> axon >>> dendrite.

M **8.** Neurons and other cells that produce action potentials are said to show
    a. polarity.
    b. saltatory conduction.
*   c. excitability.
    d. capacitance.
    e. voltage.

M **9.** Functionally speaking, a nerve impulse is
    a. a flow of electrons along the outside of the plasma membrane of a neuron.
    b. the movement of cytoplasmic elements through the core of the neuron.
*   c. a series of changes in membrane potentials.
    d. a lengthening and shortening of the membrane extensions of a neuron.
    e. generated by electrical discharge.

D **10.** When a neuron is at rest,
    a. there is a voltage difference across the membrane of about 70 millivolts.
    b. the cytoplasmic fluid is negatively charged.
    c. it is not responding to a stimulus.
    d. the fluid outside the membrane has more sodium and less potassium than the cytoplasm.
*   e. all of these

M **11.** At rest, a nerve cell has a high concentration of _?_ inside and a high concentration of _?_ outside.
    a. acetylcholine; chlorine
    b. sodium; potassium
*   c. potassium; sodium
    d. calcium; phosphorous
    e. phosphorus; calcium

M **12.** The membrane-bound enzyme system that maintains the resting membrane potential is which of the following pumps?
    a. sodium-phosphorus
*   b. sodium-potassium
    c. sodium-chlorine
    d. phosphorus-calcium
    e. phosphorus-chlorine

D   13.   Active transport
     a.   helps establish the resting potential of a neuron.
     b.   counters the process of diffusion.
     c.   allows transport of atoms across the plasma membrane of the neuron against the concentration gradient.
     d.   helps establish the resting potential of a neuron and counters the process of diffusion.
     *   e.   helps establish the resting potential of a neuron, counters the process of diffusion, and allows transport of atoms across the plasma membrane of the neuron against the concentration gradient.

D   14.   For sodium to accumulate rapidly in a neuron,
     *   a.   the cell must reach threshold potential.
     b.   the wave of repolarization must occur to reestablish a resting potential.
     c.   there must be a dramatic increase in the negative charge of the cytoplasm.
     d.   a voltage surge must cause the sodium gates to close.
     e.   the potassium gates must open first.

M   15.   Disturbances in sensory neurons will result in an action potential if the
     a.   stimulus is graded.
     b.   stimulus remains local.
     *   c.   graded stimulus reaches a trigger zone.
     d.   localized stimuli do not spread too far.
     e.   stimuli become downgraded to localized ones.

M   16.   The intensity of a nerve impulse is dependent upon the
     a.   diameter of the nerve that transmits the impulse.
     *   b.   number of impulses produced per unit time.
     c.   amount of voltage generated by the action potential.
     d.   sense organ that generates the impulse.
     e.   all of these

D   17.   What happens first following a neuron stimulation?
     *   a.   Sodium ions enter the cell.
     b.   Sodium ions leave the cell.
     c.   Potassium ions enter the cell.
     d.   Potassium ions leave the cell.
     e.   none of these is accurate

D   18.   An action potential is brought about by
     a.   a sudden membrane impermeability.
     b.   the movement of negatively charged proteins through the neuronal membrane.
     c.   the movement of lipoproteins to the outer membrane.
     *   d.   a local change in membrane permeability caused by a greater-than-threshold stimulus.
     e.   all of these

D   19.   During the passage of a nerve impulse,
     a.   sodium ions pass through gated channels.
     b.   positive feedback causes more sodium ions to enter the cell.
     c.   the interior of the cell becomes positive.
     d.   changing voltage increases the number of open gates.
     *   e.   all of these

D   20.   The phrase "all or nothing," used in conjunction with discussion about an action potential, means that
     a.   a resting membrane potential has been received by the cell.
     *   b.   nothing can stop the action potential if the threshold is reached.
     c.   the membrane either achieves total equilibrium or remains as far from equilibrium as possible.
     d.   propagation along the neuron is saltatory.
     e.   none of these

D   21.   Once a threshold is reached,
     a.   the number of sodium gates that open depends upon the strength of a stimulus.
     b.   a change in local resting membrane potential will be unable to spread to a trigger zone of the nerve membrane.
     c.   the resting potential of a neuron is restored.
     d.   the potassium channels in the input zone open.
     *   e.   the opening of sodium gates and the accompanying flow of sodium ions is an example of positive feedback.

D   22.   The reason that an action potential is so brief is that
     *   a.   following each action potential, the inside of the membrane becomes negative once again.
     b.   the opening of potassium gates allows the voltage difference across the neural membrane to be restored.
     c.   the protein channels for sodium movement remain open.
     d.   the sodium-potassium pump restores the electrical gradients.
     e.   the membrane limits electrical activity.

D   23.   Which of the following statements is FALSE?
     *   a.   An action potential can be generated in an input zone only.
     b.   A trigger zone has enough sodium gates to initiate an action potential.
     c.   Each portion of a membrane has its own refractory time.
     d.   During the refractory period, the sodium gates are shut and the potassium gates open.
     e.   During the refractory period, the resting membrane potential has not been restored.

D   24.   The occurrence of an action potential can best be compared to a(n)
     *   a.   switch to turn a lamp on and off.
     b.   volume control on a stereo.
     c.   door to the classroom.
     d.   room light dimmer switch.
     e.   accelerator on an automobile.

E 25. Before another action potential "spike" can occur,
* a. there must be a very brief restoration of the resting conditions in the membrane.
b. the membrane voltage must drop to zero.
c. the sodium-potassium pump must cease temporarily.
d. all of the membrane gates must be closed at the same time.
e. none of these

D 26. During the short recovery period before another action potential,
a. the threshold value is increased.
b. the threshold value is reduced.
* c. the sodium gates are shut and the potassium gates are opened.
d. both sodium and potassium gates are shut.
e. the nerve is said to be at the resting potential.

HOW MESSAGES FLOW FROM CELL TO CELL

M 27. Which of the following statements is FALSE?
* a. Synapses are direct contacts between nerves.
b. Both sensory and motor neurons use action potentials to transmit information.
c. Only the central nervous system is able to interpret the meaning of a stimulus.
d. Sensory neurons carry impulses toward the central nervous system.
e. Motor neurons carry impulses away from the central nervous system.

M 28. Following their action, transmitter substances
a. are expelled from the presynaptic cells by exocytosis.
b. tend to destroy acetylcholine.
c. enter the postsynaptic cell to continue the passage of the impulse.
d. interact with membrane receptors of the postsynaptic cells.
* e. diffuse away or are broken down by enzymes.

M 29. Which of the following is a junction between two neurons?
a. Schwann cell
* b. chemical synapse
c. node of Ranvier
d. sodium gate
e. all of these

D 30. The operation of a synapse
a. results from the passage of an electrical charge across the gap.
* b. involves neurotransmitter molecules from vesicles in the presynaptic neuron that act upon a receptor site in the postsynaptic neuron.
c. occurs only between two nerves.
d. is limited only by the action of acetylcholinesterase.
e. occurs between dendrites and cell body.

M 31. Which of the following bridges the gap between a neuron sending a message and the neuron receiving it?
a. threshold value
b. action potential
* c. neurotransmitter molecules
d. neurohormone
e. all of these

D 32. The presynaptic neuron and postsynaptic neuron do not directly contact each other because
a. one would inhibit the actions of the other.
b. they never grow to sufficient length.
c. the synaptic vesicles keep them apart.
* d. this would cause continuous impulse transmission.
e. acetylcholine prevents this action.

M 33. Neurotransmitters
a. include acetylcholine.
b. change the permeability of postsynaptic cells.
c. may be inhibitory or stimulatory.
d. elicit graded potentials near the synapse.
* e. all of these

D 34. Which of the following statements is FALSE?
a. A nerve will not fire unless a stimulus exceeds the threshold.
b. An action potential is an all-or-nothing event.
* c. An action potential continues indefinitely until a quenching signal is released.
d. An action potential is self-propagating.
e. An action potential transmission depends on activities at the membrane.

D 35. Which of the following neurotransmitters is mismatched?
a. substance P—acts to arouse the body to flee or fight
b. endorphin—suppresses pain
c. norepinephrine—arouses the body
* d. serotonin—sexual function
e. dopamine and GABA—act on the brain

D 36. Organophosphate insecticides kill by inhibiting acetylcholinesterase, an enzyme that degrades acetylcholine. What effect does this have?
a. It allows continuous volleys of impulses.
b. Control of vital organs is disrupted.
c. "Start/stop" signals for breathing and heartbeat are not possible.
d. Control of vital organs is disrupted and "start/stop" signals for breathing and heartbeat are not possible.
* e. Control of vital organs is disrupted; "start/stop" signals for breathing and heartbeat are not possible; and it allows continuous volleys of impulses.

M   37.   Endorphins are
         a.   neuromodulators.
         b.   stimulators of brain and nervous activity.
         c.   inhibitors of pain perception.
         d.   neuromodulators and stimulators of brain and
              nervous activity.
    *   e.   inhibitors of pain perception.

M   38.   Synaptic integration means that
         a.   all positive or excitatory stimuli are added
              together.
         b.   the positive and negative ions neutralize each
              other.
    *   c.   excitatory and inhibitory signals are combined in
              a neuron.
         d.   the adjacent neurons interact so that excitatory
              and inhibitory stimuli cancel each other out.
         e.   all of these

THE PATHS OF INFORMATION FLOW

D   39.   When an impulse passes from one neuron to the next,
         it
         a.   is passed directly from dendrite to axon.
         b.   passes from axon to cell body to dendrite.
         c.   can bypass the cell bodies of both.
    *   d.   passes from axon to dendrite.
         e.   undergoes repolarization.

M   40.   By definition, a "nerve" is
    *   a.   a bundle of axons.
         b.   a bundle of sensory neurons, dendrites, and axons
              of sensory neurons, or both.
         c.   the same as a neuron within the central nervous
              system.
         d.   a dendrite.
         e.   a fiber more than 10 inches in length.

M   41.   The myelin sheath
         a.   insulates axons.
         b.   enhances conduction of action potentials along an
              axon.
         c.   does not surround all nerves.
         d.   is composed of neuroglial cells.
    *   e.   all of these

M   42.   The spaces that separate adjacent Schwann cells are
         called
         a.   neuroglia.
         b.   myelin sheaths.
    *   c.   nodes.
         d.   dendrites.
         e.   synapses.

M   43.   Conduction from node to node
         a.   occurs only in the central nervous system.
         b.   is a quicker type of nerve conduction.
         c.   occurs between nerves and muscles.
         d.   involves the "jumping" of impulses.
    *   e.   is a quicker type of nerve conduction and involves
              the "jumping" of impulses from node to node.

D   44.   A deterioration in the myelin sheaths of motor axons
         to the lower leg would be expected to
         a.   remove the restraints to ion movement and speed
              up impulse transmission.
         b.   cause immobility of the leg due to cessation of
              impulses to leg muscles.
    *   c.   slow the rate of transmission and cause lack of
              motor control.
         d.   have little effect because the sheaths are for
              insulation only.

M   45.   What is the name of the condition in which there is a
         deterioration of the myelin sheaths of the neurons in
         the spinal cord?
         a.   muscular dystrophy
         b.   cancer
         c.   diabetes
    *   d.   multiple sclerosis
         e.   Alzheimer disease

E   46.   The most ancient path of information flow is
         a.   located in the midbrain.
    *   b.   the reflex arc.
         c.   found in the lower part of the brain.
         d.   found in the autonomic nervous system.
         e.   in the flow of information from a sense receptor to
              the brain.

M   47.   One example of a simple reflex arc involves the
    *   a.   contraction of a muscle when it is stretched.
         b.   conscious message to move part of the body.
         c.   receptor, the brain, and the effector.
         d.   muscle action in a salute when a
              noncommissioned combatant sees an officer.
         e.   contraction of an antagonistic muscle when its
              opposite muscle relaxes.

D   48.   The stretch reflex is
         a.   an adaptation that enables humans to stand
              upright.
         b.   activated by stretch-sensitive receptors inside the
              muscle spindles.
         c.   a simple, stereotyped, and repeatable motor
              action.
         d.   elicited by a sensory stimulus.
    *   e.   all of these

M   49.   Which of the following statements is FALSE?
         a.   Reflexes are the simplest of all nervous reactions.
         b.   The nervous system required sense organs before
              organisms could perceive their environment.
    *   c.   Motor neurons lead toward the brain or central
              nervous system.
         d.   Reflex actions are stereotyped and repeatable.
         e.   All of these statements are true.

M 50. A reflex pathway is the simplest reaction unit because it
   a. involves only one synapse.
   b. is evaluated and integrated by the medulla, not the cerebrum.
 * c. involves only two or three neurons.
   d. does not involve the central nervous system in any way.
   e. uses only acetylcholine.

D 51. In terms of evolution, which of the following is considered to be the oldest?
   a. cephalization
   b. information storage
   c. eyes
 * d. reflexes
   e. reasoning

TYPES OF NERVOUS SYSTEMS

M 52. *Hydra,* a cnidarian relative of sea anemones, has
   a. radial symmetry.
   b. a "nerve net."
   c. tentacles.
   d. a single opening to the digestive tract.
 * e. all of these

D 53. Which of the following is incorrect concerning a nerve net?
   a. found in animals with radial symmetry
   b. used in reflex actions
 * c. shows evolution of cephalization
   d. operates cells with contractile properties
   e. utilizes sensory cells

M 54. Cephalization refers to a
   a. type of symmetry.
   b. type of segmentation characteristic of lower forms of life.
   c. group of protective cells found in the tentacles of a polyp.
   d. transitional state in the life cycle of a jellyfish.
 * e. none of these

M 55. Which of the following is the more advanced nervous system?
   a. a diffuse system with scattered nerves
   b. a bilaterally symmetrical system
   c. a radially symmetrical system
 * d. paired nerves, paired sensory structures, and paired brain centers
   e. a nerve net

E 56. Clusters of cell bodies of neurons outside the central nervous system are known as
   a. nerve cords.
 * b. ganglia.
   c. a plexus.
   d. notochords.
   e. nerves.

D 57. Which of the following terms is NOT directly connected with the nervous system?
 * a. spinal column
   b. spinal cord
   c. neural tube
   d. nerve cord
   e. All of these are associated with the nervous system.

M 58. The two major divisions of the vertebrate nervous system are the
   a. autonomic and peripheral systems.
   b. sympathetic and parasympathetic systems.
   c. cranial and spinal nerves.
 * d. central and peripheral nervous systems.
   e. brain and spinal cord.

M 59. Which of the following would NOT be defined as a part of the central nervous system?
   a. brain
   b. cerebellum
   c. medulla
 * d. spinal nerves
   e. neuroglia cells

THE PERIPHERAL NERVOUS SYSTEM

M 60. Which of the following statements concerning the peripheral nervous system is FALSE?
   a. Spinal nerves lead to and from the spinal cord.
   b. There are 31 pairs of spinal nerves.
 * c. Cranial nerves lead from the brain directly to the spinal cord.
   d. Some nerves carry only sensory information.
   e. Some nerves are both sensory and motor.

M 61. The major divisions of the peripheral nervous system are
 * a. somatic and autonomic systems.
   b. sympathetic and parasympathetic systems.
   c. peripheral and central systems.
   d. afferent and autonomic systems.
   e. cranial and skeletal nerves.

E 62. All nerves that conduct impulses away from the central nervous system are
 * a. motor only.
   b. sensory only.
   c. motor or sensory depending on body location.
   d. spinal nerves.
   e. cranial nerves.

M 63. The sequence of a simple reaction to a stimulus is
* a. sense organ, sensory neuron, interneuron, motor neuron, effector.
b. sense organ, sensory neuron, motor neuron, interneuron, effector.
c. sense organ, motor neuron, sensory neuron, interneuron, effector.
d. sense organ, motor neuron, interneuron, sensory neuron, effector.
e. sense organ, interneuron, sensory neuron, motor neuron, effector.

M 64. The autonomic subdivision of the vertebrate nervous system would innervate all but which of the following?
a. intestinal muscles
* b. skeletal muscles
c. heart
d. glands
e. smooth muscles

D 65. Which nerves generally dominate internal events when environmental conditions permit normal body functioning?
a. ganglia
b. pacemaker
c. sympathetic
* d. parasympathetic
e. all of these

D 66. Which of the following statements is TRUE?
a. Both the parasympathetic and sympathetic nervous systems send nerves to all organs.
b. The sympathetic nervous system that supplies an organ will also provide parasympathetic nerves to it.
c. Both the sympathetic and parasympathetic have either excitatory or inhibitory effects.
* d. The sympathetic branch of the sympathetic system usually speeds up the activities of the body.
e. The parasympathetic system usually speeds up the activities of the body.

M 67. Signals from the parasympathetic nervous system cause which of the following?
a. rise in blood pressure
b. increase in pulse rate
* c. increase in digestive activities
d. rise in blood sugar level
e. rise in metabolic rate

D 68. Activation of the sympathetic nervous system
* a. causes the pupils of the eye to dilate.
b. increases the flow of watery saliva.
c. stimulates peristaltic contractions of the intestinal system.
d. slows heartbeat and lowers blood pressure.
e. allows the body to relax rather than prepare for fight or flight.

D 69. The word that best describes the interaction of the sympathetic and parasympathetic systems is
* a. antagonistic.
b. cooperative.
c. overriding.
d. subversive.
e. ineffective.

M 70. The part of the central nervous system that is composed of parts that are antagonistic to each other is the
* a. autonomic nervous system composed of the sympathetic and parasympathetic subsystems.
b. central nervous system composed of the brain and spinal cord.
c. peripheral nervous system composed of the cranial and spinal nervous system.
d. none of these; the muscular system is the only system with antagonistic subsets.

D 71. During the "fight-flight" response, which of the following would be in use?
a. sympathetic nervous system
b. parasympathetic nervous system
c. epinephrine
* d. sympathetic nervous system and epinephrine
e. parasympathetic nervous system and epinephrine

E 72. Interneurons are found mostly in the
a. dorsal root.
* b. spinal cord.
c. sensory neurons.
d. motor neurons.
e. autonomic nervous system.

THE CENTRAL NERVOUS SYSTEM

M 73. The hindbrain includes the
a. thalamus.
b. pineal gland.
c. cerebellum.
d. medulla oblongata.
* e. cerebellum and medulla oblongata.

E 74. The part of the brain that connects one brain center with another is the
a. cerebrum.
* b. pons.
c. cerebellum.
d. fissure of Rolando.
e. hypothalamus.

M 75. The center for coordinating limb movements and posture is the
a. cerebrum.
b. pons.
* c. cerebellum.
d. thalamus.
e. hypothalamus.

M   76.   The part of the brain that controls the basic responses necessary to maintain life processes (breathing, heartbeat) is the
*   a. medulla oblongata.
    b. corpus callosum.
    c. fissure of Rolando.
    d. cerebellum.
    e. cerebral cortex.

M   77.   The pituitary gland assists the _?_ in some of its roles
    a. pineal gland
    b. medulla oblongata
*   c. hypothalamus
    d. thalamus
    e. cerebrum

M   78.   The center of conscious behavior and intelligence is the
    a. medulla oblongata.
    b. thalamus.
    c. pons.
    d. cerebellum.
*   e. cerebrum.

M   79.   Which part of the mammalian brain is disproportionately larger than the corresponding part of a fish brain?
    a. medulla oblongata
    b. thalamus
    c. pons
    d. cerebellum
*   e. cerebrum

M   80.   The part of the brain that shows the greatest proportional increase in size from the lower vertebrates to humans is the increase in the
    a. cerebellum.
*   b. cerebrum.
    c. medulla oblongata.
    d. hypothalamus.
    e. thalamus.

M   81.   The part of the brain that deals with the basic drives such as hunger, sex, and thirst is the
    a. cerebrum.
    b. pons.
    c. cerebellum.
    d. thalamus.
*   e. hypothalamus.

M   82.   The major relay station of the brain for conducting sensory signals is the
    a. cerebrum.
    b. olfactory area.
    c. cerebellum.
*   d. thalamus.
    e. hypothalamus.

M   83.   The mechanism that regulates the movement of substances into and out of the cells of the brain is the
    a. cerebrospinal fluid.
    b. reticular formation.
    c. tectum.
*   d. blood-brain barrier.
    e. brain stem.

E   84.   The protective covering of the brain is the
    a. ventricles.
*   b. meninges.
    c. tectum.
    d. olfactory and optic bulbs.
    e. pineal gland.

E   85.   The outer layer of gray matter of the brain is associated with the
*   a. cerebral cortex.
    b. pons.
    c. optic chiasma.
    d. corpus callosum.
    e. thalamus.

E   86.   The cerebral hemispheres communicate with each other by means of the
    a. cerebral cortex.
    b. corpora cardiaca.
    c. corporothalamus.
*   d. corpus callosum.
    e. corpus allata.

M   87.   The left hemisphere of the brain is responsible for
    a. music.
    b. artistic ability.
    c. spatial relationships.
*   d. analytical skills and speaking.
    e. abstract abilities.

M   88.   The right hemisphere of the cerebrum is specialized for
    a. verbal ability.
    b. mathematics.
*   c. music and visual-spatial relationships.
    d. control over the right side of the body.
    e. walking.

M   89.   Emotional states and memory are the responsibility of the
    a. medulla.
    b. corpus callosum.
*   c. limbic system.
    d. cerebral cortex.
    e. cerebellum.

DRUGGING THE BRAIN

E   90.   Active chemicals found in chocolate, tea, coffee, and soft drinks are examples of which of the following?
    a. depressant
*   b. stimulant
    c. narcotic analgesic
    d. hallucinogen or psychedelic
    e. antipsychotic

E   91.   Pain relievers such as endorphins and enkephalins are
  a. depressants.
  b. stimulants.
 * c. natural analgesics.
  d. hallucinogens or psychedelics.
  e. antipsychotics.

M   92.   Substances that lower the activity of the brain and inhibit transmission at a synapse are
 * a. depressants.
  b. stimulants.
  c. narcotic analgesics.
  d. hallucinogens or psychedelics.
  e. antipsychotics.

E   93.   Substances that could be called hypnotics and that induce sleep are
 * a. depressants.
  b. stimulants.
  c. narcotic analgesics.
  d. hallucinogens or psychedelics.
  e. antipsychotics.

M   94.   A chemical substance that behaves as a natural analgesic is
  a. an amphetamine.
  b. LSD.
  c. epinephrine.
 * d. endorphin.
  e. none of these

M   95.   A group of chemicals that at low doses reduce fatigue and increase alertness but at larger doses, induces clumsiness and mental incoherence are
  a. depressants.
 * b. stimulants.
  c. narcotic analgesics.
  d. hallucinogens or psychedelics.
  e. antipsychotics.

E   96.   Substances that alter sensory perception, cause disorientation, and inhibit the ability to perform complex tasks are
  a. depressants.
  b. stimulants.
  c. narcotic analgesics.
 * d. hallucinogens or psychedelics.
  e. antipsychotics.

E   97.   Barbiturates are
 * a. depressants.
  b. stimulants.
  c. narcotic analgesics.
  d. hallucinogens or psychedelics.
  e. antipsychotics.

E   98.   Substances that cause euphoria, relieve pain, and cause addiction are
  a. depressants.
  b. stimulants.
 * c. narcotic analgesics.
  d. hallucinogens or psychedelics.
  e. antipsychotics.

OVERVIEW OF SENSORY SYSTEMS

M   99.   Which sense utilizes mechanical energy?
  a. sense of touch
  b. muscle sense
  c. sense of hearing
  d. body position
 * e. all of these

D   100.   Which of the following animals does NOT have a sensory system?
  a. free-living flatworms
  b. tapeworms
  c. cnidarians
 * d. sponges
  e. nematodes

D   101.   The difference in "sensation" and "perception" when referring to a stimulus lies in
  a. the type of receptor stimulated.
 * b. understanding what a stimulus means.
  c. the number of receptors that depolarize.
  d. feeling exactly what is happening at the site.
  e. responding to the stimulus.

M   102.   The major function of a receptor is to
  a. control the autonomic functions of the body.
  b. stabilize the internal environment to achieve homeostasis.
  c. produce responses to the various stimuli the body receives.
 * d. respond to particular types of stimuli.
  e. decode the stimulus.

M   103.   Which of the following statements is FALSE?
 * a. All animals placed in the same environment will have the same awareness of it.
  b. Humans and insects see flowers differently.
  c. The carotid bodies monitor the concentration of carbon dioxide in the blood.
  d. Olfactory receptors detect odors.
  e. Pacinian corpuscles are examples of mechanoreceptors.

D   104.   Which of the following statements is FALSE?
  a. Sensory receptors are able to detect specific stimuli only.
  b. Sensation is an awareness of a change in external or internal conditions.
 * c. A stimulus will generate impulses that are different depending on where the signals are sent in the brain.
  d. Information about a stimulus is coded in the quantity and frequency of action potentials sent to the brain.
  e. Specific regions of the brain translate the information about the signal and convert it into a sensation.

M 105. Which of the following is NOT characteristic of sensation?
   a. Some sense cells can be activated only by chemicals.
   b. Nerve impulses for each of the five senses are essentially the same regardless of the sense considered.
   c. Sensory nerve impulses follow the all-or-none law.
 * d. All organisms perceive their environments by the same sense organs.
   e. Sensation is "awareness."

D 106. Differences in intensity of a stimulus
   a. do not affect the impulse transmitted.
   b. are indicated by the number of nerves activated.
   c. control the part of the brain that receives the stimulus.
   d. are encoded in the frequency of action potentials on a single axon.
 * e. are indicated by the number of nerves activated and are encoded in the frequency of action potentials on a single axon.

D 107. Which of the following statements is FALSE?
   a. It is assumed that lower animals are incapable of perception.
 * b. Humans, as the most complex organisms, have all of the sensory organs found in lower forms.
   c. Mechanoreceptors are responsible for the senses of equilibrium and hearing.
   d. Infrared radiation is detected by thermoreceptors.
   e. A lobster can react to the boiling water in which it is placed to cook.

D 108. Which of the following statements is TRUE?
   a. All action potentials for the same nerve are alike.
   b. Receptors respond to a change in resting membrane potential.
   c. Different nerves convey different information by going to different areas of the brain.
   d. Differences in intensities may be due to the number of receptors and nerves involved in response.
 * e. all of these

M 109. A loud sound can be distinguished from a soft whisper because
   a. more neurons depolarize.
   b. each receptor depolarizes more fully.
   c. the frequency of depolarizing neurons increases.
 * d. more neurons depolarize and the frequency of depolarizing neurons increases.
   e. more neurons depolarize, the frequency of depolarizing neurons increases, and each receptor depolarizes more fully.

M 110. Which of the following statements is FALSE?
   a. Neurons in the brain can interpret incoming action potentials only in certain ways.
   b. Optic nerve impulses can only be interpreted as light.
 * c. Sensory neurons do not follow the all-or-none law.
   d. The stronger the stimulus, the more action potentials are generated.
   e. A strong stimulus activates many adjacent receptors, thereby increasing the number of action potentials and the level of awareness for the stimulus.

D 111. Which of the following is NOT an example of nerve adaptation?
   a. a loss of the sense of pressure of clothes against the skin
   b. adjustment to repeated jumping into a body of cold water
 * c. response to lack of oxygen at high altitudes
   d. eventual loss of awareness of a constant noise
   e. the loss of the ability to smell a person's perfume or cologne after being in that person's presence for some time

SOMATIC SENSATIONS

D 112. The extent to which a sense can detect a particular sensation is mainly due to the
   a. sensitivity of its receptors.
   b. speed of nerve transmission.
 * c. brain area devoted to interpretation.
   d. transmitter substances in the synapses.
   e. amount of stimulus.

M 113. The somatic senses include all EXCEPT which one of the following sensations?
 * a. balance
   b. pain near the body surface
   c. temperature
   d. touch
   e. pressure

M 114. Somatic sensations include all EXCEPT which one of the following?
   a. heat and cold
   b. pressure and touch
   c. pain
   d. limb motions and the position of the body in space
 * e. sound

M 115. According to the classification given by your authors, somatic senses
 * a. are distributed in several locations over the body.
   b. reside in certain receptor organs located at a few specific locations.
   c. are exemplified by ears and eyes.
   d. include sight and sound.
   e. all of these but "are distributed in several locations over the body"

M 116. Mechanoreceptors are located in
   a. internal organs.
   b. skin.
   c. joints.
   d. tendons.
  * e. all of these

D 117. The feeling of pressure on the skin is the result of
   a. bending of mechanoreceptors.
   b. stimulation only when the stimulus is first applied.
   c. constant stimulation.
  * d. mechanoreceptors and constant stimulation.
   e. bending of mechanoreceptors and stimulation only when the stimulus is first applied.

E 118. The Pacinian corpuscle is used in sensing
   a. sound.
  * b. fine textures.
   c. chemicals.
   d. sight.
   e. chemical differences.

M 119. A stretch receptor is classified as a
   a. chemoreceptor.
  * b. mechanoreceptor.
   c. photoreceptor.
   d. thermoreceptor.
   e. all of these

THE SPECIAL SENSES

E 120. Olfactory centers are responsive to
   a. touch.
  * b. smell.
   c. taste.
   d. sound.
   e. sight.

M 121. Receptors in the human nose are
  * a. chemoreceptors.
   b. mechanoreceptors.
   c. photoreceptors.
   d. nocireceptors.
   e. none of these

M 122. Pheromones
   a. are social signals.
   b. identify individuals who belong to a group in case they get separated.
   c. may serve as sex attractants.
   d. may be used for an alarm signal.
  * e. all of these

E 123. Female silk moths secrete a pheromone as a(n)
   a. way to gather young when they scatter.
   b. message to stay close to the cocoon.
   c. alarm signal.
  * d. sexual attractant.
   e. territory marker.

M 124. Functionally, the two most closely associated senses are
   a. sight and sound.
   b. touch and sight.
  * c. taste and smell.
   d. temperature and pain.
   e. touch and balance.

E 125. One's equilibrium is sensed by a
   a. chemoreceptor.
  * b. mechanoreceptor.
   c. photoreceptor.
   d. thermoreceptor.
   e. none of these

M 126. Hair cells are important in the sense of
   a. equilibrium.
   b. hearing.
   c. taste.
   d. smell.
  * e. both equilibrium and hearing.

E 127. The sense of equilibrium or balance can detect
   a. motion.
   b. acceleration.
   c. gravity.
   d. position.
  * e. all of these

M 128. The semicircular canals are
   a. empty.
   b. filled with gas.
  * c. filled with a liquid.
   d. filled with bones or stones.
   e. filled with sand grains.

E 129. How many semicircular canals are in each organ of balance?
   a. 2
  * b. 3
   c. 4
   d. 5
   e. more than 6

E 130. The organ of Corti has _?_ attached to its inner basilar membrane.
   a. chemoreceptors
  * b. mechanoreceptors
   c. photoreceptors
   d. nocireceptors
   e. all of these

M 131. The principal place in the human ear where sound waves are amplified by means of the vibrations of tiny bones is the
   a. pinna.
   b. ear canal.
  * c. middle ear.
   d. organ of Corti.
   e. all of these

M 132. The place where vibrations are translated into patterns of nerve impulses is the
    a. pinna.
    b. ear canal.
    c. middle ear.
*   d. organ of Corti.
    e. none of these

E 133. The organ of Corti is located in the
    a. thoracic cavity.
*   b. inner ear.
    c. abdominal cavity.
    d. brain stem.
    e. semicircular canals.

D 134. In hearing, the last place that pressure or sound waves pass through is the
    a. bones of the middle ear.
    b. tympanic membrane.
    c. oval window.
    d. round window.
*   e. tectorial membrane.

E 135. How many coiled and fluid-filled ducts are found in each cochlea?
    a. 1
    b. 2
*   c. 3
    d. 4
    e. 5 or more

D 136. The sense of hearing in both invertebrates and vertebrates is dependent on
    a. fluid displacement.
    b. hair bending.
    c. echolocation.
*   d. vibration of a membrane.
    e. all of these

D 137. The sense in which amplitude and frequency can be detected with some accuracy is
    a. sight.
*   b. hearing.
    c. balance.
    d. taste.
    e. smell.

M 138. Movable bones are features of the sense organs associated with
    a. sight.
*   b. hearing.
    c. taste.
    d. smell.
    e. touch.

M 139. Movable bones are found in the
    a. cochlea.
    b. external ear.
*   c. middle ear.
    d. inner ear.
    e. organ of Corti.

M 140. The organ of Corti
    a. functions in the awareness of motion and the sense of equilibrium.
    b. controls the sense of depth perception.
*   c. converts sound vibrations into impulses that enable hearing.
    d. secretes cerebrospinal fluid.
    e. detects light energy.

E 141. Eyes are
    a. chemoreceptors.
    b. mechanoreceptors.
*   c. photoreceptors.
    d. nocireceptors.
    e. none of these

E 142. The layer of the eye where photoreceptors are located is the
    a. lens.
    b. cornea.
    c. pupil.
    d. iris.
*   e. retina.

M 143. The adjustable ring of contractile and connective tissues that controls the amount of light entering the eye is the
    a. lens.
    b. cornea.
    c. pupil.
*   d. iris.
    e. retina.

E 144. The white, protective fibrous tissue of the eye, often called the white of the eye, is the
    a. lens.
*   b. sclera.
    c. pupil.
    d. iris.
    e. retina.

E 145. The darkly pigmented middle layer of the eye that prevents the scattering of light is the
    a. fovea.
    b. retina.
    c. sclera.
*   d. choroid.
    e. cornea.

M 146. Accommodation involves the ability to
    a. change the sensitivity of the rods and cones by means of neurotransmitters.
    b. change the curvature of the cornea.
*   c. change the shape of the lens by contracting or relaxing a ciliary muscle.
    d. adapt to large changes in light intensity.
    e. all of these

M   147.   The ciliary muscle
           a.   controls the eardrum.
      *   b.   controls the shape of the lens to allow focusing.
           c.   holds the bones of the middle ear in place.
           d.   enables the eyeball to move so that a person may
                see an object without moving the head.
           e.   is responsible for the size of the pupil in different
                light intensities.

M   148.   If the ciliary muscle of the eye is damaged, then
           a.   color vision will be lost.
           b.   the amount of light entering the eye cannot be
                regulated.
      *   c.   proper focusing will be impossible.
           d.   only peripheral vision is available.
           e.   "night blindness" will become more evident.

E   149.   The transparent outer protective cover of the eyeball is
           the
           a.   fovea.
           b.   retina.
           c.   sclera.
           d.   choroid.
      *   e.   cornea.

E   150.   The part of the eye that may be pigmented (e.g.,
           brown, green, or gray) is the
           a.   retina.
           b.   sclera.
           c.   choroid.
           d.   cornea.
      *   e.   iris.

E   151.   Rod and cone cells are located in the
           a.   lens.
           b.   cornea.
           c.   pupil.
           d.   iris.
      *   e.   retina.

E   152.   The highest concentration of cones is in the
      *   a.   fovea.
           b.   blind spot.
           c.   sclera.
           d.   ommatidium.
           e.   choroid.

D   153.   The fovea
           a.   is the blind spot produced by the optic nerve
                entering the eye.
      *   b.   is the region of the retina filled with cones that
                allows the most visual acuity.
           c.   is the region of the retina that has the greatest
                concentration of rods that enable sight under
                extremely dim conditions.
           d.   focuses light on the retina.
           e.   is the anterior fluid-filled chamber of the eye.

M   154.   In the human eye, what provides the greatest visual
           acuity (the precise discrimination between adjacent
           points in space)?
           a.   photoreceptors in the sclera.
      *   b.   photoreceptors in the fovea.
           c.   protein filaments in the lens.
           d.   photoreceptors in the optic nerve.
           e.   none of these

E   155.   Cones are
           a.   sensitive to red light.
           b.   sensitive to green light.
           c.   sensitive to blue light.
           d.   relatively insensitive to dim light.
      *   e.   all of these

M   156.   Where are bipolar, amacrine, and ganglion cells
           located?
           a.   sclera
           b.   thalamus
           c.   organ of Corti
      *   d.   retina
           e.   all of these

E   157.   Nearsightedness is caused by
      *   a.   eye structure that focuses an image in front of the
                retina.
           b.   uneven curvature of the cornea.
           c.   uneven curvature of the lens.
           d.   eye structure that focuses an image posterior to
                the retina.
           e.   all of these

Matching Questions

D **158.** Matching I. Choose the most appropriate answer.

1. ___ effector
2. ___ interneuron
3. ___ myelin sheath
4. ___ neuroglia
5. ___ rest period
6. ___ sodium-potassium pump
7. ___ transmitter substance
8. ___ autonomic nervous system
9. ___ cerebellum
10. ___ hypothalamus
11. ___ medulla oblongata
12. ___ nerve net
13. ___ peripheral nervous system
14. ___ meninges
15. ___ ganglion

    A. cells that support neurons
    B. motor neurons that are divided into sympathetic and parasympathetic divisions
    C. a neuron cannot propagate an action potential at this time
    D. acetylcholine
    E. coordinates posture and limb movement
    F. establishes basis of resting membrane potential
    G. group of nerve cell bodies that function as a local integrating center
    H. contains centers concerned with body temperature regulation and adjusts fluid volume
    I. integrator cell between sensory and motor
    J. reflex control center for respiration and circulation
    K. in cnidarians; based on reflex pathways devoted to swimming and feeding
    L. all parts of nerve cells outside the brain and spinal cord
    M. motor neuron
    N. has an insulating function
    O. membrane coverings over the brain and spinal cord

Answers: 1. M 2. I 3. N 4. A
          5. C 6. F 7. D 8. B
          9. E 10. H 11. J 12. K
          13. L 14. O 15. G

D **159.** Matching II. Choose the one appropriate answer for each.

1. ___ amplitude
2. ___ cochlea
3. ___ eardrum
4. ___ iris
5. ___ oval window
6. ___ pheromone
7. ___ hammer
8. ___ pitch
9. ___ retina
10. ___ round window
11. ___ semicircular canals

    A. dissipates excess vibrational energy to the middle ear
    B. contains the organ of Corti
    C. separates the outer and middle ears
    D. A vibrating middle ear bone transmits pressure waves to this.
    E. consists of tissue containing rods and cones
    F. bone in middle ear
    G. peak height and valley depth of sound waves are its basis
    H. maintain balance and position; detect acceleration
    I. depends on how many wave changes per second occur
    J. a signaling molecule
    K. regulates size of pupil and amount of incoming light

Answers: 1. G 2. B 3. C 4. K
          5. D 6. J 7. F 8. I
          9. E 10. A 11. H

Classification Questions

Answer questions 160–164 in reference to the four cell types listed below.

    a. sensory neurons
    b. interneurons
    c. motor neurons
    d. Schwann cells

M   **160.**   Nerve cells that carry signals to muscle cells are these.

M   **161.**   Formed by neuroglial cells wrapped like jelly rolls around axons.

E   **162.**   Enhances conduction of action potentials along an axon.

E   **163.**   Found mostly inside the brain and spinal cord.

E   **164.**   This cell type picks up environmental signals.

Answers: 160. c   161. d   162. d

           163. b   164. a

Answer questions 165–169 in reference to the five regions of the vertebrate brain listed below.

    a. cerebrum
    b. hypothalamus
    c. pons
    d. cerebellum
    e. medulla oblongata

D   **165.**   This region of the brain contains the reflex centers involved in respiration.

D   **166.**   This region of the brain controls neural-endocrine activities such as temperature control of the internal environment.

D   **167.**   Governs behaviors affecting organ functions such as thirst, hunger, and sex.

M   **168.**   This part of the brain controls the complex coordination of posture and limb movement.

D   **169.**   This region controls signal flow between the cerebellum and forebrain integrating centers.

Answers: 165. e   166. b   167. b

           168. d   169. e

Answer questions 170–174 in reference to the four kinds of energy listed below.

    a. chemical
    b. mechanical
    c. thermal
    d. light

E   **170.**   Receptors on the tongue detect variation in this kind of energy.

M   **171.**   Olfactory receptors detect this kind of energy.

D   **172.**   Ears monitor this kind of energy.

E   **173.**   Ultraviolet radiation detected by insects is in this category.

M   **174.**   The pain you feel from fire is a result of detecting this kind of energy.

Answers: 170. a   171. a   172. b

           173. d   174. c

Answer questions 175–179 in reference to the five eye structures listed below.

    a. cornea
    b. lens
    c. retina
    d. iris
    e. vitreous body

D   **175.**   This structure regulates the amount of light that enters the eye.

M   **176.**   This structure forms the transparent front of the eye.

E   **177.**   This structure primarily acts to focus light waves.

M   **178.**   This structure is composed of rod- and cone-shaped cells in mammals and birds.

M   **179.**   This structure acts to maintain the shape of the eye and to transmit light to other structures.

Answers: 175. d   176. a   177. b

           178. c   179. e

Selecting the Exception

M   **180.**   Four of the five answers listed below are actively involved in nerve impulse transmission. Select the exception.
    *   a. neuroglia
         b. neuron
         c. ganglia
         d. nerves
         e. tracts

D   **181.**   Four of the five answers listed below are true of a neuron at resting potential. Select the exception.
    *   a. Interior of neuron is positive.
         b. Exterior of neuron has negative charge.
         c. More sodium ions are outside neuron.
         d. More potassium ions are inside neuron.
         e. Membrane of neuron is polarized.

D   **182.**   Four of the five answers listed below are used in descriptions of neuron membranes. Select the exception.
         a. gate
         b. pump
         c. wave of depolarization
         d. channel
    *   e. synaptic cleft

D   183.   Four of the five answers listed below are used in descriptions of the nerve sheath. Select the exception.
         a. neuroglial cells
    *   b. threshold
         c. myelin sheath
         d. saltatory conduction
         e. node of Ranvier

M   184.   Four of the five answers listed below are participants in a common function. Select the exception.
         a. sensory neuron
    *   b. medulla
         c. interneuron
         d. effector
         e. receptor

D   185.   Four of the five answers listed below are characteristic of bilaterally symmetrical forms. Select the exception.
    *   a. sessile, nonmoving
         b. segmentation
         c. cephalization
         d. paired nerves, muscles, sensory structures
         e. right and left halves of the body

M   186.   Four of the five answers listed below are parts of the central nervous system. Select the exception.
         a. spinal cord
         b. medulla
    *   c. ganglia
         d. cerebellum
         e. cerebrum

M   187.   Four of the five answers listed below are innervated by the autonomic nervous system. Select the exception.
    *   a. skeletal muscles
         b. smooth muscles
         c. heart
         d. endocrine glands
         e. exocrine glands

D   188.   Four of the five answers listed below are actions mediated by the sympathetic nervous system. Select the exception.
         a. pulse increases
    *   b. blood glucose levels drop
         c. metabolism increases
         d. digestion slows down
         e. pupils of the eyes dilate

M   189.   Four of the five answers listed below are stimulants. Select the exception.
    *   a. heroin
         b. caffeine
         c. nicotine
         d. cocaine
         e. amphetamine

D   190.   Four of the five answers listed below are analgesics. Select the exception.
         a. endorphin
         b. fentanyl
         c. heroin
         d. enkephalin
    *   e. lithium

D   191.   Four of the five answers listed below are related by a similar sense receptor. Select the exception.
         a. touch or pressure
    *   b. olfaction
         c. balance (equilibrium)
         d. hearing
         e. muscle sense

M   192.   Four of the five answers listed below are somatic senses. Select the exception.
    *   a. light
         b. pressure
         c. touch
         d. temperature
         e. pain

M   193.   Four of the five answers listed below are parts of the inner ear. Select the exception.
    *   a. eardrum
         b. oval window
         c. scala tympani
         d. basilar membrane
         e. cochlea

M   194.   Four of the five answers listed below are parts of the same sense organ. Select the exception.
         a. choroid
         b. retina
         c. vitreous humor
    *   d. ampulla
         e. sclera

M   195.   Four of the five answers listed below are parts of the same sense organ. Select the exception.
    *   a. cochlea
         b. cornea
         c. sclera
         d. choroid
         e. fovea

D   196.   Three of the four answers listed below are colors for which the cone cells have pigments. Select the exception.
         a. red
    *   b. yellow
         c. blue
         d. green
         e. All of these are colors for which the cone cells have pigments.

Labeling

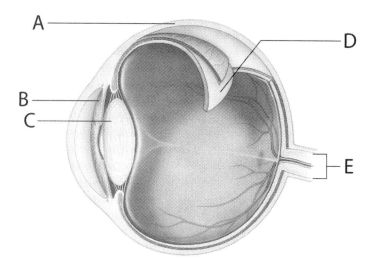

Match the function to the structure in the figure by choosing the appropriate letter:

E   **197.**   This absorbs and transduces light energy.

E   **198.**   This focuses light images on photoreceptors.

E   **199.**   This protects the exterior of the eyeball.

E   **200.**   This carries signals to the brain.

E   **201.**   This adjusts the amount of incoming light.

Answers: 197. D   198. C   199. A

200. E   201. B

CHAPTER 26
ENDOCRINE CONTROLS

Multiple-Choice Questions

HORMONES AND OTHER SIGNALING MOLECULES

M   **1.** Target cells
    a. are found only in specific endocrine glands.
    b. are equipped with specific receptor molecules.
    c. are muscle cells.
    d. may occur in any part of the body.
   * e. are equipped with specific receptor molecules and may occur in any part of the body.

M   **2.** Which of the following statements is TRUE?
   * a. Although hormones are carried to all parts of the body, they produce effects only in cells with proper receptors.
    b. Hormones are limited to steroid compounds.
    c. Hormones are secreted by specialized exocrine glands.
    d. Most hormones are controlled by positive feedback mechanisms involving the pituitary gland.
    e. Hormones are electrochemical events.

M   **3.** The important feature of all cells that react to a specific hormone is the
    a. type of blood supply they receive.
    b. proximity of the endocrine gland.
   * c. presence of an appropriate receptor molecule.
    d. characteristics of their plasma membranes.
    e. presence of specific genes responsive to the hormone.

E   **4.** Most hormones are distributed throughout the body by the
    a. exocrine system.
    b. lymphatic system.
    c. nervous system.
   * d. blood system.
    e. integumentary system.

D   **5.** The overall purpose of the endocrine system is to
    a. provide a mechanism for rapid response to changes in the body.
   * b. maintain a relatively constant internal environment.
    c. ensure proper growth and development.
    d. allow for a mechanism to control gene action.
    e. all of these

M   **6.** In the androgen insensitivity syndrome,
    a. no testosterone is produced.
    b. chemicals circulating in the blood deactivate the male hormone.
   * c. the cellular receptor for testosterone in the target cells is defective.
    d. the male with this defect is normal in all respects except that he is sterile.
    e. all of these

D   **7.** The reason that some individual hormones have so many different effects is that
    a. they influence gene transcription.
    b. they trigger a second messenger system that produces a cascade of effects.
   * c. there are a great many different cells in different tissues that have specific receptors for the hormone.
    d. the hormone is carried throughout the body and only a small amount is needed to produce its effect.
    e. all of these

M   **8.** Steroid hormones do not require a membrane receptor because they
    a. are small enough to pass directly through the membrane.
   * b. diffuse across the target cell's plasma membrane.
    c. pass through special channels.
    d. are water-soluble.
    e. dissolve in the cholesterol of the membranes.

M   **9.** The release of cyclic AMP as a second messenger is a response to
    a. peptide hormones.
    b. steroid hormones.
    c. glycoprotein hormones.
   * d. protein and glycoprotein hormones.
    e. protein, steroid, and glycoprotein hormones.

M   **10.** Which is the predominant second messenger involved in regulating glucose metabolism?
    a. insulin
    b. glucagon
    c. adenyl cyclase
   * d. cAMP
    e. all of these

M   **11.** Second messengers are molecules of
    a. steroid compounds.
   * b. cyclic AMP.
    c. ADP.
    d. prostaglandin.
    e. intermedin.

E   12.   If you were cast up on a desert island with no fresh water to drink, the level of which of the following would rise in your bloodstream in an effort to conserve water?
       a. erythropoietin
       b. oxytocin
       c. insulin
*   d. antidiuretic hormone
       e. glucose

THE HYPOTHALAMUS AND PITUITARY GLAND

E   13.   Which two glands are together referred to as the "master integrating center?"
       a. pineal and pituitary
*   b. pituitary and hypothalamus
       c. thyroid and pancreas
       d. adrenal and hypothalamus
       e. thyroid and adrenal

E   14.   The pituitary gland is controlled by the
       a. pons.
       b. corpus callosum.
       c. medulla oblongata.
       d. thalamus.
*   e. hypothalamus.

D   15.   The hypothalamus and pituitary link the activities of the endocrine system and nervous system by
*   a. neurohormones being secreted in response to the summation of neural messages that enter the hypothalamus.
       b. shifts in hormonal concentrations being detected by the anterior pituitary.
       c. pheromones being secreted as a response to photoperiodic stimuli.
       d. the nervous tissue of the anterior lobe of the pituitary sending stimuli to the glandular tissue of the posterior pituitary to produce hormones that will be secreted by the hypothalamus.
       e. all of these

M   16.   Which of the following statements is TRUE?
       a. The anterior pituitary gland is essentially nervous tissue.
       b. The anterior pituitary gland secretes only two hormones.
       c. The posterior pituitary gland is the master gland.
*   d. The posterior pituitary gland only stores hormones produced by the hypothalamus.
       e. all of these

E   17.   The antidiuretic hormone
       a. controls water balance.
       b. affects social behavior.
       c. influences blood pressure.
       d. causes the body to conserve water.
*   e. all of these

E   18.   Oxytocin affects the
*   a. uterine wall.
       b. voluntary muscles throughout the body.
       c. nervous tissue.
       d. target cells in the brain.
       e. target cells in the digestive tract.

M   19.   The control over milk production, water balance, and labor in childbirth is mediated by the _?_ gland.
       a. pineal
       b. anterior pituitary
*   c. posterior pituitary
       d. parathyroid
       e. thyroid

D   20.   A drop in blood volume would trigger the body to secrete
       a. parathyroid hormones.
       b. somatotropin.
*   c. antidiuretic hormone.
       d. insulin.
       e. glucocorticoids.

D   21.   Positive feedback systems are characteristic of the
       a. male reproductive system and the pituitary gland.
       b. relative amounts of insulin and glucagon circulating in the bloodstream.
*   c. secretion of oxytocin and the onset and continuation of labor.
       d. release of antidiuretic hormone and the excretion of sodium by the kidney.
       e. decrease in insulin supply following a meal.

E   22.   The anterior pituitary secretions produce their effects in the
       a. gonads.
       b. thyroid glands.
       c. adrenal glands.
       d. mammary glands.
*   e. all of these

E   23.   ACTH (adrenocorticotropin)
       a. is secreted by the posterior pituitary.
       b. has target cells in the autonomic nervous system.
*   c. has target cells in the adrenal glands.
       d. has target cells in the adrenal medulla.
       e. initiates the autoimmune response.

M   24.   The luteinizing hormone
*   a. has roles in gamete formation and other reproductive aspects in both sexes.
       b. has no function in males.
       c. is produced by the corpus luteum.
       d. stimulates milk production.
       e. promotes sperm formation.

M   25.   The pituitary hormone associated with metabolic rate and with growth and development is
       a. ACTH.
       b. TSH.
       c. FSH.
       d. LH.
*   e. STH or GH.

M   26. The most general of the pituitary hormones, in that it
          has targets in most tissues, is
          a. the adrenocorticotropic hormone.
          b. the thyroid-stimulating hormone.
          c. gonadotropin.
     *   d. somatotropin.
          e. prolactin.

M   27. Prolactin
     *   a. stimulates the mammary glands to produce milk.
          b. affects only animals with mammary glands.
          c. causes the development of breasts and other
              secondary sexual characteristics in the male.
          d. acts in concert with FSH to produce milk.
          e. has secondary effects on reducing the size of the
              uterus after birth.

E   28. The growth hormone is also called
          a. prolactin.
          b. adrenalin.
          c. thyroxine.
          d. ACTH.
     *   e. somatotropin.

D   29. Which of the following hormones is different from the
          others based upon the extent of effects on target cells?
          a. corticotropin
          b. luteinizing hormone
     *   c. somatotropin
          d. thyrotropin
          e. follicle-stimulating hormone

E   30. Dwarfism may be due to insufficient production of
          a. mineralocorticoid.
          b. glucocorticoid.
          c. calcitonin.
     *   d. somatotropin or GH.
          e. the parathyroid hormone.

M   31. Acromegaly is the result of excessive secretion of
          which of the following by adults?
          a. mineralocorticoid
          b. glucocorticoid
          c. thyroxine
          d. testosterone
     *   e. somatotropin

THYMUS, THYROID, AND PARATHYROID GLANDS

M   32. The thymus gland has a direct influence on
          a. the pituitary gland.
     *   b. infection-fighting T cells.
          c. glucose metabolism.
          d. stress management.
          e. growth of bones.

E   33. A goiter is an enlarged form of which gland?
          a. adrenal
          b. pancreas
     *   c. thyroid
          d. parathyroid
          e. thymus

M   34. A goiter is caused by a deficiency in
          a. thyroxine.
          b. triiodothyronine.
          c. calcium.
     *   d. iodine.
          e. both thyroxine and triiodothyronine.

M   35. If you eliminated all sources of calcium (dairy
          products, some vegetables) from your diet, the level of
          which of the following would rise in an attempt to
          supply calcium stored in your body to the tissues that
          need it?
          a. aldosterone
          b. calcitonin
          c. mineralocorticoids
     *   d. parathyroid hormone
          e. all of these

M   36. Which of the following glands produces only one type
          of hormone?
          a. adrenal medulla
          b. adrenal cortex
          c. pancreas
     *   d. parathyroid
          e. pituitary

E   37. The normal human individual has how many
          parathyroid glands?
          a. 2
          b. 3
     *   c. 4
          d. 5
          e. 6

ADRENAL GLANDS AND STRESS RESPONSES

M   38. Cortisol and aldosterone
          a. are secreted by the adrenal cortex.
          b. influence carbohydrate, fat, and protein
              metabolism.
          c. function during infection and injury as part of the
              defense response.
          d. are steroid hormones.
     *   e. all of these

E   39. The adrenal medulla produces
          a. mineralocorticoids.
     *   b. epinephrine.
          c. cortisol.
          d. testosterone.
          e. glucocorticoids.

M   40. Cushing syndrome exhibits
          a. a fatty trunk.
          b. elevated levels of cortisol.
          c. a puffy, rounded, "moon face."
          d. abnormally high blood sugar and blood pressure.
     *   e. all of these

M 41. The hormone whose levels remain high when the body is suffering from inflammation and stress is
   * a. cortisol.
     b. somatotropin.
     c. thymosin.
     d. prolactin.
     e. parathyroid hormone.

D 42. The only endocrine gland whose secretory function is under direct control by sympathetic nerves is the
     a. pancreas.
     b. thyroid.
   * c. adrenal medulla.
     d. thymus.
     e. testis.

THE PANCREAS AND GLUCOSE HOMEOSTASIS

M 43. The actions of insulin and glucagon could be described as
     a. synergistic.
   * b. antagonistic.
     c. cooperative.
     d. permissive.
     e. mutualistic.

D 44. The pancreatic secretions governing glucose levels are precisely controlled by
     a. neural connections to the pancreas.
     b. the blood-brain barrier.
     c. cooperative interactions.
   * d. two hormones working antagonistically.
     e. releasing factors.

M 45. The hormone that is antagonistic in action to glucagon is
     a. norepinephrine.
   * b. insulin.
     c. thyroxine.
     d. epinephrine.
     e. mineralocorticoids.

M 46. Insulin directly affects the
     a. secretion of saliva.
     b. storage of proteins.
     c. secretion of pancreatic juices.
   * d. metabolism of sugar.
     e. utilization of fat reserves.

D 47. Which of the following does NOT affect blood sugar levels?
     a. glucagon
     b. epinephrine
   * c. parathyroid hormones
     d. glucocorticoids
     e. insulin

E 48. Glucagon is produced by the
     a. adrenal cortex.
     b. adrenal medulla.
     c. thyroid.
     d. kidneys.
   * e. pancreas.

M 49. Which gland is both an exocrine and endocrine gland?
   * a. pancreas
     b. adrenal
     c. ovary
     d. thyroid
     e. pituitary

E 50. Excess glucose is converted into glycogen in the
     a. pancreas.
   * b. liver.
     c. thymus.
     d. thyroid.
     e. none of these

E 51. Specialized islet cells that secrete hormones are found scattered throughout the
     a. adrenal cortex.
     b. liver.
     c. thymus.
     d. adrenal medulla.
   * e. pancreas.

D 52. If you skip a meal, which of the following conditions would prevail?
     a. Insulin levels would rise.
     b. Glucagon levels would rise.
     c. Glycogen would be converted to glucose.
     d. Insulin levels would rise and glycogen would be converted to glucose.
   * e. Glucagon levels would rise and glycogen would be converted to glucose.

D 53. Which of the following is true of "type 1 diabetes"?
     a. Insulin levels are near normal.
     b. Target cells do not respond to insulin.
     c. It is the more common form of diabetes.
   * d. It is thought to be an autoimmune disease.
     e. It usually occurs in middle-aged people.

D 54. Which of the following hormones is different from the others based upon its chemical structure?
   * a. glucagon
     b. cortisol
     c. estrogen
     d. testosterone
     e. mineralocorticoids

HORMONES AND REPRODUCTIVE BEHAVIOR

M 55. Which of the following is NOT true of the sex hormones?
     a. They are produced in the gonads.
   * b. They are protein hormones.
     c. Estrogen is an example.
     d. They influence gender and sex differences.
     e. They are derived from the steroid cholesterol.

M 56. Which of the following is TRUE of sex hormones at puberty?
   a. Estrogen production in males is higher than in females.
   b. Progesterone quantities fall.
   c. Removal of the ovaries causes progesterone levels to rise.
 * d. Testosterone production rises.
   e. Estrogen production in males causes penis development.

M 57. Which gland is associated with biological clocks or biorhythms?
 * a. pineal
   b. parathyroid
   c. hypothalamus
   d. pituitary
   e. thymus

E 58. Which gland is associated with seasonal affective disorder (SAD)?
 * a. pineal
   b. pituitary
   c. thyroid
   d. parathyroid
   e. thymus

M 59. The gland that functions in controlling the reproductive cycle is the
   a. thyroid.
 * b. pineal.
   c. thymus.
   d. pancreas.
   e. kidney.

Matching Questions

D 60. Matching. Choose the one most appropriate answer for each.
   1. ___ adrenal cortex
   2. ___ adrenal medulla
   3. ___ anterior lobe of pituitary
   4. ___ exocrine glands
   5. ___ insulin
   6. ___ gonad
   7. ___ hypothalamus
   8. ___ cAMP
   9. ___ steroid hormone
   10. ___ pancreatic islets
   11. ___ parathyroid gland
   12. ___ pineal gland
   13. ___ posterior lobe of pituitary
   14. ___ thymus gland
   15. ___ thyroid gland

   A. secretes thyroxine and triiodothyronine
   B. secrete insulin and glucagon
   C. secretes hormones that prepare accessory reproductive structures for reproduction
   D. involved in lymphocyte maturation and immune response
   E. secretes ACTH, TSH, FSH, growth hormone and prolactin
   F. secretes sex hormones, cortisol, and aldosterone
   G. a second messenger
   H. soluble in the lipids of the cell membrane
   I. participates in reproductive physiology and senses photoperiods
   J. secretes (releases into bloodstream) oxytocin and antidiuretic hormone
   K. secretes a hormone that promotes calcium release from bone storage sites
   L. produces oxytocin and antidiuretic hormone
   M. hormone that lowers blood glucose levels
   N. secretes epinephrine and norepinephrine
   O. secrete pheromones, milk, tears, sweat, and mucus

Answers:
1. F	2. N	3. E	4. O
5. M	6. C	7. L	8. G
9. H	10. B	11. K	12. I
13. J	14. D	15. A	

Classification Questions

Answer questions 61–65 in reference to the five endocrine glands listed below.

     a. pituitary
     b. adrenal
     c. pancreas
     d. thyroid
     e. pineal

M   **61.**   This gland is the target for corticotropin (ACTH).

E   **62.**   Melatonin is produced in this gland.

M   **63.**   Antidiuretic hormone is produced in this gland.

M   **64.**   This gland produces a hormone that regulates metabolism and has roles in growth and development.

E   **65.**   Insulin is produced in this gland.

Answers: 61. b   62. e   63. a

               64. d   65. c

Answer questions 66–70 in reference to the five pituitary hormones listed below.

     a. glucagon
     b. epinephrine
     c. somatotropin
     d. oxytocin
     e. antidiuretic hormone

M   **66.**   This hormone controls water retention and loss.

M   **67.**   The mammary glands are the target for this hormone.

D   **68.**   This hormone induces protein synthesis and cell division in young animals.

D   **69.**   The pancreas is the source of this hormone.

M   **70.**   Fight or flight is induced by this hormone.

Answers: 66. e   67. d   68. c

               69. a   70. b

Answer questions 71–75 in reference to the five endocrine glands listed below.

     a. adrenal cortex
     b. pituitary
     c. pineal
     d. parathyroid
     e. thymus

D   **71.**   This gland controls biological rhythms.

D   **72.**   This gland plays a central role in the immune response.

D   **73.**   This gland is divided into two lobes.

M   **74.**   Cortisone is produced by this gland.

M   **75.**   Calcium concentration in the blood is controlled by this gland.

Answers: 71. c   72. e   73. b

               74. a   75. d

Selecting the Exception

E   **76.**   Four of the five answers listed below are endocrine glands. Select the exception.
        a. thymus gland
   *   b. salivary gland
        c. parathyroid gland
        d. thyroid gland
        e. pituitary gland

D   **77.**   Four of the five answers listed below are produced by the same lobe of the pituitary. Select the exception.
   *   a. antidiuretic hormone
        b. prolactin
        c. corticotropin
        d. somatotropin
        e. luteinizing hormone

M   **78.**   Four of the five answers listed below affect blood glucose level. Select the exception.
   *   a. calcitonin
        b. glucagon
        c. glucocorticoid
        d. insulin
        e. epinephrine

D   **79.**   Four of the five answers listed below are related by the same action. Select the exception.
        a. activates vitamin D
        b. induces reabsorption of calcium by the kidney
        c. removes calcium and phosphate from bones
   *   d. regulates blood volume
        e. involved in the biofeedback control of extracellular calcium

Labeling

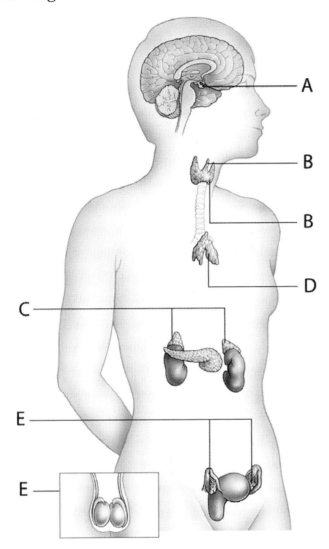

E   **80.**   The organs at letter _?_ produce hormones and gametes.

E   **81.**   Cortisol steroids are produced at letter _?_.

E   **82.**   This gland is sometimes called the "master gland" because of the wide variety of hormones it produces.

E   **83.**   The gland at letter _?_ has close ties to the immune system.

E   **84.**   The glands at letter _?_ have powerful influences on metabolism and calcium levels in the body.

Answers: 80. E   81. C   82. A

            83. D   84. B

CHAPTER 27
REPRODUCTION AND DEVELOPMENT

Multiple-Choice Questions

METHODS OF REPRODUCTION

M 1. Which of the following is NOT true of asexual reproduction?
   a. It is more suitable for reproduction in animals in stable environments.
   b. It results in offspring that are identical to each other.
 * c. It promotes genetic variation in each successive generation.
   d. Budding is one type of asexual reproduction.
   e. The offspring are genetically identical to the parents.

M 2. Which of the following statements is NOT an advantage of asexual reproduction?
   a. Asexual reproduction is more efficient than sexual reproduction.
   b. An individual organism can reproduce asexually by itself.
 * c. Asexual reproduction promotes variation.
   d. Asexual reproduction produces fewer offspring than sexual reproduction.
   e. Asexual reproduction does not require the searching for a reproductive partner.

D 3. Which of the following is NOT one of the factors contributing to the high cost of sexual reproduction?
   a. specialized reproductive structures such as the male penis
   b. production of excessive numbers of gametes
   c. development of elaborate courtship rituals
 * d. production of the cytoplasm for millions of reproductive buds
   e. nourishment of offspring

D 4. Which of the following animals would fit this description: "Eggs fertilized outside the body, minimum of yolk, rapid development."
   a. bird
 * b. sea urchin
   c. bony fish
   d. reptile
   e. human

PROCESSES OF ANIMAL DEVELOPMENT

M 5. Gastrulation, produces
   a. hollow balls of cells.
 * b. embryos with germ layers.
   c. solid balls of cells.
   d. maternal messages.
   e. all of these

E 6. The heart, muscles, bones, and blood develop primarily from
   a. ectoderm.
 * b. mesoderm.
   c. endoderm.
   d. the placenta.
   e. the gray crescent.

M 7. Which embryonic tissue is incorrectly associated with its derivative?
 * a. skin from mesoderm
   b. nervous system from ectoderm
   c. liver from endoderm
   d. circulatory system from mesoderm
   e. muscles from mesoderm

E 8. Muscles differentiate from which tissue?
   a. ectoderm
   b. endoderm
 * c. mesoderm
   d. plasmoderm
   e. all of these

M 9. The mesoderm is responsible for the formation of all EXCEPT which of the following adult tissues?
   a. reproductive system
   b. circulatory system
 * c. nervous system
   d. muscle system
   e. excretory system

M 10. If an experimenter interferes with the mesoderm in an egg, which of the following systems would NOT be affected by the experimenter?
   a. circulatory system
   b. muscular system
   c. reproductive system
 * d. integumentary (skin) system
   e. excretory system

D 11. Select the correct sequence of animal developmental events.
   a. fertilization >>> cleavage >>> gastrula >>> blastula
 * b. fertilization >>> cleavage >>> blastula >>> gastrula
   c. fertilization >>> blastula >>> cleavage >>> gastrula
   d. fertilization >>> gastrula >>> blastula >>> cleavage
   e. none of these is correct

E 12. In the following list of developmental events, which occurs last?
* a. growth and tissue specialization
b. gamete formation
c. gastrulation
d. cleavage
e. organ formation

D 13. In the human, which of the following events would occur over the longest period of time?
a. sperm production
b. cleavage
c. fertilization
d. gastrulation
* e. growth and tissue specialization

M 14. Maternal control elements in the oocyte's cytoplasm consist largely of
a. DNA.
* b. enzymes and mRNA transcripts.
c. HeLa cells.
d. puffs.
e. all of these

D 15. Although the genetic contributions of egg and sperm nuclei are equal, the egg contributes more than the sperm to cell differentiation because of its
a. larger size.
b. cytoplasmic determinants.
c. proteins.
d. cytoplasmic determinants and proteins, only.
* e. cytoplasmic determinants, proteins, and larger size.

D 16. Which of the following affects the developmental pathways that different embryonic cells eventually will follow?
a. sperm nucleus
b. egg nucleus
c. sperm cytoplasm
* d. egg cytoplasm
e. none of these

E 17. Which stage in development occurs first?
a. cleavage
b. morula
c. gastrula
* d. zygote
e. blastula

E 18. Which of the following is a single-layered, hollow ball of cells?
a. cleavage
b. morula
c. gastrula
d. zygote
* e. blastula

E 19. The process of cleavage most commonly produces a
a. zygote.
* b. blastula.
c. gastrula.
d. puff.
e. third germ layer.

E 20. Shortly after fertilization, successive cell divisions convert the zygote into a multicellular embryo during a process known as
a. meiosis.
b. parthenogenesis.
c. embryonic induction.
* d. cleavage.
e. invagination.

E 21. Which of the following structures is a hollow ball composed of a single layer of cells?
a. zygote
b. morula
c. gastrula
* d. blastula
e. yolk sac

D 22. In the process of blastula formation,
a. the size of individual cells decreases.
b. the number of cells increases.
c. the total amount of cytoplasm remains about the same.
d. the size of individual cells decreases and the number of cells increases.
* e. the size of individual cells decreases, the number of cells increases, but the total amount of cytoplasm remains about the same.

E 23. Which of the following is the space inside the blastula?
a. blastocyst
b. blastofurrow
c. blastocell
* d. blastocoel
e. blastodisk

E 24. The germ layers are formed in which of the following stages?
a. cleavage
b. morula
* c. gastrula
d. zygote
e. blastula

D 25. Which of the following events is NOT included in what embryologists refer to as gastrulation?
a. cell rearrangements
b. formation of the archenteron
* c. organ formation
d. formation of germ layers
e. establishment of the body axis

M 26. During which of the following stages do cell lineages of identical genetic makeup become structurally and functionally different from one another according to the genetically controlled developmental program of the species?
a. cleavage
* b. differentiation
c. morphogenesis
d. metamorphosis
e. ovulation

M 27. In the process of differentiation,
   a. some daughter cells usually receive varying assortments of genes.
 * b. cells with identical assortments of genes come to have different individual genes expressed.
   c. cells become specialized as a result of meiosis.
   d. daughter cells acquire different characteristics as a result of mutations that have occurred.
   e. all of these

D 28. The explanation for the differences between a cell from the human liver and a cell from the skin is the
   a. maternal and paternal origins of the cell types.
   b. gene content of the two cells.
 * c. expression of the genes in the two cells.
   d. fact that they are in different parts of the body.
   e. fact that they contain different genes.

M 29. Cells migrate during morphogenesis in response to
   a. chemical gradients.
   b. recognition proteins.
   c. adhesive cues.
   d. chemical gradients and recognition proteins.
 * e. gene products from cells in different tissues, signaling molecules, and adhesive proteins.

D 30. Formation of the human hand involves
   a. morphogenesis.
   b. apoptosis.
   c. embryonic induction.
   d. pattern formation.
 * e. all of these

M 31. The differentiation of a body part in response to signals from an adjacent body part is
   a. contact inhibition.
   b. ooplasmic localization.
 * c. embryonic induction.
   d. pattern formation.
   e. all of these

M 32. The mechanism of embryonic induction involves
 * a. gene products from other cells in different tissues.
   b. electrical signals.
   c. touch.
   d. chemicals and touch.
   e. electrical signals and touch.

M 33. The process in which the fate of a group of cells is controlled by substances produced by other embryonic cells is known as
 * a. embryonic induction.
   b. cytoplasmic localization.
   c. cellular differentiation.
   d. morphogenesis.
   e. formation of the gray crescent.

M 34. Products of homeotic genes
   a. cause lethal mutations.
 * b. control blocks of genes necessary for the basic body plan.
   c. are found only in fruit flies where they are responsible for odd placement of appendages.
   d. are also known as "fate maps."
   e. operate only in individuals with two genes of the same kind.

M 35. Signaling molecules responsible for embryonic induction are called
   a. crystallins.
 * b. morphogens.
   c. mutagens.
   d. inducagens.
   e. homeoboxes.

REPRODUCTIVE SYSTEM OF HUMAN MALES

M 36. The major difference between the male and female reproductive systems is the
 * a. provision of a site for fertilization and development in the female.
   b. production of haploid gametes by the male only.
   c. diploid polar bodies of the female.
   d. generation of millions of eggs but only thousands of sperm each month.
   e. number of gamete-producing organs.

E 37. In the human male, several hundred million sperm are produced in the
   a. interstitial cells.
   b. prostate.
 * c. seminiferous tubules of the testes.
   d. vas deferens.
   e. epididymis.

E 38. Sperm are produced in the
 * a. testes.
   b. vas deferens.
   c. epididymis.
   d. prostate gland.
   e. penis.

M 39. Seminal fluid is produced by the
   a. prostate gland.
   b. seminal vesicle.
   c. bulbourethral gland.
   d. urinary bladder.
 * e. all except "urinary bladder"

D 40. The seminal vesicles ("sperm vessels") are misnamed. Sperm are actually stored in the
   a. vas deferens.
 * b. epididymis.
   c. prostate.
   d. scrotum.
   e. urethra.

D 41. Which of the following is the site where sperm are stored?
   a. ureter
   b. urethra
   c. vas deferens
   d. vas efferens
 * e. epididymis

M 42. Which of the following is the last structure that a sperm travels through as it leaves the body?
   a. ureter
 * b. urethra
   c. vas deferens
   d. vas efferens
   e. epididymis

M 43. Which of the following is part of the urinary system, not the reproductive system?
 * a. ureter
   b. urethra
   c. vas deferens
   d. vas efferens
   e. epididymis

M 44. Which of the following cells are diploid?
   a. spermatids
   b. primary spermatocytes
   c. secondary spermatocytes
   d. spermatogonia
 * e. both primary spermatocytes and spermatogonia

M 45. Which cells are produced during meiosis I?
   a. spermatogonia
   b. primary spermatocytes
 * c. secondary spermatocytes
   d. spermatids
   e. sperm

D 46. Leydig cells in the testes produce
   a. semen.
   b. LH.
 * c. testosterone.
   d. FSH.
   e. GnRH.

D 47. All EXCEPT which of the following are the products of meiosis?
   a. male gametes
   b. spermatids
   c. sperm
   d. secondary spermatocytes
 * e. spermatogonia

M 48. Meiosis I results directly in the production of
   a. spermatids.
   b. spermatogonial cells.
   c. primary spermatocytes.
 * d. secondary spermatocytes.
   e. sperm.

M 49. Sertoli cells
   a. start sperm production.
   b. provide a "cap" for each sperm.
   c. secrete testosterone.
 * d. support and nourish maturing sperm.
   e. become primary spermatocytes.

D 50. The release of testosterone requires
   a. luteinizing hormone.
   b. GnRH.
   c. Sertoli cells.
 * d. luteinizing hormone and GnRH.
   e. luteinizing hormone, GnRH, and Sertoli cells.

D 51. Which of the following structures is NOT found as part of a mature sperm?
   a. DNA molecules
   b. cap with enzymes
   c. mitochondria
   d. whiplike tail
 * e. ribosomes

REPRODUCTIVE SYSTEM OF HUMAN FEMALES

E 52. The female reproductive system includes all EXCEPT which of the following?
   a. clitoris
   b. vagina
   c. oviduct
   d. ovary
 * e. mammary gland

E 53. The primary reproductive organ in the human female is the
   a. uterus.
 * b. ovary.
   c. vagina.
   d. clitoris.
   e. vulva.

M 54. The passageway that channels ova from the ovary into the uterus is known as
   a. a vagina.
   b. a uterus.
 * c. an oviduct.
   d. an endometrium.
   e. all of these

M 55. The _?_ is one of a pair of ciliated channels through which oocytes are conducted.
   a. ovary
   b. uterus
   c. vagina
 * d. oviduct
   e. follicle

M 56. Which of the following statements is FALSE?
    a. A female has more oocytes before she is born than at any time during her life.
    b. Meiosis II will not occur in an oocyte unless it is fertilized.
*   c. Fertilization occurs in the vagina.
    d. Implantation occurs in the uterus.
    e. The vagina serves as the birth canal.

E 57. The cervix is part of the
    a. vulva.
    b. ovary.
*   c. uterus.
    d. oviduct.
    e. vagina.

D 58. Which of the following is NOT *required* in the reproductive process?
    a. ovary
    b. oviduct
*   c. clitoris
    d. vagina
    e. uterus

E 59. The cessation of regular menstrual cycles due to age is called
*   a. menopause.
    b. the luteal phase.
    c. oogenesis.
    d. coitus.
    e. parturition.

M 60. Which of the following is FALSE?
    a. Menstrual cycles are controlled by hormones.
    b. All primates have a menstrual cycle.
    c. All female primates can be physically and behaviorally receptive to sexual activity at any time.
    d. Eggs released by older women have a greater chance of producing a Down syndrome child.
*   e. The human menstrual cycle lasts about 14 days.

D 61. Which of the following is NOT an active participant in human reproduction?
*   a. polar bodies
    b. oocytes
    c. sperm
    d. endometrium
    e. FSH

M 62. Which of the following statements is NOT true of the human female?
    a. She produces all the eggs that she ever will before she is born.
    b. The process of meiosis may take 30 to 50 years to complete.
    c. The primary oocytes lay dormant until puberty.
*   d. She will normally produce more gametes than her male counterpart.
    e. It is possible that more than one egg will be released at ovulation.

M 63. FSH and LH are secreted by the
    a. hypothalamus.
    b. ovaries.
*   c. anterior pituitary.
    d. testes.
    e. uterus.

M 64. Ovulation is triggered by
*   a. high levels of LH.
    b. low levels of LH.
    c. high levels of chorionic gonadotropin.
    d. high levels of estrogen.
    e. high levels of progesterone.

E 65. Menstrual flow results in the discharge of
    a. the follicle.
    b. the corpus luteum.
*   c. the lining of the uterus.
    d. surface cells from the vagina.
    e. blood from the blood vessels on the outer surface of the uterus.

M 66. Ovulation is triggered primarily by
*   a. a surge of LH that occurs halfway through the menstrual cycle.
    b. the falling levels of estrogen and progesterone.
    c. the rising levels of progesterone.
    d. both a surge of LH that occurs halfway through the menstrual cycle and the rising levels of progesterone.
    e. adrenalin.

M 67. Ovulation involves the
    a. production of the first polar body.
*   b. release of a secondary oocyte.
    c. beginning of the follicular phase of the menstrual cycle.
    d. suspension of the meiotic process.
    e. deterioration of the corpus luteum.

M 68. Ovulation is triggered by a surge in the level of _?_ in the circulatory system.
    a. estrogen
    b. follicle-stimulating hormone
*   c. luteinizing hormone
    d. progesterone
    e. human chorionic gonadotropin

M 69. Destruction of the corpus luteum, if pregnancy does NOT occur, results from the action of
    a. chorionic gonadotropin.
    b. luteinizing hormone.
    c. progesterone.
*   d. prostaglandins.
    e. estrogen.

E 70. Breaking down of the endometrium begins in response to
    a. rising levels of FSH and LH.
    b. falling levels of estrogen.
    c. falling levels of progesterone.
*   d. falling levels of estrogen and progesterone.
    e. falling levels of FSH and LH.

D   71. Which of the following serves to end each menstrual
          cycle?
          a. a surge in luteinizing hormone
          b. the secretion of human chorionic gonadotropin
     *   c. the secretion of prostaglandins by the corpus
              luteum that lead to its self-destruction
          d. a rise in the level of progesterone
          e. a drop in the level of gonadotropic hormones in
              the blood

D   72. Using your knowledge of the feedback loops of human
          female hormones, which of the following would you
          predict is the result of high levels of estrogen and
          progesterone in the blood?
          a. lack of growth of the corpus luteum
     *   b. absence of monthly ovulation
          c. increased secretion of FSH
          d. increased levels of LH
          e. all of these

D   73. The menstrual flow is the result of
          a. no implantation of a zygote.
          b. decreased levels of progesterone.
          c. discarded uterine linings.
          d. no implantation of a zygote and discarded uterine
              linings.
     *   e. no implantation of a blastocyst, discarded uterine
              linings, and decreased levels of progesterone.

HOW PREGNANCY HAPPENS

M   74. Orgasm is necessary for
     *   a. ejaculation of semen.
          b. pregnancy.
          c. erection.
          d. sexual arousal.
          e. all of these

E   75. Fertilization in mammals occurs in the
          a. ovary.
          b. uterus.
          c. vagina.
     *   d. oviduct.
          e. follicle.

E   76. The average number of sperm that enter the vagina
          during an ejaculation is between
          a. 150,000 and 350,000.
          b. 1.5 and 3.5 million.
          c. 15 and 35 million.
     *   d. 150 and 350 million.
          e. 1.5 and 3.5 billion.

D   77. If the vas deferens tubes are cut and tied (vasectomy),
          the semen will not contain
          a. fructose.
          b. buffers.
          c. mucus.
     *   d. sperm.
          e. any of these

D   78. Which of the following is the most effective
          contraceptive approach *of those listed*?
          a. withdrawal
     *   b. diaphragm
          c. condoms alone
          d. douching
          e. rhythm method

E   79. The type of contraception that functions by preventing
          implantation (even after successful fertilization) is
          a. tubal ligation.
          b. spermicidal jelly.
          c. birth control pills.
     *   d. morning after pills.
          e. diaphragm.

E   80. The type of contraception that works because
          ovulation is prevented is
          a. rhythm.
          b. tubal ligation.
     *   c. birth control pills.
          d. diaphragm.
          e. condom.

M   81. Which of the following is NOT a temporary method of
          contraception?
          a. birth control pills
     *   b. vasectomy
          c. condoms
          d. IUD plus spermicide
          e. spermicidal jelly or foam

E   82. *Of the following*, which is the least successful method
          of birth control?
          a. early withdrawal
          b. a condom alone
          c. a spermicidal jelly or foam alone
     *   d. douching
          e. the Pill

M   83. A contraceptive pill contains
          a. estrogen.
          b. progesterone.
          c. the follicle-stimulating hormone.
          d. the luteinizing hormone.
     *   e. both estrogen and progesterone-like hormones.

SEXUALLY TRANSMITTED DISEASES

M   84. Which of the following is NOT true of STDs?
          a. can cause PID
          b. some are viral
     *   c. can be cured
          d. number of cases increasing
          e. can be passed to newborn

M   85. This viral STD is similar to cold sores in its
          manifestation.
     *   a. genital herpes
          b. HPV
          c. chlamydia
          d. gonorrhea
          e. AIDS

M 86. This STD initially forms a painless chancre (sore) but later can cause mental deterioration.
    a. gonorrhea
    b. AIDS
    c. trichomoniasis
  * d. syphilis
    e. HPV

M 87. This STD is also commonly spread by infected blood.
    a. syphilis
  * b. AIDS
    c. chlamydia
    d. herpes
    e. warts

HUMAN PRENATAL DEVELOPMENT

E 88. The embryo is recognizable as human and is called a fetus by which week of pregnancy?
  * a. eighth
    b. twelfth
    c. sixteenth
    d. twentieth
    e. twenty-fourth

M 89. During a human pregnancy, implantation occurs at which stage?
    a. zygote
    b. early cleavage
  * c. blastocyst
    d. gastrula
    e. morula

E 90. Implantation occurs in the
    a. ovary.
  * b. uterus.
    c. vagina.
    d. oviduct.
    e. follicle.

E 91. During human development, which of the following gives rise to the embryo?
    a. trophoblast
    b. amnion
  * c. embryonic disk
    d. chorion
    e. placenta

M 92. The first several cleavages after fertilization occur in the
    a. uterus.
    b. ovary.
    c. vagina.
  * d. oviduct.
    e. either a or b above

M 93. Which of the following statements is FALSE?
    a. Ovulation occurs when the follicle ruptures and releases an oocyte.
    b. Cleavage occurs when the zygote divides.
    c. Fertilization occurs in the upper regions of the oviduct.
    d. The blastocyst implants in the endometrial lining of the uterus.
  * e. Implantation occurs about 36 hours after fertilization.

M 94. The presence of which hormone in a mother's urine indicates that she is pregnant?
    a. luteinizing hormone
    b. follicle-stimulating hormone
  * c. human chorionic gonadotropin
    d. progesterone
    e. estrogen

M 95. Which of the following hormones is produced only when a woman is pregnant?
    a. testosterone
    b. gonadotropic-releasing hormone
  * c. human chorionic gonadotropin
    d. estrogen
    e. progesterone

M 96. The fact that a blastocyst has been implanted on the uterine wall can be demonstrated by the presence of
  * a. human chorionic gonadotropin.
    b. progesterone.
    c. estrogen.
    d. testosterone.
    e. a second polar body.

M 97. Which of the following membranes is associated with waste storage?
    a. amnion
    b. yolk sac
    c. chorion
  * d. allantois
    e. none of these

M 98. Which of the following membranes is associated with the formation of the placenta?
    a. amnion
    b. yolk sac
  * c. chorion
    d. allantois
    e. none of these

M 99. In humans, the fluid immediately surrounding the embryo is contained in the
    a. allantois.
    b. placenta.
    c. chorion.
  * d. amnion.
    e. yolk sac.

M   100.   The membrane that contacts the endometrium is the
          a. amnion.
          b. allantois.
     *   c. chorion.
          d. yolk sac.
          e. umbilical cord.

M   101.   Which of the following systems is the first of those listed to begin development in the human embryo?
     *   a. nervous system
          b. excretory system
          c. reproductive system
          d. skeletal system
          e. endocrine system

D   102.   Which of the following does NOT occur in the first trimester?
          a. formation of a heart
          b. disappearance of the tail
          c. formation of internal organs
     *   d. detection of movement of the fetus
          e. segmentation and development of somites

E   103.   In humans, the embryonic development of a four-chambered heart and the nerve cord is present by which week?
          a. third
     *   b. fourth
          c. fifth
          d. sixth
          e. seventh

E   104.   Which drug, if taken during pregnancy, results in the production of infants without arms or legs?
          a. tetracycline
     *   b. thalidomide
          c. streptomycin
          d. salicylic acid
          e. codeine

M   105.   Which disease may produce a malformed embryo if the mother develops the disease early in pregnancy?
     *   a. German measles (rubella)
          b. chicken pox
          c. red measles
          d. hepatitis
          e. mumps

FROM BIRTH ONWARD

M   106.   The female hormones that participate in milk production for the newborn are
     *   a. prolactin and oxytocin.
          b. prolactin and estrogen.
          c. prolactin and progesterone.
          d. oxytocin and estrogen.
          e. oxytocin and progesterone.

M   107.   _?_ stimulates the growth of cells that will produce milk proteins.
          a. estrogen.
     *   b. prolactin.
          c. oxytocin.
          d. prostaglandin.
          e. progesterone.

E   108.   Postnatal growth is most rapid in a human child
          a. during the first two weeks.
          b. from two weeks to fifteen months.
          c. from infancy to ten years.
     *   d. from ages thirteen to nineteen.
          e. during adulthood.

D   109.   Which of the following is NOT currently a possible explanation of the process of aging?
          a. limited number of mitosis cycles
          b. autoimmune attack
     *   c. increased mutation rate
          d. mistakes by DNA repair mechanisms
          e. limited division potential

M   110.   The programmed life span hypothesis of aging takes note of
          a. telomere mutation.
     *   b. telomere deletions.
          c. nothing concerning telomeres.
          d. telomere additions.
          e. DNA deterioration.

M   111.   Aging caused by accumulation of damage at the molecular and cellular levels includes
          a. DNA structural changes.
          b. DNA repair problems.
          c. telomeres.
          d. free radicals.
     *   e. all except "telomeres"

Matching Questions

D 112. Matching I. Choose the one best answer for each numbered item.

1. ___ parthenogenesis
2. ___ cleavage
3. ___ differentiation
4. ___ embryonic induction
5. ___ fertilization
6. ___ gastrula
7. ___ gastrulation
8. ___ morphogenesis
9. ___ ectoderm
10. ___ asexual

   A. the formation of two or three embryonic tissue layers
   B. the union of male and female gametes
   C. selective gene expression results in different cell types
   D. subdividing of the zygote by mitosis; no growth occurs
   E. development of offspring from unfertilized egg
   F. an embryonic stage of development that has three embryonic tissue layers
   G. source of the nervous system and outer body coverings
   H. one body part develops in response to signals from an adjacent part
   I. development of tissues and organs in a programmed, orderly sequence
   J. reproduction produces identical offspring

Answers: 1. E   2. D   3. C   4. H
          5. B   6. F   7. A   8. I
          9. G   10. J

D 113. Matching II. Choose the one most appropriate answer for each.

1. ___ abortion
2. ___ abstention
3. ___ coitus
4. ___ douching
5. ___ ejaculation
6. ___ implantation
7. ___ lactation
8. ___ menopause
9. ___ menstruation
10. ___ miscarriage
11. ___ orgasm
12. ___ ovulation
13. ___ tubal ligation
14. ___ vasectomy

   A. the production and secretion of milk
   B. twilight of a female's reproductive capacity
   C. birth control exercised after development begins
   D. an abortion that occurs spontaneously
   E. the burrowing of the blastocyst into the uterus
   F. the release of an egg from the ovary
   G. the release of semen from the male reproductive tract
   H. a 100-percent-effective method of preventing conception
   I. a highly ineffective form of birth control
   J. the periodic elimination of the uterine lining
   K. characterized by involuntary muscle contractions, release of tension, and warmth
   L. sexual intercourse
   M. the oviduct is blocked or cut
   N. cutting or blocking each vas deferens

Answers: 1. C   2. H   3. L   4. I
          5. G   6. E   7. A   8. B
          9. J   10. D   11. K   12. F
          13. M   14. N

D 114. Matching III. Choose the one most appropriate answer for each.

1. ___ penis
2. ___ allantois
3. ___ blastocyst
4. ___ cervix
5. ___ clitoris
6. ___ endometrium
7. ___ epididymis
8. ___ FSH
9. ___ Leydig cells
10. ___ LH
11. ___ placenta
12. ___ coitus
13. ___ seminal vesicles
14. ___ thalidomide
15. ___ vas deferens

A. in females, a midcycle surge acts on a ruptured follicle to produce corpus luteum

B. structures that secrete mucus and nutrients absorbable by sperm; open into the ejaculatory duct

C. forms an outpouching of the yolk sac; becomes part of the placenta

D. a drug that causes severely deformed arms and legs in developing embryos

E. two of these connect seminiferous tubules with vas deferens

F. opening between uterus and vagina

G. organ that supplies the embryo/fetus with nutrients and removes wastes

H. connects epididymis with ejaculatory duct

I. another name for sexual intercourse

J. male organ for sperm delivery

K. attaches to uterine wall

L. testosterone produced by these

M. develops from the same embryonic tissues as does the penis in males; has many sensory receptors

N. the uterine lining

O. begins sperm production at puberty

Answers:
1. J   2. C   3. K   4. F
5. M   6. N   7. E   8. O
9. L   10. A   11. G   12. I
13. B   14. D   15. H

Classification Questions

Answer questions 115–119 in reference to the five stages of development listed below.

a. zygote
b. blastula
c. morula
d. gastrula
e. embryo

M 115. This stage appears as a multicellular, hollow ball.

E 116. This is the fertilized egg.

D 117. This stage might contain only 16 cells.

D 118. The gut cavity of an animal forms during this stage.

D 119. The major germ layers are formed during this stage.

Answers: 115. b   116. a   117. c
118. d   119. d

Answer questions 120–124 in reference to the five stages of sperm development listed below.

a. spermatogonium
b. secondary spermatocyte
c. primary spermatocyte
d. spermatid
e. sperm

D 120. At this stage of development, the male sex cell is first in the haploid condition.

M 121. This continues to undergo mitosis throughout the reproductive life of the male.

D 122. This represents the product of the first meiotic division.

D 123. This is a mitotic product that then undergoes meiosis.

M 124. At this stage of development, the male sex cell is fully motile.

Answers: 120. b   121. a   122. b
123. c   124. e

Selecting the Exception

M 125. Four of the five answers listed below are events occurring after fertilization. Select the exception.
    a. cleavage
* b. gamete formation
    c. blastula
    d. gastrulation
    e. organogenesis

E 126. Four of the five answers listed below possess large amounts of yolk. Select the exception.
*   a. human egg
     b. snake egg
     c. bird egg
     d. turtle egg
     e. fish egg

M 127. Four of the five answers listed below are produced by the same germ layer. Select the exception.
*   a. nervous system
     b. muscle system
     c. circulatory system
     d. reproductive system
     e. excretory system

M 128. Three of the four answers listed below produce portions of the semen. Select the exception.
*   a. epididymis
     b. prostate
     c. seminal vesicle
     d. bulbourethral gland

M 129. Three of the four answers listed below are related by the number of chromosomes present. Select the exception.
     a. sperm
*   b. spermatogonia
     c. secondary spermatocyte
     d. spermatids

E 130. Three of the four answers listed below are all parts of a sperm. Select the exception.
     a. flagella
     b. midpiece
     c. acrosome
*   d. polar body

D 131. Four of the five answers listed below are related by a common quality. Select the exception.
*   a. urethra
     b. testis
     c. ejaculatory duct
     d. vas deferens
     e. epididymis

D 132. Four of the five answers listed below are true of testosterone. Select the exception.
     a. promotes secondary sex characteristics
     b. controls sexual behavior
     c. necessary for growth and function of male reproductive tract
     d. stimulates spermatogenesis
*   e. produced by spermatogonia cells

E 133. Four of the five answers listed below are related by gender. Select the exception.
*   a. Sertoli cells
     b. cervix
     c. clitoris
     d. myometrium
     e. vulva

M 134. Four of the five answers listed below are related by a common location. Select the exception.
     a. follicle
     b. corpus luteum
*   c. cervix
     d. oogonium
     e. oocyte

D 135. Four of the five answers listed below are related by a matching feature. Select the exception.
*   a. blastocyst
     b. amnion
     c. allantois
     d. yolk sac
     e. chorion

M 136. Four of the five answers listed below are related by a common theme. Select the exception.
     a. alcohol
     b. thalidomide
     c. German measles
*   d. vitamins
     e. antibiotics

M 137. Four of the five answers listed below are related by a similar effectiveness. Select the exception.
     a. the Pill
     b. tubal ligation
     c. vasectomy
*   d. douching
     e. IUD

Labeling

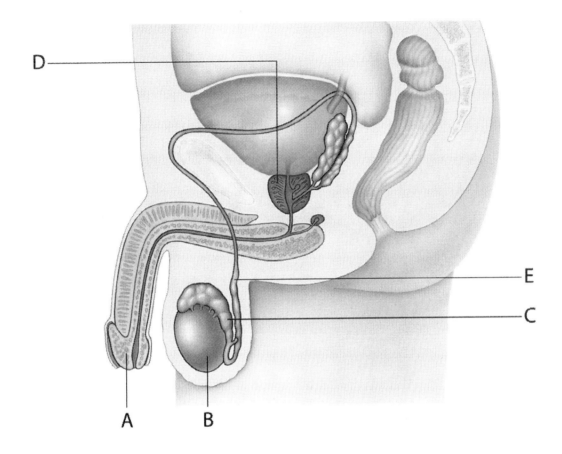

E   **138.**   Sperm are stored to allow for maturation in the structure at letter _?_.

E   **139.**   The organ at letter _?_ is the male counterpart to the female ovary.

E   **140.**   The organ at letter _?_ can become troublesome and cancerous in older men, causing restricted urine flow.

Answers: 138. C   139. B   140. D

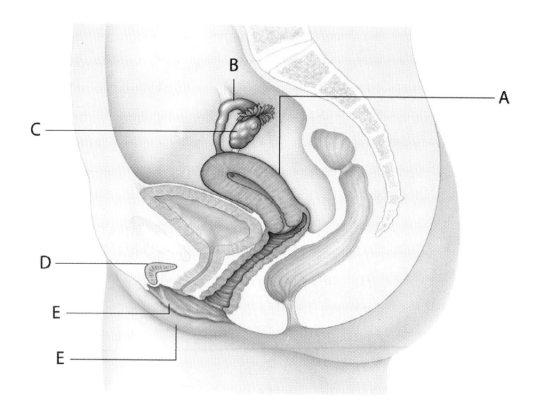

E   **141.**   The organ at letter _?_ is lined with endometrium.

E   **142.**   The organ that produces eggs and hormones is at letter _?_.

E   **143.**   What letter indicates female tissue that is homologous to tissue at the head of the male penis?

Answers: 141. A   142. C   143. D

CHAPTER 28
POPULATION ECOLOGY

Multiple-Choice Questions

CHARACTERISTICS OF POPULATIONS

E 1. The number of individuals that make up a population's gene pool is the
    a. population distribution.
    b. population growth.
    c. population birth rate.
*   d. population size.
    e. carrying capacity.

M 2. The number of individuals of the same species in some specified area or volume of habitat is the
*   a. population density.
    b. population growth.
    c. population birth rate.
    d. population size.
    e. carrying capacity.

M 3. To a person studying utilization of classroom space on campus, the most useful data concerning students in a classroom would be expressed by the number of
    a. total individuals.
*   b. individuals per square yard.
    c. individuals per room.
    d. rooms per building.
    e. students of each age.

D 4. Which of the following is NOT one of the factors that control the dispersion of organisms in nature?
*   a. Most environmental resources are randomly distributed.
    b. Biological conditions tend to be patchy.
    c. Dispersal of seeds and young organisms is often limited or controlled by environmental factors.
    d. The development of societies in some populations controls distribution.
    e. Physical features in the environment are not generally uniform.

D 5. Which of the following would provide a chicken rancher using a noncaged arrangement for his flock the data necessary to ensure maximum survival of his hens?
*   a. distribution
    b. number of individuals
    c. individuals per square foot
    d. size of room
    e. age structure

M 6. The distribution of the human population in the United States is
*   a. clumped.
    b. random.
    c. uniform.
    d. constant.
    e. undetermined.

M 7. What distribution pattern is the most common in the natural world?
    a. random
    b. uniform
*   c. clumped
    d. stratified or layered
    e. bimodal

M 8. Uniform distribution of human habitats would likely be the result of _?_ whereas habitats of other animals would be due to _?_.
    a. competition; social interaction
*   b. community planning; competition
    c. social interaction; chemical avoidance
    d. limited mobility; contact inhibition
    e. random chance; planning

POPULATION SIZE AND EXPONENTIAL GROWTH

M 9. Population size depends upon
    a. deaths.
    b. births.
    c. migration.
    d. immigration.
*   e. all of these

M 10. The size of a population is controlled by all EXCEPT which of the following?
    a. biotic potential
*   b. feeding level
    c. carrying capacity of the environment
    d. death rate
    e. birth rate

D 11. A population
    a. is the unit of evolution.
    b. consists of interbreeding members of the same species.
    c. shares the same gene pool.
    d. grows at an exponential rate when the birth rate exceeds the death rate at a constant differential, no matter how slight the difference.
*   e. all of these

M 12. Zero population growth is achieved when
  a. a population reaches the carrying capacity of the environment.
  * b. an interval during which the number of births and the number of deaths are balanced.
  c. births exceed deaths.
  d. deaths exceed births.
  e. migration is prevented.

D 13. If the effects of death are imposed on the birth rate of a population,
  a. the growth rate will slow down.
  b. the time scale of population growth changes.
  c. eventually—as the environment is overexploited—deaths will exceed births.
  d. an exponential growth curve will be produced if births exceed deaths at a constant level.
  * e. all of these

D 14. The biotic potential
  a. varies from one species to another.
  b. is controlled by the timing of the first reproduction.
  c. is controlled by the frequency of reproduction.
  d. is controlled by the number of offspring produced.
  * e. all of these

D 15. A situation in which the birth rate plus immigration equals the death rate plus emigration is called
  a. an intrinsic limiting factor.
  b. exponential growth.
  c. saturation.
  * d. zero population growth.
  e. geometric growth.

D 16. The rate of increase for a population (r) refers to what kind of relationship between birth rate and death rate?
  a. their sum
  b. their product
  c. the doubling time between them
  * d. the difference between them
  e. reduction in each of them

M 17. Which characteristic of a population is a convenient way to express the rate of change within a population?
  a. size
  * b. growth
  c. density
  d. carrying capacity
  e. age

M 18. A population that is growing exponentially in the absence of limiting factors can be illustrated by which curve?
  a. S-shaped
  * b. J-shaped
  c. one that terminates in a plateau phase
  d. bimodal
  e. binomial

M 19. Which concept is a way to express the growth rate of a given population?
  * a. doubling time
  b. population density
  c. population size
  d. carrying capacity
  e. all of these

D 20. A population of 1,000 individuals with an $r = 1$ in an unlimited environment will number _?_ four years later.
  a. 1,000
  b. 1,004
  c. 4,000
  * d. 16,000
  e. 160,000

D 21. If K for a population is 1,200 and $r = 0.1$, which of the following populations will show the greatest increase over the course of one year?
  a. $N = 100$
  b. $N = 200$
  c. $N = 300$
  * d. $N = 700$
  e. $N = 900$

D 22. If K for a population is 1,200 and $r = 0.9$, which of the following populations will show the greatest increase over the course of one year?
  a. $N = 100$
  b. $N = 200$
  c. $N = 300$
  * d. $N = 700$
  e. $N = 900$

M 23. For a population in a limited environment, _?_ is a variable function that depends on the relationship between _?_ and _?_.
  a. $K; r; N$
  b. $N; K; r$
  * c. $r; K; N$
  d. $r; K; N$-1
  e. $r; K; N$-2

D 24. If a population has an $r = 0.02$, which of the following statements must be true?
  a. Two of every 100 individuals will give birth over the course of a year.
  b. Two individuals will be born for every 100 individuals in the population over the course of a year.
  c. Births will exceed deaths by 2 percent over the course of a year.
  d. The number of individuals added to the population will be 2 percent greater than the number of individuals removed from the population over the course of a year.
  * e. none of these

D   25.   In a population growing exponentially,
a. the number of individuals added to the population next year is greater than the number added this year.
b. the population growth rate increases year after year.
c. net reproduction per individual increases year after year.
* d. the number of individuals added to the population next year is greater than the number added this year and the population growth rate increases year after year.
e. the number of individuals added to the population next year is greater than the number added this year, the population growth rate increases year after year, and net reproduction per individual increases year after year.

D   26.   A population will exhibit a negative growth rate if
a. predation continues indefinitely.
b. N is greater than $1/2K$.
c. number of births + number of immigrants equals number of deaths + number of emigrants.
* d. r is less than 0.
e. none of these

LIMITS ON THE GROWTH OF POPULATIONS

M   27.   Populations
a. are limited by only one factor at a time.
b. increase arithmetically.
c. increase indefinitely.
* d. are limited by the carrying capacity.
e. are represented by a minimum of two different sizes.

D   28.   In natural communities, feedback mechanisms called _?_ operate when the size of a population changes.
a. density-dependent controls
b. density-independent factors
c. biotic factors
d. physical factors
* e. density-dependent controls and biotic factors

M   29.   The maximum number of individuals of a species that a given environment can sustain indefinitely defines
* a. the carrying capacity of the environment.
b. exponential growth.
c. the doubling time of a population.
d. density-independent factors.
e. all of these

D   30.   Limiting factors
a. produce more pronounced effects as a population grows.
b. prevent a population from producing a J-shaped curve.
c. can be either density-dependent or density-independent.
d. act together in concert to form the environmental resistance to population growth.
* e. all of these

D   31.   A J-shaped growth curve is converted to an S-shaped one
a. when the parents are past reproductive age.
b. if the data are plotted in reverse.
* c. when the carrying capacity is reached.
d. if reproduction stops.
e. only for fast-growing populations such as bacteria.

D   32.   The carrying capacity of an environment is determined by
a. the net rate of reproduction of the female members.
b. an S-shaped curve.
c. the predation rate on the females.
d. diseases suffered by both sexes.
* e. the sustainable supply of resources it provides.

M   33.   Carrying capacity of an environment is increased by
a. pollution.
b. predation.
c. disease.
d. population growth.
* e. none of these

D   34.   In natural communities, some feedback mechanisms operate whenever populations change in size; they are
* a. density-dependent factors.
b. density-independent factors.
c. always intrinsic to the individuals of the community.
d. always extrinsic to the individuals of the community.
e. none of these

M   35.   A change in a population that is NOT related strictly to the size of the population is best described as
a. density-dependent.
* b. density-independent.
c. intrinsic.
d. an S-shaped curve.
e. a J-shaped curve.

M   36.   In itself, a flood that washes away an entire population of rabbits is
a. a density-dependent factor.
b. an intrinsic limiting factor.
c. a consequence of exponential growth.
* d. density-independent.
e. all of these

M   37.   Density-independent controls over population growth include
a. parasites.
* b. temperature.
c. disease.
d. competition.
e. all of these

M 38. Which density-dependent factor controls the size of a population?
    a. wind velocity
    b. light intensity
*   c. nutrient supply
    d. rainfall
    e. wave action in an intertidal zone

M 39. In ecosystems, the factors that tend to reduce the size of some populations, regardless of how large the population is, are called
    a. density-dependent factors.
*   b. density-independent factors.
    c. ecological factors.
    d. abiotic factors.
    e. essential factors.

E 40. Which is NOT a density-dependent, growth-limiting factor?
    a. predation
*   b. drought
    c. parasitism
    d. competition
    e. species interaction

M 41. As population density increases, the chance of _?_ also increases.
    a. parasitism
    b. pathogens
    c. predation
    d. competition
*   e. all of these

E 42. The greatest reduction of human population in recorded history was the result of
    a. a global ice age.
    b. two world wars.
*   c. bubonic plague.
    d. family planning.
    e. ozone depletion.

LIFE HISTORY PATTERNS

M 43. A cohort is
*   a. a collection of same-aged individuals of the same species.
    b. any member of the same species.
    c. any member of the same species and sex within a population.
    d. a sexual mate.
    e. a litter mate or sibling within a large population.

M 44. Two populations of the same species have equal immigration, emigration, and death rates, and the females in each population produce four offspring on average during their reproductive years. If the two populations have different net reproductive rates, it is because
    a. one population has more food than the other.
    b. one population has less disease than the other.
*   c. one population breeds at later ages than does the other.
    d. one population has more food than the other and one population has less disease than the other.
    e. one population has more food than the other, one population has less disease than the other, and one population breeds at later ages than does the other.

E 45. Life tables provide data concerning
    a. expected life span.
    b. reproductive age.
    c. death rate.
    d. birth rate.
*   e. all of these

D 46. Type II survivorship curves
    a. are characteristic of humans and elephants.
*   b. typify a population in which all ages have an equal chance of surviving.
    c. indicate a high mortality rate in the very young.
    d. show that very few young are produced, that each is given parental support, and that most individuals live a relatively long life and die of old age.
    e. are typical of annual plants.

D 47. A study of a cohort of 1,000 newborn animals showed a death rate per individual in year one of 60 percent and a death rate per individual in year two of 20 percent. The quantity of survivors after two years is
    a. 120.
*   b. 200.
    c. 320.
    d. 400.
    e. 1,000.

M 48. A type III survivorship curve is characteristic of
    a. monkeys.
    b. horses.
    c. eagles.
*   d. sea urchins.
    e. humans.

M 49. A type III survivorship curve (mortality high at birth and decreasing with age) is characteristic of all EXCEPT which species?
    a. flies
*   b. humans
    c. frogs
    d. reptiles
    e. fish

D 50. The work of Reznick and Endler with guppies has shown that
 a. the *r* of a population is determined by natural selection.
 b. the average age at which individuals attain sexual maturity is determined by natural selection.
 c. the *r* of a population has a genetic basis.
 d. the *r* of a population is determined by natural selection and the average age at which individuals attain sexual maturity is determined by natural selection.
 * e. the *r* of a population is determined by natural selection, the average age at which individuals attain sexual maturity is determined by natural selection, and the *r* of a population has a genetic basis.

D 51. Killifish and pike-cichlids raised in natural conditions will
 a. control the size of the guppies that live with them.
 b. function as predators of guppies.
 c. determine the growth rate of guppies.
 d. control the evolution of size and color of the guppies.
 * e. all of these

HUMAN POPULATION GROWTH

E 52. The leading cause of human deaths around the world is
 a. heart disease.
 b. cancer.
 * c. malnutrition and starvation.
 d. war.
 e. accidents.

D 53. All EXCEPT which one of the following are the reasons for the rapid population explosion of humans?
 a. increases in carrying capacity
 b. expansion into new habitats
 c. removal of limiting factors
 d. reproduction occurring earlier in the life cycle
 * e. longer generation times

M 54. The tremendous increase in the number of human beings over the course of the past 100 years is attributable to
 a. immunization and vaccination programs.
 b. colonization of previously underutilized habitat.
 c. more equal distribution of patchy resources.
 d. immunization and vaccination programs plus colonization of previously underutilized habitat.
 * e. immunization and vaccination programs, colonization of previously underutilized habitat, and more equal distribution of patchy resources.

M 55. Which of the following is NOT a factor that has led to the dramatic increase in the human population?
 a. increase of carrying capacity
 b. removal of several limiting factors
 c. human invasion of new habitats and climatic zones
 * d. an increase in the levels of pollution in the world
 e. the development of public health and the germ theory of disease

D 56. Which of the following is NOT subject to the limits imposed by the principles of logistic growth?
 a. bacteria
 b. fungi
 c. small animals
 d. humans
 * e. All of these are subject to such limits.

D 57. If all disease is eradicated and food supply exceeds demand indefinitely, the human population on the planet Earth will NOT continue to grow at an exponential rate indefinitely because
 a. a new disease organism will evolve.
 b. density-independent factors will always remove individuals.
 * c. space will become a limiting factor.
 d. the few humans left will war and kill each other.
 e. all of these

M 58. The most reasonable method of limiting human population growth is
 a. increasing carrying capacity.
 * b. decreasing birth rate.
 c. decreasing competition.
 d. increasing death rate.
 e. exploiting outer space.

M 59. If the reproductive rate drops to the maintenance level (zero population growth), how many years would it take for world population to stop growing?
 a. 1
 b. 20
 c. 50
 * d. 60
 e. 150

E 60. Which of the following countries has established the most extensive family-planning program?
 a. the United States
 b. Brazil
 * c. China
 d. Japan
 e. Pakistan

M 61. When the human population growth of the world is calculated, the doubling time is
 a. about the same as it was 20 years ago.
 * b. decreasing at an accelerated pace.
 c. increasing slowly.
 d. in a gradual decline.
 e. about 1.8 percent.

M   62. The age-structure diagram for rapidly growing populations
        a. is in the form of a pyramid.
        b. is characterized by a large percentage of the population in the postreproductive years.
        c. has a very broad base showing a large number of young.
        d. has about equal distribution among all age groups.
    *   e. is in the form of a pyramid and has a very broad base showing a large number of young.

D   63. If reproduction occurs early in the life cycle, what occurs?
    *   a. Population growth rate increases.
        b. Population size declines.
        c. Population size is not affected.
        d. Generation time increases.
        e. Growth rate remains unchanged.

D   64. In which demographic model is population growth the fastest?
        a. preindustrial
    *   b. transitional
        c. industrial
        d. postindustrial
        e. transformational

Matching Questions

D   65. Matching. Choose the one most appropriate answer for each.
        1. ____ age structure
        2. ____ population growth rate
        3. ____ J-shaped curve
        4. ____ limiting factor
        A. describes a population that is experiencing unrestrained growth
        B. the birth rate minus the death rate plus any inward migration or minus any outward migration
        C. how individuals are distributed at each age level for a population
        D. the amount of glucose in a culture flask containing bacteria, for example

Answers: 1. C   2. B   3. A   4. D

Classification Questions

Answer questions 66–70 in reference to the four levels of organization listed below.
        a. population
        b. community
        c. ecosystem
        d. biosphere

E   66. This is composed of producers, consumers, decomposers, and the abiotic environment.

E   67. All of the individuals of a single species living in a region constitute this.

M   68. A group of different species living together in a single habitat is this.

M   69. This is the basic functional unit of ecology.

E   70. This contains all of the others.

Answers: 66. c   67. a   68. b
              69. c   70. d

Answer questions 71–75 in reference to the five terms listed below that are used by ecologists.
        a. carrying capacity
        b. net reproductive rate
        c. age structure
        d. survivorship
        e. growth rate

D   71. The average number of offspring born to each female over her reproductive lifetime is known as this.

M   72. The number of individuals in each of several age categories is known as this.

M   73. The maximum number of individuals that a given habitat can support is known as this.

D   74. A change in the available food supply in a habitat will affect all of these terms, except this.

E   75. This term is equal to the birth rate minus the death rate of a species.

Answers: 71. b   72. c   73. a
              74. c   75. e

Selecting the Exception

E   **76.**   Four of the five answers listed below are parts of the ecosystem. Select the exception.
*   a. energy
      b. raw materials and nutrients
      c. decomposers
      d. producers
      e. consumers

D   **77.**   Four of the five answers below are limits to achieving a population's full biotic potential. Select the exception.
      a. lack of nutrients
      b. predation
*   c. exponential growth
      d. competition for space
      e. waste buildup

E   **78.**   Four of the five answers listed below are components of the abiotic (nonliving) environment. Select the exception.
      a. soil
      b. rainfall
*   c. competitors
      d. temperature
      e. sunlight

E   **79.**   Four of the five answers listed below are factors that affect population size. Select the exception.
      a. births
*   b. distribution
      c. emigration
      d. immigration
      e. deaths

D   **80.**   Four of the five answers listed below follow a type II survivorship curve. Select the exception.
      a. songbirds
*   b. large mammals with extended parental care
      c. small mammals
      d. lizards
      e. seeds prior to germination

D   **81.**   Four of the five answers listed below follow a type III survivorship curve. Select the exception.
      a. most insects
      b. most reptiles
      c. many fishes
*   d. humans
      e. most marine invertebrates

M   **82.**   Four of the five answers listed below are density-independent factors. Select the exception.
*   a. nutrient supply
      b. temperature drop
      c. drought
      d. volcanic eruption
      e. hard freeze

CHAPTER 29
COMMUNITY STRUCTURE AND BIODIVERSITY

Multiple-Choice Questions

WHICH FACTORS SHAPE COMMUNITY STRUCTURE?

E 1. All of the populations of different species that occupy and are adapted to a given habitat are referred to by which term?
   a. biosphere
 * b. community
   c. ecosystem
   d. niche
   e. ecotone

M 2. Which of the following would be more likely to affect an animal's habitat than its niche?
 * a. rainfall
   b. prey abundance
   c. predators
   d. defense mechanisms
   e. competitors

M 3. What term denotes the range of all factors that influence whether a species can obtain resources essential for survival and reproduction?
   a. habitat
 * b. niche
   c. carrying capacity
   d. ecosystem
   e. community

M 4. When Shakespeare wrote about the world as a stage and each of us being players, he was unknowingly referring to the biological concept of
   a. succession.
 * b. the niche.
   c. different habitats.
   d. feeding levels.
   e. interspecific competition.

E 5. Niche refers to the
   a. home range of an animal.
   b. preferred habitat for an organism.
 * c. functional role of a species in a community.
   d. territory occupied by a species.
   e. locale in which a species lives.

E 6. A relationship in which benefits flow both ways between the interacting species is
   a. a neutral relationship.
   b. commensalism.
   c. competitive exclusion.
 * d. mutualism.
   e. parasitism.

E 7. A one-way relationship in which one species benefits and directly hurts the other is called
   a. commensalism.
   b. competitive exclusion.
 * c. parasitism.
   d. obligate mutualism.
   e. neutral relationship.

D 8. Which of the following is NOT characteristic of parasites?
   a. They are specialists and usually are able to affect only one variety of hosts.
 * b. They inflict serious injury and kill their hosts.
   c. Some reside inside their hosts, whereas others live outside their hosts.
   d. Their host may be a plant as well as an animal.
   e. They are dependent on hosts.

M 9. The weakest symbiotic attachment, in which one species simply lives better in the presence of another species without harming it is
 * a. commensalism.
   b. competitive exclusion.
   c. mutualism.
   d. facultative obligate mutualism.
   e. parasitism.

E 10. Species interactions differ in
   a. the extent to which one species is helped or harmed by the presence of another.
   b. degree of dependence.
   c. how exclusive the attachments are.
 * d. all of these
   e. none of these

M 11. Fruit flies probably have what type of relationship with humans?
   a. parasitic
   b. mutualistic
   c. obligate
 * d. commensal
   e. saprobic

E 12. In the food chain grass >>> rabbit >>> eagle, the relationship between the grass and eagle is
   a. predation.
   b. commensalism.
   c. competition.
 * d. indirect interaction.
   e. mutualism.

D   13. Which of the following is NOT usual as a result of predation?
        a. The level of the predator population is maintained near or below the carrying capacity.
        b. Both predator and prey undergo selection leading to coevolution.
    *   c. The predator or prey becomes extinct.
        d. The level of the prey population is maintained near or below the carrying capacity of the environment.
        e. The predators need prey.

E   14. The interaction in which one species benefits and the second species is neither harmed nor benefited is
        a. mutualism.
        b. parasitism.
    *   c. commensalism.
        d. competition.
        e. predation.

E   15. The interaction between two species in which one species benefits and the other species is harmed is
        a. mutualism.
        b. commensalism.
        c. competition.
    *   d. predation.
        e. none of these

MUTUALLY BENEFICIAL INTERACTIONS

M   16. The relationship between an insect and the plants it pollinates is best described as
    *   a. mutualism.
        b. competitive exclusion.
        c. parasitism.
        d. commensalism.
        e. all of these

E   17. The relationship between the yucca plant and the yucca moth that pollinates it is best described as
        a. camouflage.
        b. commensalism.
        c. competitive exclusion.
    *   d. mutualism.
        e. all of these

E   18. An interaction between two species in which both species benefit is known as
    *   a. mutualism.
        b. parasitism.
        c. commensalism.
        d. competition.
        e. predation.

COMPETITIVE INTERACTIONS

M   19. The interaction between two species in which both species may be harmed is known as
        a. mutualism.
        b. parasitism.
        c. commensalism.
    *   d. competition.
        e. predation.

M   20. A male wolf who is courting a female bares his teeth when a second male approaches the same female. The second male retreats. This series of events provides an example of
        a. a neutral interaction.
        b. exploitation competition.
    *   c. interference competition.
        d. competitive exclusion.
        e. commensalism.

M   21. The construction of a fence around your yard would establish a relationship with the neighbor's dog that would be described as
        a. succession.
    *   b. interference competition.
        c. commensalism.
        d. mutualism.
        e. a niche.

M   22. Overlap in requirements initially leads to
        a. mutualism.
        b. commensalism.
    *   c. competition.
        d. predation.
        e. parasitism.

M   23. Competitive exclusion is the result of
        a. mutualism.
        b. commensalism.
    *   c. competition.
        d. predation.
        e. parasitism.

M   24. In Gause's experiments with *Paramecium* growing in test tubes, he demonstrated that
        a. organisms with similar niches will evolve enough to survive in different niches.
        b. organisms with slightly different feeding habits will change to become exclusive competitors.
    *   c. organisms with similar feeding habits may compete to the point of extinction.
        d. organisms with slightly different feeding habits will change to become exclusive competitors and organisms with similar feeding habits may compete to the point of extinction.
        e. organisms with similar niches will evolve enough to survive in different niches, and organisms with similar feeding habits may compete to the point of extinction.

M   25.   Gause's exclusion principle refers to
          a. isolation.
     *   b. competition.
          c. habitat preference.
          d. physiological adaptation.
          e. habitat destruction.

M   26.   Competitive exclusion is based upon the idea that
          a. one species will voluntarily allow the other to
              survive.
     *   b. no two species can completely occupy the same
              niche.
          c. the larger species will dominate the smaller.
          d. competition is overrated as a factor in species
              survival.
          e. two species can live together if they share the
              same niche but only at alternate times.

M   27.   The subdividing of some category of similar resources
          in a way that allows competing species to exist is
          a. competition.
          b. social parasitism.
          c. predation.
          d. mimicry.
     *   e. resource partitioning.

M   28.   Coexistence of twelve species of fruit-eating pigeons
          in a New Guinea forest is an example of
     *   a. resource partitioning
          b. competition
          c. predation
          d. parasitism
          e. parasitoidism

PREDATOR-PREY INTERACTIONS

E   29.   A goat eating by pulling a plant out of the ground is an
          example of
          a. parasitism.
     *   b. predation.
          c. competition.
          d. commensalism.
          e. mutualism.

D   30.   In general, a predator is _?_ than its _?_.
          a. smaller; host
          b. larger; host
          c. smaller; prey
     *   d. larger; prey
          e. the same size

D   31.   In contrast to a predator, a parasite *usually*
     *   a. does not kill the animal on which, or in which, it
              lives.
          b. kills its host.
          c. is a short-term visitor.
          d. is larger than its host.
          e. does not kill the animal on which or in which it
              lives and is larger than its host.

D   32.   Conditions of stable coexistence between predator and
          prey include
          a. high predator reproductive rate relative to that of
              the prey.
          b. a carrying capacity for prey which is not high.
          c. large predator size relative to that of the prey.
     *   d. high predator reproductive rate relative to that of
              the prey and a carrying capacity for prey which is
              not high.
          e. high predator reproductive rate relative to that of
              the prey, a carrying capacity for prey which is not
              high, and large predator size relative to that of the
              prey.

D   33.   Humans hunt the black rhinoceros, which is rapidly
          approaching extinction as a result of this predation.
          What accounts for the absence of stable coexistence
          between the two species?
          a. Predator and prey have not coevolved.
          b. Human predation is not necessarily density-
              dependent.
          c. The prey reproductive rate is greater than that of
              the predator.
     *   d. Predator and prey have not coevolved and human
              predation is not necessarily density-dependent.
          e. Predator and prey have not coevolved, human
              predation is not necessarily density-dependent,
              and the prey reproductive rate is greater than that
              of the predator.

D   34.   Ladybugs are effective natural control agents against
          pest insects, but as gardeners soon find out, they do
          not reduce pest populations to zero because
          a. they can't fly to find pests on nearby plants.
          b. of their very selective feeding habits.
     *   c. to do so would jeopardize their own existence.
          d. they don't live long enough.
          e. their reproductive capacity is nonexistent.

D   35.   Without intervention by humans, cockroaches will
          overrun a kitchen until
          a. the carrying capacity is reached.
          b. predators attack.
          c. parasites invade the roaches' bodies.
          d. density-independent factors such as cold
              intervene.
     *   e. all of these

M   36.   Populations are held in check by
          a. resource partitioning.
          b. predation.
          c. social parasitism.
          d. competition.
     *   e. all of these

D   37.   Which is NOT an example of coevolution?
          a. insect and flower
          b. predator and prey
          c. host and parasite
          d. model and mimic
     *   e. sharks and dolphins

M 38. Which of the following is an adaptation against predation?
   a. thorns
   b. social behavior
   c. mimicry
   d. thorns and social behavior
 * e. thorns, social behavior, and mimicry

M 39. Chemicals in both plants and animals serve as which of the following to predators?
   a. warnings
   b. repellents
   c. toxins
   d. bad tastes
 * e. all of these

D 40. Hover flies like to drop in at outdoor picnics to sample the sweets, but the reaction of the humans is to flee the scene because of the flies' uncanny resemblance to bees. Thus, the survival of the hover fly is enhanced by
 * a. mimicry.
   b. display behavior.
   c. warning coloration.
   d. chemical defenses.
   e. camouflage.

PARASITES AND PARASITOIDS

D 41. Which of the following statements about parasites is TRUE?
   a. Parasites usually do not kill their hosts.
   b. The parasite species that infects a particular host species becomes less virulent over evolutionary time.
   c. Warm-blooded animals are frequently infected by parasites.
   d. Parasites usually do not kill their hosts and the parasite species that infects a particular host species becomes less virulent over evolutionary time.
 * e. Parasites usually do not kill their hosts, the parasite species that infects a particular host species becomes less virulent over evolutionary time, and warm-blooded animals are frequently infected by parasites.

D 42. Which of the following does NOT apply to parasitoids?
   a. insects
   b. kill animals on which they feed
 * c. host usually survives
   d. smaller in size than prey
   e. effective biocontrol agents

D 43. Actual physical contact between interacting organisms does not necessarily occur
   a. between parasitoid and prey.
 * b. in social parasitism.
   c. in a predator-prey reaction.
   d. when a parasite feeds on a host.
   e. in any of the above.

M 44. Which of the following is NOT a desirable attribute of effective parasitoid control agents?
   a. They are well adapted to the host.
 * b. They have limited search capability.
   c. The reproductive rate is high.
   d. They are mobile.
   e. They are capable of quick responses to host population change.

CHANGES IN COMMUNITY STRUCTURE OVER TIME

D 45. During the process of community succession,
   a. the total biomass remains constant.
 * b. there are increasing possibilities for resource partitioning.
   c. the pioneer community gives way quickly to the climax community, followed by a succession of more diverse arrays of organisms.
   d. nutrients cycle more rapidly with time.
   e. all of these

M 46. Which of the following statements is FALSE?
   a. Succession is highly predictable.
   b. Pioneer species have wide ranges of tolerances.
   c. Pioneer plant species are usually small annuals with an abundance of easily dispersed seeds.
 * d. The succession that occurs after a large fire is primary succession.
   e. Climax species are those that are best adapted to the specific climate where the succession occurs.

M 47. Secondary succession is likely to occur in
   a. a deciduous forest only.
   b. a shallow lake only.
   c. an abandoned field only.
   d. a deciduous forest or a shallow lake only.
 * e. a deciduous forest, a shallow lake, or an abandoned field.

M 48. Pioneer plant species are usually characterized by
   a. small size.
   b. efficient dispersal mechanisms.
   c. slow maturation.
 * d. small size and efficient dispersal mechanisms.
   e. small size, efficient dispersal mechanisms, and slow maturation.

M 49. Which of the following represent an early stage in primary succession?
   a. pine trees
 * b. moss and lichens on bare rock
   c. weedy annual plants in an open field
   d. climax species in succession
   e. fields of food crops

M   50.   Secondary succession can occur
     *   a.   after a fire.
           b.   on a new sand dune.
           c.   on bare rock.
           d.   immediately after the formation of a man-made
                lake.
           e.   on a glacier.

M   51.   The plants and animals *now present* on acreage from
           which the trees were removed ten years earlier
           represent
           a.   primary succession.
           b.   a climax forest.
           c.   pioneer species.
     *   d.   secondary succession.
           e.   species introductions.

D   52.   Farmland that is under regular and continued tillage
           will not
           a.   undergo succession.
     *   b.   produce a climax community.
           c.   experience competition.
           d.   suffer from the effects of disturbance.
           e.   develop species diversity.

M   53.   The climax community
           a.   is formed by species with the least range of
                environmental tolerance.
           b.   is usually the most common community found in
                an area.
           c.   remains unchanged once it is established.
     *   d.   is well adapted to the present climate conditions
                but can restore itself if something destroys it.
           e.   is the initial collection of species in an area.

FORCES CONTRIBUTING TO COMMUNITY INSTABILITY

E   54.   A keystone species is
           a.   a single dominant species.
           b.   in control of the prey species.
           c.   exemplified by the sea star.
           d.   a single dominant species and is exemplified by
                the sea star.
     *   e.   a single dominant species, exemplified by the sea
                star, and in control of the prey species.

M   55.   Many introduced species have had deleterious effects
           on communities and ecosystems because
     *   a.   coevolved parasites and pathogens are absent.
           b.   the introduced species are long-lived.
           c.   predators prefer the introduced species, and the
                local prey therefore proliferate to dangerously
                high levels.
           d.   the communities from which they came lost an
                important predator, competitor, or parasite.
           e.   human beings do not know how to appreciate
                them.

PATTERNS OF SPECIES DIVERSITY

M   56.   There are more insect species per square kilometer in a
           Brazilian rainforest than there are in a redwood forest
           of the Pacific Northwest of the United States.
           According to contemporary ecological hypotheses, an
           explanation for this finding is that
           a.   Tropical latitudes intercept more intense sunlight.
           b.   Resource availability is greater.
           c.   Tropical communities have been evolving longer.
           d.   Species diversity might be self-reinforcing.
     *   e.   all of these

D   57.   An equilibrium population of five individuals on an
           island is more likely to go extinct than an equilibrium
           population of 50 individuals because
           a.   intraspecific competition is more intense in
                smaller groups.
     *   b.   density-independent factors are more likely to
                eliminate smaller rather than larger groups.
           c.   there is more ecological space for predators if
                there are fewer prey.
           d.   predation pressure increases as prey populations
                decrease.
           e.   five individuals is not enough for reproduction.

CONSERVATION BIOLOGY

M   58.   Recovery from a mass extinction requires about how
           long?
           a.   100,000 years
           b.   none of these because recovery is never possible
           c.   about as long as the extinction required
           d.   less than one million years
     *   e.   20 to 100 million years

M   59.   Which of the following is LEAST likely to be a cause
           of extinction?
           a.   asteroid impact
           b.   human activity
     *   c.   adaptive radiation
           d.   tectonic activity
           e.   climate change

M   60.   Which of the following is MOST likely to be the cause
           of the current extinction crisis?
           a.   asteroid impact
     *   b.   human activity
           c.   adaptive radiation
           d.   tectonic activity
           e.   climate change

E   61.   Any species that is extremely vulnerable to extinction
           is designated as
           a.   riparian.
           b.   endemic.
     *   c.   endangered.
           d.   fragmented.
           e.   an indicator.

E   62. Endemic means a species
*   a. evolved in one geographic region and does not
         live elsewhere.
     b. could cause an epidemic at any time.
     c. is on its way to extinction.
     d. can live in only one habitat.
     e. is extinct.

E   63. Which of the following would NOT be a contributing
          factor in species extinction?
     a. habitat loss
     b. overharvesting
     c. habitat fragmentation
*   d. conservation biology
     e. illegal wildlife trading

M   64. Habitat fragmentation can reduce biodiversity by
*   a. creating patches too small to maintain breeding.
     b. increasing the effects of chemical pollution.
     c. eliminating vast tracts of forests.
     d. introducing exotic species into a habitat.
     e. all of these

M   65. Natural areas that are surrounded by a "sea" of habitat
          that has been degraded by human activities describes
     a. indicator species.
     b. ecoregions.
     c. hot spots.
*   d. habitat islands.
     e. biogeography.

E   66. Because migratory birds live in all major regions and
          climate zones, they are one of the
     a. habitat island indicators.
     b. exotic species.
*   c. key indicator species.
     d. habitat fragmenters.
     e. pollution carriers.

M   67. Exotic species that are introduced into a non-native
          habitat usually
     a. interbreed with native species.
*   b. drive endemic species to extinction.
     c. die out due to competition from native species.
     d. blend in with endemic species.
     e. create habitat islands for themselves.

D   68. The wild maize (*Zea diploperennis*) found by a
          Mexican college student was significant because it
     a. lives more than one growing season.
     b. is more resistant to disease.
*   c. lives more than one growing season and is more
         resistant to disease.
     d. produces much greater yields per acre than
         domestic corn.
     e. lives more than one growing season, is more
         resistant to disease, and produces much greater
         yields per acre than domestic corn.

M   69. Conservation biology includes a(n)
     a. survey of biological diversity.
     b. look at the evolutionary origins of diversity.
     c. ecological consideration of diversity.
     d. effort to maintain biodiversity.
*   e. all of these

E   70. Habitats with the most species in greatest danger of
          extinction are called
     a. ecoregions.
     b. indicator species.
     c. riparian zones.
*   d. hot spots.
     e. conservation islands.

M   71. Which of the following pairs of words are most
          closely related?
*   a. hot spots—indicator species
     b. habitat island—strip logging
     c. conservation—habitat loss
     d. coral reef—Rachel Carson
     e. endemic—exotic

M   72. In making a systematic survey of biodiversity, the
          initial work has focused
     a. at the ecoregion level.
     b. among the riparian zones.
*   c. in hot spots.
     d. at the regional research station.
     e. on a global scale.

E   73. A broad land or ocean region defined by climate,
          geography, and producer species is called
*   a. an ecoregion.
     b. a hot spot.
     c. a realm.
     d. a habitat island.
     e. a biosphere.

M   74. Future value of ecoregions can be determined by
     a. destroying portions of the regions.
     b. indicator species.
*   c. bioeconomic analysis.
     d. selling them on the global market.
     e. introducing new species.

M   75. Bioeconomic analysis looks at
     a. long-term economic benefits.
     b. short-term gains.
     c. cost/benefit ratios.
     d. sustainability of biodiversity.
*   e. all of these

E   76. Given a choice, most humans will choose to
     a. protect endangered species.
     b. do what is best for mankind.
     c. conserve.
     d. maintain biodiversity for all humankind.
*   e. preserve their own lives.

M 77. Gary Hartshorn has proposed a profitable, sustainable method of harvesting called
  a. riparian ranching.
  b. habitat fragmentation.
  * c. strip logging.
  d. sustainable forestation.
  e. clear cutting.

M 78. A relatively narrow corridor of vegetation along a stream or river is called a(n)
  a. ecoregion.
  * b. riparian zone.
  c. habitat island.
  d. hot zone.
  e. refuge.

Matching Questions

D 79. Matching I. Choose the one most appropriate answer for each.
  1. ___ camouflage
  2. ___ commensalism
  3. ___ competitive exclusion
  4. ___ habitat
  5. ___ mimicry
  6. ___ mutualism
  7. ___ parasitism
  8. ___ primary succession
  9. ___ climax community
  10. ___ secondary succession
  11. ___ succession
  A. blending in and being hidden by the background
  B. where an organism is generally located in an environment
  C. one organism benefits at another organism's expense
  D. a self-sustaining array of interacting organisms that is best suited for a particular environment
  E. lichens on newly hardened, newly cooled lava
  F. robins and human populations
  G. the yucca moth and the yucca
  H. one species is forced from an area of niche overlap
  I. repugnant species resemble tasty ones
  J. the process that converts a pioneer community to a climax community
  K. natural reforestation of burned-over forest

Answers: 1. A   2. F   3. H   4. B
          5. I   6. G   7. C   8. E
          9. D   10. K   11. J

D 80. Matching II. Choose the one most appropriate answer for each.
  1. ___ conservation biology
  2. ___ biodiversity
  3. ___ ecoregion
  4. ___ endangered species
  5. ___ habitat fragmentation
  6. ___ habitat island
  7. ___ habitat loss
  8. ___ hot spot
  9. ___ indicator species
  10. ___ strip logging
  11. ___ riparian zone
  A. a reduction in suitable places to live
  B. organisms that give "early warning" signal of changes in biodiversity
  C. new method of harvesting trees to preserve diversity
  D. a field of research whose goal is conservation of biodiversity
  E. endemic species vulnerable to extinction
  F. broad land or ocean region defined by climate, geography, and producer species
  G. encompassed in genes, species, and habitats
  H. locations where species are in greatest danger of extinction
  I. a national park is an example
  J. narrow corridor of vegetation along stream or river
  K. isolated patches of habitat

Answers: 1. D   2. G   3. F   4. E
          5. K   6. I   7. A   8. H
          9. B   10. C   11. J

Classification Questions

Answer questions 81–85 in reference to the five kinds of species interactions listed below.

a. competition
b. predation
c. mutualism
d. commensalism
e. parasitism

E **81.** In this interaction, one species benefits while the other is neither harmed nor benefited.

M **82.** In this interaction between two species, both species are harmed in some way.

M **83.** In this interaction, both species benefit.

E **84.** In this interaction, one individual or species is usually killed while the other benefits by eating the first.

M **85.** In this interaction, one species is harmed, but usually not killed, to the benefit of the other that lives on or in the first.

Answers: 81. d   82. a   83. c

    84. b   85. e

Answer questions 86–90 in reference to the five kinds of species interactions listed below.

a. competition
b. parasitoidism
c. mutualism
d. commensalism
e. parasitism

E **86.** The relationship between a dog and a wood tick is this kind of relationship.

M **87.** The interaction between a human and the intestinal bacterium *E. coli* is usually this kind of relationship.

M **88.** The interaction between two closely related species of woodpeckers that live in a temperate forest is likely to be this.

M **89.** If a wasp lays its eggs inside the larva of a fly, the interaction is this.

M **90.** When a tropical bird places its nest in association with a wasp nest on the same tree, the interaction is this.

Answers: 86. e   87. c   88. a

    89. b   90. d

Answer questions 91–95 in reference to the four "habitat" items listed below.

a. habitat fragmentation
b. habitat island
c. habitat loss
d. habitat

M **91.** This describes where a species lives.

M **92.** This could reduce a habitat's boundaries, making species more vulnerable to predators.

M **93.** This could be the result of chemical pollution.

D **94.** This is inhabited area surrounded by unsuitable habitat.

D **95.** This action may result in a lack of sufficient resources to sustain the population.

Answers: 91. d   92. a   93. c

    94. b   95. a

Selecting the Exception

M **96.** Four of the five answers listed below are relationships in which at least one of the interactants benefits. Select the exception.
  * a. competition
    b. parasitism
    c. mutualism
    d. commensalism
    e. predation

D **97.** Four of the five answers listed below are examples of mutualism. Select the exception.
    a. plants and pollinators
    b. plants and seed dispersal by seed-eating animals
    c. mycorrhizae
  * d. antibiotics
    e. lichen

E **98.** Four of the five answers listed below are examples of defense coloration. Select the exception.
    a. industrial melanism
    b. warning coloration
    c. camouflage
  * d. albinism
    e. mimicry

E **99.** Four of the five answers listed below are defense chemicals. Select the exception.
  * a. perfume
    b. warning odors
    c. poisons
    d. alarm substances
    e. repellents

M **100.** Four of the five answers below are related by role.
Select the exception.
   a. scavenger
* b. intestinal tract
   c. saprobe
   d. producer
   e. decomposer

M **101.** Four of the five answers listed below are events that
lead to secondary succession. Select the exception.
   a. opening the canopy in a tropical rain forest
   b. abandoning a cotton field
* c. retreat of a glacier in Alaska
   d. the finish of a fire
   e. growth of weeds in a lawn that is not mowed

M **102.** Four of the five answers listed below can become
threats to species survival. Select the exception.
   a. habitat losses
   b. introduction of exotic species
   c. overharvesting
   d. illegal wildlife trading
* e. strip logging

CHAPTER 30
ECOSYSTEMS

Multiple-Choice Questions

THE NATURE OF ECOSYSTEMS

E **1.** In a natural community, the primary consumers are
*   a. herbivores.
    b. carnivores.
    c. scavengers.
    d. decomposers.
    e. all of these

E **2.** Which of the following is usually a primary carnivore?
    a. chicken
    b. cow
    c. rabbit
*   d. wolf
    e. squirrel

M **3.** Which of the following is a primary consumer?
*   a. cow
    b. dog
    c. hawk
    d. fox
    e. snake

M **4.** Most living organisms are dependent upon plants because
    a. plants produce oxygen as a by-product of photosynthesis.
    b. as producers, they form the base of food chains.
    c. they function to prevent erosion and reduce desertification.
    d. as they remove carbon dioxide from the atmosphere, they reduce the problems generated by the greenhouse effect.
*   e. all of these

D **5.** Which of the following combinations of organisms could be expected to survive in isolation from other forms of life available?
*   a. producers and decomposers
    b. producers and carnivores
    c. carnivores and decomposers
    d. herbivores, carnivores, and decomposers
    e. producers only

M **6.** Wastes would accumulate and the recycling of most nutrients would stop if the _?_ in the ecosystem died.
    a. protozoans and protistans
*   b. bacteria and fungi
    c. flatworms, roundworms, and earthworms
    d. insects
    e. plants

E **7.** Herbivores represent the
*   a. primary consumers.
    b. secondary consumers.
    c. tertiary consumers.
    d. primary producers.
    e. secondary producers.

D **8.** Photoautotrophs are
    a. primary consumers.
    b. secondary consumers.
    c. tertiary consumers.
*   d. primary producers.
    e. secondary producers.

M **9.** Detritivores are
    a. bacteria.
    b. plants.
    c. fungi.
*   d. animals.
    e. both bacteria and fungi.

E **10.** An array of organisms together with their physical environment is which of the following?
    a. population
    b. community
*   c. ecosystem
    d. biosphere
    e. species

M **11.** A community differs from an ecosystem in that the former does NOT include
    a. unicellular organisms.
    b. decomposers.
*   c. abiotic (nonliving) factors.
    d. unicellular organisms and decomposers.
    e. unicellular organisms, decomposers, and abiotic factors.

M **12.** Which of the following are NOT heterotrophs?
    a. primary carnivores
    b. herbivores
    c. detritivores
    d. decomposers
*   e. All of these are heterotrophs.

D **13.** Which of the following is NOT dependent on the others as a food supply?
    a. carnivores
    b. herbivores
*   c. producers
    d. detritivores
    e. decomposers

E 14. Which of the following is the correct word meaning "nourishment"?
    a. tropic
*   b. trophic
    c. topic
    d. tophic
    e. tropical

D 15. Most of the energy available to a primary consumer
*   a. will be used up in various biological activities.
    b. will be converted into biomass.
    c. is obtained directly from solar energy.
    d. will be passed on to the animal that feeds upon it.
    e. is passed on to decomposers.

M 16. Which of the following is NOT true of ecosystems?
    a. Although they may include many different species, many features of ecosystem structure and function are alike.
    b. Autotrophs secure energy and nutrients that are then used by heterotrophs.
*   c. Energy cycles and minerals flow through ecosystems.
    d. Many different niches are represented in most ecosystems.
    e. Ecosystems are characterized by relatively few trophic levels.

D 17. Which of the following statements is TRUE?
    a. A population cannot exceed the carrying capacity even temporarily.
*   b. An organism can occupy more than one trophic level, depending upon the feeding habits of the organism.
    c. Once populations of organisms become isolated, they remain so by various types of isolation mechanisms.
    d. The limits of a population are all traced to climatic or physical factors.
    e. Organisms with different evolutionary backgrounds can occupy the same niche at the same time.

M 18. The primary consumer is also
    a. the second link in a food chain.
    b. a herbivore.
    c. an animal.
    d. a herbivore and an animal.
*   e. the second link in a food chain, a herbivore, and an animal.

D 19. A secondary consumer usually eats
    a. only herbivores.
    b. only primary producers.
    c. primary carnivores.
*   d. anything "below" it in the food web.
    e. decomposers.

D 20. Food chains rarely have more than three levels of consumers because
    a. the animals are too large to search for prey.
    b. the growing season of plants is not long enough.
    c. pyramids do not go that high.
*   d. the amount of energy still available is too small.
    e. they tire easily.

M 21. Detritus specifically includes
    a. organic wastes.
    b. toxic materials.
    c. dead and partially decayed material.
    d. living bacteria and fungi.
*   e. both organic wastes plus dead and partially decayed material.

D 22. The amount of energy that flows through a detrital food web is _?_ that which flows through a grazing web.
    a. the same as
*   b. greater than
    c. less than
    d. the sum of
    e. the difference of

D 23. Which of the following statements is FALSE?
    a. Heat loss represents a one-way loss of energy from an ecosystem.
*   b. Organisms in the food chain can use all the energy contained in the food that they eat.
    c. In some ecosystems, the majority of the energy stored in plants does not become available until the plants die.
    d. Heat and energy are lost by each organism in the ecosystem.
    e. The two food webs are classified as grazing and detrital.

M 24. Decomposers perform their recycling efforts on organisms
    a. at the end of a food chain.
    b. on the top of a pyramid.
    c. that are producers.
    d. that are consumers.
*   e. all of these

M 25. Decomposers
    a. are able to enter a food chain at any trophic level.
    b. are the most numerous organisms in an ecosystem.
    c. include bacteria and fungi.
*   d. all of these
    e. none of these

M 26. Primary carnivores are
    a. tertiary consumers in the third trophic level.
*   b. secondary consumers in the third trophic level.
    c. secondary consumers in the second trophic level.
    d. tertiary consumers in the fourth trophic level.
    e. also primary producers in aquatic ecosystems.

M 27. Which of the following CANNOT be placed in a single trophic level?
- a. oak tree
- b. zebra
- *c. mushroom
- d. rabbit
- e. earthworm

BIOLOGICAL MAGNIFICATION IN FOOD WEBS

M 28. Biological magnification refers to the
- a. increase in size of animals as they progress through a food chain.
- b. increase in size of organisms as they progress through ecological succession.
- c. increase in the efficiency of energy utilization as organisms progress through a food chain.
- *d. accumulation of toxic pollutants as animals pass through a food chain.
- e. increase in numbers of animals over time.

E 29. In biological magnification,
- *a. poisons build up in food chains and webs so that the concentration is highest at the high end of the food chain.
- b. there is a tendency for an environment to change when organisms first invade.
- c. more highly evolved forms are able to build large populations under favorable conditions.
- d. parasites spread rapidly through congested populations.
- e. sediments fill in aquatic environments so that succession will occur if organisms disturb the aquatic habitat.

M 30. Which substance is magnified during transfers in ecosystems?
- *a. fat-soluble pesticides
- b. carbohydrates
- c. inorganic phosphates
- d. fat-soluble pesticides and carbohydrates
- e. fat-soluble pesticides, carbohydrates, and inorganic phosphates

M 31. The release of DDT into the environment to control some insect pests will result in the highest detectable concentrations
- a. at the bottom of the food chain.
- b. in the targeted insect pest.
- c. in the middle of the food chain.
- *d. at the end of the food chain.
- e. in the plants that may receive spray.

M 32. Long-lasting pesticides such as DDT
- a. are target specific.
- b. are the most effective control over pests.
- *c. build up in concentration as they pass through a food chain.
- d. break down after the organism that receives the pesticide dies.
- e. are increasing in usage.

STUDYING ENERGY FLOW THROUGH ECOSYSTEMS

D 33. Net primary production is the
- a. rate of photosynthesis.
- b. rate of energy flow.
- c. amount of energy stored in the ecosystem.
- d. amount of energy utilized.
- *e. is the fraction of trapped energy that producers funnel into growth and reproduction.

M 34. Gross primary production refers to the total
- a. energy reaching the ecosystem in a given period of time.
- b. energy reaching the ecosystem in a given area.
- *c. energy initially trapped by the producers.
- d. energy used by the heterotrophic part of the ecosystem in a given period of time.
- e. energy produced minus the energy used.

E 35. The ultimate source of all energy in a terrestrial ecosystem is
- a. the organic matter in all the organisms of the ecosystem.
- b. water.
- *c. sunlight.
- d. carbon dioxide.
- e. carbon.

E 36. Most of the energy within an ecosystem is lost
- a. when organisms disperse.
- b. when organisms die.
- *c. as a result of metabolism.
- d. by organisms at the top of the food web.
- e. during breathing.

E 37. At the bottom or base of a pyramid of energy are the
- *a. primary producers.
- b. secondary producers.
- c. primary consumers.
- d. secondary consumers.
- e. tertiary consumers.

E 38. At the top of a pyramid of biomass are the
- a. primary producers.
- b. secondary producers.
- c. primary consumers.
- d. secondary consumers.
- *e. tertiary consumers (third level).

M 39. The biomass of a community is the dry weight of the
- a. material decomposed in a year.
- b. producers.
- *c. living organisms.
- d. consumers.
- e. decomposers.

D   40.   The pyramid of energy is
            a. a demonstration of the first law of
                thermodynamics.
     *   b. a result of the decline in the energy available as
                energy travels through the trophic levels.
            c. fundamentally different from the pyramid of
                biomass and the pyramid of numbers.
            d. just one of the manifestations of competition.
            e. the result of eating the correct foods.

D   41.   Energy pyramids are characteristic of ecosystems
            because
            a. not all of what is eaten is absorbed by a consumer.
            b. not all of what is killed is eaten by a predator.
            c. not all of what is produced in one trophic level is
                consumed by organisms in the next highest
                trophic level.
            d. not all of what is eaten is absorbed by a consumer
                and not all of what is killed is eaten by a predator.
     *   e. not all of what is eaten is absorbed by a consumer,
                not all of what is killed is eaten by a predator, and
                not all of what is produced in one trophic level is
                consumed by organisms in the next highest
                trophic level.

M   42.   The simple food chain grass >>> zebra >>> lion
            provides a good example of a pyramid of
            a. energy.
            b. heat.
            c. biomass.
     *   d. both energy and biomass.
            e. energy, heat, and biomass.

E   43.   Energy flow in an ecosystem is
            a. cyclical.
     *   b. one-way.
            c. two-way.
            d. reversible under different conditions.
            e. a conservation mechanism.

GLOBAL CYCLING OF WATER AND NUTRIENTS

E   44.   Materials in sedimentary cycles
            a. pass through both a solid and a gaseous phase.
     *   b. do not commonly move gases in the ecosystem.
            c. are present as liquids in the earth but as gases in
                the atmosphere.
            d. pass through both a solid and a gaseous phase and
                are present as liquids in the earth but as gases in
                the atmosphere.
            e. remain as solids.

E   45.   Which of the following does NOT cycle through an
            ecosystem?
            a. water
            b. carbon
     *   c. energy
            d. phosphorus
            e. nitrogen

M   46.   The chemical elements that are available to producers
            are usually in what form?
     *   a. ions
            b. gases
            c. solids
            d. compounds
            e. hydrocarbons

D   47.   Which of the following statements is FALSE?
            a. Ecologists use models to represent relationships
                between biogeochemical cycles and most
                ecosystems.
     *   b. The physical environment has virtually no
                reservoir for most elements.
            c. Inputs from the physical environment and
                recycling made possible by decomposers and
                detritivores maintain the nutrient reserves in an
                ecosystem.
            d. In most major ecosystems, the amount of nutrients
                that is cycled within the ecosystem is greater than
                the amount entering or leaving the ecosystem in a
                given year.
            e. Once elements are in the biological parts of the
                biogeochemical cycles, they are unlikely to leave
                until the organism dies.

M   48.   The Hubbard Brook watershed studies revealed the
            importance of tree roots in preventing loss of calcium
            from an ecosystem. Calculation of calcium loss is
            performed by sampling
            a. the roots of the trees.
            b. the soil of the watershed.
     *   c. the stream exiting the watershed.
            d. the roots of the trees and the soil of the watershed.
            e. the roots of the trees, the soil of the watershed,
                and the stream exiting the watershed.

M   49.   Most of the water vapor in the Earth's atmosphere
            comes from evaporation from
            a. lakes.
            b. rivers.
            c. land.
     *   d. oceans.
            e. plants.

D   50.   Of all the water on the Earth's surface, most of it is
            NOT fit for human consumption because it contains
            a. microbial pollutants.
     *   b. salt.
            c. heavy metals.
            d. pesticides.
            e. CFCs.

M   51.   Large-scale agriculture accounts for about what
            percent of freshwater use?
            a. one-fifth
            b. one-tenth
            c. three-fourths
            d. one-half
     *   e. two-thirds

D   52.   Which of the following is NOT a result or effect of irrigation?
     a. increased food production
     b. waterlogging of soil
     c. raised water tables
*   d. alteration of soil type
     e. salinization

CARBON CYCLE

M   53.   Which gas is increasing in the atmosphere and amplifying the greenhouse effect?
*   a. carbon dioxide
     b. carbon monoxide
     c. ozone
     d. fluorocarbons
     e. oxygen

E   54.   Carbon is stored in what form?
     a. biomass
     b. fossil fuels
     c. limestone rocks
     d. shells of animals
*   e. all of these

M   55.   Carbon is introduced into the atmosphere by all EXCEPT which of the following means?
     a. respiration
     b. volcanic eruptions
     c. burning of fossil fuels
*   d. wind erosion
     e. combustion

D   56.   A significant fraction of the Earth's carbon is found in all EXCEPT which of the following?
     a. carbonate
     b. carbon dioxide
     c. cellulose
*   d. carbon monoxide
     e. All of these are significant in holding the Earth's carbon.

D   57.   Carbon enters the biomass of animal bodies in the form of
     a. carbon dioxide.
     b. carbon monoxide.
*   c. carbohydrates.
     d. fossil fuels.
     e. calcium carbonate.

D   58.   Most of the carbon now present in the Earth's atmosphere will eventually end up in what two "holding stations"?
     a. plants and animals
     b. plants and decomposers
     c. plants and soil
*   d. plants and oceans
     e. plants and fossil fuels

D   59.   In which of the following locations does carbon remain for the shortest time?
     a. peat bogs
*   b. tropical forests
     c. marshes
     d. sea shells
     e. fossil fuels

GREENHOUSE GASES, GLOBAL WARMING

E   60.   Carbon dioxide in the atmosphere
     a. is destroying the ozone layer.
*   b. has dramatically increased in the last few decades.
     c. is one of the prime reasons for acid rain.
     d. is a waste gas produced by respiration and has no biological use.
     e. can change spontaneously to carbon monoxide in sunlight.

M   61.   The warming action on Earth's atmosphere is referred to as
     a. respiration accumulation.
*   b. greenhouse effect.
     c. the smog problem.
     d. the blanket phenomenon.
     e. ozone depletion.

E.   62.   Air pollution
     a. reduces visibility.
     b. corrodes buildings.
     c. causes various human diseases.
     d. damages plants.
*   e. all of these

M   63.   Greenhouse gases include all the following except
     a. methane.
*   b. oxygen.
     c. carbon dioxide.
     d. nitrous oxide.
     e. chlorofluorocarbons.

M   64.   Carbon dioxide is a pollutant because it
     a. is absorbed by the ocean and converted into insoluble carbonates.
     b. is utilized when fossil fuel is burned.
     c. is a waste product of photosynthesis.
*   d. cannot be recycled at a rate equal to its present production.
     e. is replacing oxygen as the most abundant gas in the air.

NITROGEN CYCLE

E   **65.** The greatest concentration of nitrogen on Earth is found in
    a. living organisms, including bacteria.
  * b. the atmosphere.
    c. soil minerals.
    d. fossil fuels.
    e. oceans.

E   **66.** Nitrogen is released into the atmosphere by
    a. nitrogen fixation.
  * b. denitrification.
    c. nitrification.
    d. ammonification.
    e. decomposition.

E   **67.** Which plants are grown to increase the amount of nitrogen in the soil?
    a. watermelon and cantaloupe vines
  * b. legumes
    c. mints
    d. grasses
    e. heaths

PHOSPHORUS CYCLE

D   **68.** Animals obtain minerals such as phosphorus
    a. primarily dissolved in drinking water.
    b. by inhalation.
    c. in meats.
    d. by eating plants.
  * e. in meats and by eating plants.

M   **69.** A dramatic enrichment of nutrients in an ecosystem is referred to as
    a. autotrophication.
    b. decomposition.
    c. energy transfer.
  * d. eutrophication.
    e. detritus.

Matching Questions

D   **70.** Matching. Choose the one most appropriate answer for each.

   1. ___ biological magnification
   2. ___ detritus
   3. ___ legumes
   4. ___ net primary production
   5. ___ primary productivity
   6. ___ ruminant animals (cows)
   7. ___ gross primary production

   A. rate at which producers capture and store energy in their tissues during a given interval
   B. total amount of solar energy initially trapped by the producers
   C. convert low-grade plant protein into high-grade meat protein by harboring cellulose-degrading microbes in their gut
   D. the fraction of trapped energy that producers funnel into growth and reproduction
   E. DDT spraying program in Borneo
   F. a kind of plant that often harbors symbiotic nitrogen fixers in its roots
   G. particles of organic waste products, dead or partly decomposed tissues

Answers: 1. E   2. G   3. F   4. D
             5. A   6. C   7. B

Classification Questions

Answer questions 71–75 in reference to the five trophic categories of an ecosystem listed below.

    a. producer
    b. herbivore
    c. carnivore
    d. detritivore
    e. decomposer

M   **71.** A primary consumer is this.

M   **72.** An eagle attacking a fish.

M   **73.** Most mushrooms function as this.

M   **74.** A crab functions as this.

E   **75.** A bear eating blueberries is functioning as this.

Answers: 71. b   72. c   73. e
            74. d   75. b

Selecting the Exception

M   **76.**   Four of the five answers listed below are heterotrophic. Select the exception.
      a. consumers
      b. carnivores
      c. herbivores
      d. parasites
   *   e. producers

M   **77.**   Four of the five answers listed below are related by a common action. Select the exception.
      a. volcanic eruption
   *   b. photosynthesis
      c. respiration
      d. fire
      e. decomposition

CHAPTER 31
THE BIOSPHERE

Multiple-Choice Questions

AIR CIRCULATION AND CLIMATES

M 1. All EXCEPT which of the following are affected by climate?
   a. land surface
   b. lakes
   c. oceans
   d. atmosphere
   * e. hydrothermal vents

E 2. The amount of ultraviolet radiation hitting the Earth's surface is greatly reduced by which gas in the atmosphere?
   * a. ozone
   b. oxygen
   c. water vapor
   d. carbon dioxide
   e. nitrogen

D 3. Chlorofluorocarbons (CFCs) are pollutants because
   * a. biogeochemical mechanisms for their removal have not yet appeared in the biosphere.
   b. they combine with water to form hydrochloric and hydrofluoric acids.
   c. they are found in smog.
   d. they are photochemical oxidants.
   e. they reduce the amount of sun reaching the Earth's surface.

M 4. The atmosphere above which region is known to have a hole in the ozone layer?
   * a. Antarctica
   b. eastern North America
   c. northern Europe
   d. the western Pacific
   e. Africa

E 5. What gas is important in the absorption of ultraviolet radiation?
   a. N_2
   * b. O_3
   c. CO_2
   d. SO_2
   e. SiO_2

M 6. The amount of solar energy that any spot on the surface of the Earth receives is controlled by
   a. the photoperiod or duration of light.
   b. the angle at which the sun strikes the Earth.
   c. the amount of atmosphere above the spot.
   d. the particulate matter and pollution in the atmosphere.
   * e. all of these

M 7. At how many degrees north and south of the equator does air rise as a result of differential heating and cooling?
   a. 10
   b. 30
   c. 40
   * d. 60
   e. 75

M 8. Major air masses rise from the Earth's surface at
   a. the equator and 30-degree latitudes.
   b. 30-degree and 60-degree latitudes.
   * c. the equator and 60-degree latitudes.
   d. 30-degree latitudes and the poles.
   e. 45-degree latitudes and the poles.

M 9. Which factor has the LEAST effect on the amount of incoming light that strikes an area?
   a. latitude
   * b. temperature
   c. the degree that a slope is exposed to the incoming light
   d. the amount of recurring cloud cover
   e. water

E 10. Transportation-produced smog causes air to turn
   a. gray.
   b. black.
   * c. brown.
   d. red.
   e. blue.

M 11. A thermal inversion refers to
   a. an abnormal occurrence not predicted by meteorologists.
   b. an Indian summer.
   c. an unusually quick change in weather patterns.
   d. the process of cool air drainage at night.
   * e. a layer of cool air trapped underneath a warm-air blanket.

D 12. A thermal inversion
   a. occurs when rising air is blocked from rising further.
   b. is characteristic of stable air masses.
   c. occurs when a warm front rises over a stationary cold air mass.
   d. occurs only at night.
   * e. occurs when rising air is blocked from rising further and keeps pollutants in an area and thus contribute to smog.

M 13. When fossil fuel burning gives off particulates and sulfur oxides, we have
    a. photochemical smog.
*   b. industrial smog.
    c. a thermal inversion.
    d. both photochemical smog and a thermal inversion.
    e. all of these

E 14. Industrial smog causes air to turn
*   a. gray.
    b. black.
    c. brown.
    d. red.
    e. blue.

M 15. Which city is famous for its brown fog?
    a. London
*   b. Los Angeles
    c. Chicago
    d. New York
    e. Pittsburgh

M 16. Acid rain occurs when
    a. carbon dioxide combines with water in the atmosphere.
    b. phosphorus-rich water in lakes evaporates to form phosphoric acid.
*   c. sulfur released in burning fossil fuels combines with water in the atmosphere.
    d. excess hydrogen is released into the atmosphere where ozone is formed.
    e. none of these

E 17. Acid rain
    a. attacks nylons.
    b. attacks marble on buildings.
    c. causes toxic metals to become motile in the ecosystem.
    d. can be reduced in the local area by tall smokestacks.
*   e. all of these

M 18. Acid rain
    a. produces nitrogen oxides.
    b. is the major reason for the production of sterile lakes around the world.
    c. is rainwater with a pH above 7.
    d. is primarily the result of industrial pollution.
*   e. All but choice "is rainwater with a pH above 7"are correct.

M 19. The two chemical elements associated with acid deposition are
    a. nitrogen and oxygen.
    b. sulfur and oxygen.
*   c. nitrogen and sulfur.
    d. carbon and oxygen.
    e. nitrogen and carbon.

D 20. Which of the following statements is FALSE?
    a. The length of day and night are equal at any place on the Earth when the sun crosses the equator.
    b. In June, if you wanted to get in a round of golf after 7 P.M., you would have longer to play in Minneapolis than in Atlanta.
*   c. The southern end of the Earth's axis points toward the sun in the northern hemisphere's summer.
    d. The organisms living in most parts of the world are adapted to seasonal variations in environmental conditions.
    e. Seasonal changes become more pronounced the greater the latitude.

M 21. To generate electricity by using wind farms, what is a chief requirement?
    a. flat lands for building the windmills
*   b. prevailing winds of at least 7.5 meters per second
    c. fossil fuels to get the windmills turning
    d. mountain passes for the wind to squeeze through
    e. a lack of rain

THE OCEAN, LANDFORMS, AND CLIMATES

E 22. What portion of the Earth's surface is covered by oceans?
    a. less than 10 percent
    b. more than 80 percent
    c. about 50 percent
*   d. approximately 70 percent
    e. barely 20 percent

M 23. Water in the oceans tends to move in great currents from
    a. north pole to south pole.
*   b. equator to poles.
    c. poles to equator.
    d. south pole to north pole.
    e. poles to equator and back again.

M 24. Mountains produce
    a. rain shadows on the windswept sides.
    b. precipitation on the nonwindy sides.
*   c. deserts on the nonwindy sides.
    d. extensive grasslands on the windswept sides.
    e. all of these

M 25. The formation of mountains affects the climate and vegetation of the surrounding areas to the greatest extent by influencing
    a. temperature.
*   b. moisture relationships.
    c. light regimens.
    d. wind.
    e. pressure.

D   26. Temperature variations during the course of a year tend to increase with
    *   a. increasing distance from the equator and increasing distance from the oceans.
        b. increasing distance from the equator and decreasing distance from the oceans.
        c. decreasing distance from the equator and decreasing distance from the oceans.
        d. decreasing distance from the equator and increasing distance from the oceans.
        e. increasing height above sea level.

REALMS OF BIODIVERSITY

M   27. In general, which of the following lists places the terms in order of increasing size?
        a. ecosystem, biogeographical realm, biome, biosphere
        b. ecosystem, biome, biosphere, biogeographical realm
        c. biome, ecosystem, biogeographical realm, biosphere
    *   d. ecosystem, biome, biogeographical realm, biosphere
        e. biome, biosphere, biogeographical realm, ecosystem

D   28. Productivity of a biome increases as
        a. water availability increases and elevation increases.
        b. water availability decreases and elevation increases.
    *   c. water availability increases and elevation decreases.
        d. water availability decreases and elevation decreases.
        e. none of these

M   29. Distribution of biomes tends to be influenced by all EXCEPT which one of the following?
        a. topography
        b. soil
        c. latitude
    *   d. longitude
        e. climate

M   30. A particular biome is characterized by
        a. climate.
        b. vegetation.
        c. animals.
        d. vegetation and animals, only.
    *   e. vegetation, animals, and climate.

D   31. Similarity of one biome to another may be due to
        a. altitude.
        b. latitude.
        c. longitude.
    *   d. altitude and latitude, only.
        e. altitude, latitude, and longitude.

E   32. Most desert biomes are in close proximity to what other biome?
        a. tundra
    *   b. grasslands
        c. deciduous forests
        d. evergreen forests
        e. rain forests

M   33. At which latitudes are deserts usually found?
        a. 0–15
        b. 15–25
    *   c. 25–40
        d. 40–60
        e. 60–90

M   34. The only one of the following characteristics that all deserts have in common is
    *   a. low rainfall amounts.
        b. heat.
        c. sand.
        d. lack of vegetation.
        e. cacti.

D   35. The biome most in danger of desertification is
        a. desert.
    *   b. grassland.
        c. deciduous forest.
        d. tropical rain forest.
        e. taiga.

M   36. In shrublands,
    *   a. annual rainfall is less than 10 centimeters or so, and rates of evaporation are high.
        b. primary production is abundant throughout the year.
        c. there are constant cool temperatures throughout the year.
        d. winters are mild and summers are wet.
        e. precipitation occurs evenly year round.

M   37. The biome most closely associated with fire is the
        a. desert.
        b. tropical rain forest.
    *   c. chaparral (shrublands).
        d. temperate deciduous forest.
        e. taiga.

D   38. Fire in the dry shrublands does not kill the small bushy plants most probably because
        a. the plants have a tough protective bark.
        b. the leaves are very heavy and wet.
    *   c. they grow back from root crowns and fire causes their seeds to germinate.
        d. humans live close by and have fire-fighting equipment.
        e. they have natural fire-retardant chemicals.

M   39. The Dust Bowl of the 1930s was the result of
         destruction of
         a. desert.
         b. chaparral.
         c. tallgrass prairie.
     *   d. shortgrass prairie.
         e. temperate deciduous forest.

M   40. Which of the following biomes would support and be
         characterized by the greatest number and diversity of
         herbivores?
         a. tundra
         b. taiga
     *   c. grassland
         d. chaparral
         e. desert

M   41. A biome with grasses as primary producers and shrubs
         and scattered trees adapted to prolonged dry spells is
         known as a
         a. warm desert.
     *   b. savanna.
         c. tundra.
         d. taiga.
         e. chaparral.

M   42. A wind system that influences large climatic regions
         and reverses direction seasonally, producing dry and
         wet seasons, is referred to as
         a. a geothermal ecosystem.
         b. an upwelling.
         c. a taiga.
     *   d. a monsoon.
         e. a hurricane.

D   43. Grassland biomes around the Earth vary in several
         ways, but the chief factor causing the variation is
     *   a. rainfall amounts.
         b. vegetation.
         c. soil type.
         d. the animals present.
         e. prevailing winds.

E   44. The biome with the greatest diversity of life is
         a. tundra.
         b. taiga.
     *   c. tropical rain forest.
         d. desert.
         e. grassland.

M   45. In tropical rain forests,
     *   a. plants flourish with regular and heavy rainfall.
         b. diversity is limited because the tall forest canopy
             shuts out most of the incoming light.
         c. conditions are extremely favorable for growing
             luxuriant food crops.
         d. there is little competition for resources.
         e. habitat partitioning is minimal.

M   46. The removal of trees from tropical rain forest for the
         purpose of large-scale food crop agriculture is not
         recommended because
         a. the soil is poor in organic nutrients.
         b. erosion rates accelerate when trees are removed.
         c. the soil has few decomposers.
     *   d. soils are weathered, humus-deficient, and poor
             nutrient reservoirs.
         e. the soil is poor in organic nutrients, erosion rates
             accelerate when trees are removed, and the soil
             has few decomposers.

E   47. Which biome is characterized by plants whose leaves
         drop off in the wintertime?
         a. coniferous forest
         b. tundra
     *   c. deciduous broadleaf forest
         d. tropical rain forest
         e. all of these

M   48. The taiga could best be described as what type of
         forest?
         a. deciduous
         b. thorn
     *   c. evergreen coniferous
         d. broad-leafed
         e. shrub

D   49. Which is NOT true of a mature temperate deciduous
         forest?
         a. Larger predators and herbivores use the forest
             more for shelter; they tend to feed in clearings.
         b. Extensive tree roots prevent major soil erosion.
     *   c. The principal producers are the small bushes and
             low-lying grasses.
         d. The mature trees are the primary energy
             foundation for the entire community and play a
             key role in recycling nutrients.
         e. The fallen leaves decay to replenish nutrients in
             the soil.

M   50. The biome at the top of a very high mountain at the
         equator would be
     *   a. tundra.
         b. taiga (boreal forest).
         c. tropical rain forest.
         d. temperate deciduous forest.
         e. chaparral (shrublands).

E   51. Which biome is a treeless plain that occurs around the
         Arctic Circle?
         a. chaparral
         b. taiga
         c. desert
         d. grassland
     *   e. arctic tundra

M 52. Permafrost and low rainfall are characteristic of which biome?
   a. boreal forest
   b. montane coniferous forest
 * c. tundra
   d. evergreen coniferous forest
   e. deciduous forests

M 53. Low temperature, brief growing seasons, limited rainfall, and short, shallow-rooted plants characterize the
 * a. tundra.
   b. taiga.
   c. temperate deciduous forest.
   d. grassland.
   e. tropical montane forests.

E 54. The word "permafrost" is associated with which biome?
 * a. tundra
   b. taiga
   c. temperate deciduous forest
   d. grassland
   e. montane forest

D 55. Arctic and alpine tundras are alike in all EXCEPT which of the following ways?
   a. low moisture
 * b. permafrost
   c. minimal plant life
   d. cold temperatures
   e. nutrient-poor soils

E 56. If you were to travel to the equator and then to the top of Mount Kilimanjaro, the changes in vegetation you would observe would mimic the changes you would experience if you traveled
 * a. from the equator toward the poles.
   b. from the poles toward the equator.
   c. from wet to dry areas.
   d. from east to west.
   e. from continent to continent.

E 57. If you were in Central Africa and you decided to climb Mount Kilimanjaro, which biome would you expect to find at the top?
   a. tropical rain forest
   b. taiga
 * c. tundra
   d. grassland
   e. deciduous forests

THE WATER PROVINCES

M 58. The greatest diversity of organisms in lake ecosystems is found in what zone?
   a. profundal
   b. limnetic
   c. thermocline
 * d. littoral
   e. benthic

E 59. Freshwater lakes will turn over in the
   a. fall.
   b. winter.
   c. spring.
   d. summer.
 * e. both fall and spring.

M 60. In a lake, the open sunlit water that supports photosynthesis is referred to as which zone?
   a. epipelagic
 * b. limnetic
   c. littoral
   d. profundal
   e. benthic

M 61. The profundal zone is characterized by
   a. plankton.
   b. algae.
   c. plants and animals.
 * d. decomposers.
   e. all of these

M 62. Thorough mixing of oxygen and nutrients within a lake occurs in
   a. winter and summer.
   b. winter and spring.
   c. spring and summer.
 * d. spring and autumn.
   e. summer and autumn.

E 63. The upper and lower levels of a lake are separated by the
   a. limnetic zone.
 * b. thermocline.
   c. littoral zone.
   d. lentic zone.
   e. eutrophic zone.

E 64. Nutrient-poor lakes are
   a. profundal.
 * b. oligotrophic.
   c. eutrophic.
   d. benthic.
   e. pelagic.

M 65. Oligotrophic lakes are characterized by all EXCEPT which of the following?
   a. deep water
   b. clear water
   c. abundant oxygen
   d. low nutrients
 * e. high production of fish

D 66. Which of the following is mismatched?
 * a. oligotrophic lake—nutrient rich
   b. oligotrophic lake—deep, clear water
   c. eutrophic lake—shallow
   d. eutrophic lake—succession
   e. eutrophic lake—phytoplankton becomes dominant

M 67. Estuaries often exhibit a great degree of species diversity because
    a. saltwater and freshwater species are present.
    b. many species of the open ocean spend a portion of their life cycles in estuarine waters.
    c. there is a continued upwelling of nutrients.
  * d. saltwater and freshwater species are present, plus many species of invertebrates and fishes that spend their early life stages here.
    e. saltwater and freshwater species are present, many species of the open ocean spend a portion of their life cycles in estuarine waters, and there is a continued upwelling of nutrients.

M 68. Water draining from the land mixes with seawater carried in on tides in which of the following?
    a. abyssal zone
    b. rift zone
    c. upwelling
  * d. estuary
    e. pelagic zone

M 69. Which are "marine nurseries" for shrimp and many marine forms?
    a. photic zones
    b. benthic zones
  * c. estuaries
    d. pelagic zone
    e. limnetic areas

E 70. The region where freshwater and saltwater mix is the
    a. neritic zone.
  * b. estuary.
    c. lotic zone.
    d. littoral region.
    e. pelagic zone.

D 71. Which of the following factors would be likely to be limiting in the open ocean?
  * a. nutrients
    b. temperature
    c. oxygen
    d. light
    e. wind

M 72. The ocean zone that exhibits the greatest degree of species diversity is
    a. estuary.
    b. rocky intertidal.
  * c. neritic.
    d. continental shelf.
    e. profundal zone.

M 73. Which zone of the ocean is found above the continental shelf?
    a. abyssal
    b. benthic
    c. pelagic
  * d. neritic
    e. oceanic

M 74. The organisms that occupy the first trophic level near hydrothermal vents are
    a. detritivores.
  * b. chemoautotrophs.
    c. decomposers.
    d. photosynthetic bacteria.
    e. fungi.

APPLYING KNOWLEDGE OF THE BIOSPHERE

D 75. Upwelling
  * a. increases productivity by bringing nutrient-rich cool water to the surface of the ocean.
    b. occurs in freshwater lakes when the thermocline is destroyed by changing temperatures.
    c. refers to the accumulation of pollution in certain estuaries.
    d. occurs when warm ocean currents approach the edge of continents.
    e. generates the major climatic changes in the Pacific Ocean known as El Niño.

M 76. Between El Niño episodes, the cholera bacteria are reservoired in
    a. shrubs and trees.
  * b. copepods and small marine crustaceans.
    c. snails and corals.
    d. bony fish and sharks.
    e. beetles and flies.

Matching Questions

D   77.   Matching. Choose the one most appropriate answer for each.

1. ___ benthic province
2. ___ biome
3. ___ deserts
4. ___ hydrothermal vents
5. ___ estuary
6. ___ savanna
7. ___ shortgrass prairie
8. ___ taiga
9. ___ tallgrass prairie
10. ___ deciduous forest
11. ___ littoral zone
12. ___ tropical rain forest
13. ___ tundra
14. ___ upwellings
15. ___ warm deserts

    A. boreal or "swamp forests"

    B. strong vertical currents

    C. Steinbeck and Michener lamented their disruption

    D. broad belts of grasslands with a smattering of shrubs and trees

    E. a well-lit, shallow, warm region that supports many species

    F. nearly all of this has been converted to agriculture

    G. includes sediments and rocks on ocean bottom

    H. the ground heats fast in the morning, then cools fast at night

    I. decomposition and mineral cycling are rapid so litter does not accumulate

    J. places where bacteria, tubeworms, and mollusks thrive in deep ocean

    K. annual rainfall is less than 10 centimeters or so

    L. mosses, lichens, caribou, and lemmings; the summer air is thick with mosquitoes

    M. primary producers are phytoplankton and detrital food webs abound

    N. a large region characterized by its large array of dominant primary producers; subdivisions of the great realms

    O. starts in regions of mild temperatures and regular seasonal rainfall

Answers:
1. G	2. N	3. H	4. J
5. M	6. D	7. C	8. A
9. F	10. O	11. E	12. I
13. L	14. B	15. K	

Classification Questions

Answer questions 78–82 in reference to the five biomes listed below.

    a. tundra
    b. grassland
    c. desert
    d. taiga (boreal forest)
    e. savanna

M   78.   A plant community composed primarily of shrubby trees widely spaced and surrounded by grasses is this biome.

M   79.   A community composed of lichens and short, shallow-rooted plants that form the base for food webs.

E   80.   This biome is characterized by extremes of temperatures and plants that are highly resistant to water loss.

M   81.   This biome has the richest soils.

E   82.   Conifers are most likely to be found in this biome.

Answers:
78. e	79. a	80. c
81. b	82. d	

Answer questions 83–87 in reference to the five biomes listed below.

    a. tundra
    b. chaparral
    c. desert
    d. taiga (coniferous forest)
    e. deciduous forest

M   83.   In this biome you could find a thin, nutrient-poor soil.

E   84.   In this biome you are most likely to find shrubs with highly flammable leaves.

M   85.   In this biome you would expect to find voles and caribou.

D   86.   This biome would most likely be found at moist, temperate latitudes.

M   87.   This biome is most likely to have spruce and balsam fir dominating the forests.

Answers:
83. d	84. b	85. a
86. e	87. d	

Selecting the Exception

D 88. Four of the five answers below are related by inclusion in the same type of biome. Select the exception.
   a. shortgrass prairie
   b. monsoon grassland
   c. savanna
 * d. chaparral
   e. tallgrass prairie

M 89. Four of the five answers listed below are characteristics of the tropical rain forest. Select the exception.
   a. new leaves are shed and regrown all year long
   b. soils are poor nutrient reservoirs
   c. decomposition and mineral cycling are rapid
   d. annual mean temperature 25°C, humidity at least 80 percent
 * e. large herds of herbivores

M 90. Four of the five answers listed below are related by a common biome. Select the exception.
   a. no trees
   b. permafrost
   c. short growing seasons
 * d. found in the rain shadows
   e. may be found above Arctic Circle or at top of mountains

M 91. Four of the five answers listed below are human efforts to improve the carrying capacity of the Earth for humans. Select the exception.
 * a. desertification
   b. recycling
   c. green revolution
   d. irrigation
   e. conservation

CHAPTER 32
BEHAVIORAL ECOLOGY

Multiple-Choice Questions

SO WHERE DOES BEHAVIOR START?

M 1. Which of the following statements is FALSE?
   a. Behavior is controlled by the environmental stimuli an organism receives.
   b. Behavior is partially genetic so that it undergoes natural selection and evolution.
 * c. Behavior refers only to responses to external stimuli.
   d. Behavior sometimes is nonadaptive.
   e. Behavior patterns can be learned.

M 2. All EXCEPT which of the following statements concerning behavior are true?
   a. The knee-jerk reflex is a behavior.
 * b. A behavior such as a complex courtship ritual is encoded by a single gene.
   c. Behaviors are products of natural selection.
   d. Behaviors are adaptive.
   e. Behaviors are influenced by hormones.

M 3. Recent studies in humans have shown there is a close relationship between poor nutrition and poor learning ability. These studies suggest that
   a. there is only a minor genetic component to learned behavior.
 * b. behavior is modified by the environment.
   c. learning is adaptive.
   d. learning is instinctive.
   e. behavior is entirely genetic.

M 4. Behavior is the result of
   a. neural networks.
   b. hormonal interactions.
   c. genetic predisposition.
   d. environmental cues.
 * e. all of these

D 5. Oxytocin has roles in
   a. the birth process.
   b. lactation.
   c. social behavior.
   d. pair bonding.
 * e. all of these

M 6. Instinctive behavior is
   a. stereotyped.
   b. unlearned.
   c. prewired to recognize sign stimuli.
   d. triggered by limited sets of clues.
 * e. triggered by one or two simple, well-defined environmental cues.

E 7. To get a young baby to smile, simply present a
   a. parent's smiling face.
   b. parent's nonsmiling face.
   c. person's face or a mask.
   d. picture of a face.
 * e. representation of a face, so long as it has two recognizable eyes.

E 8. Konrad Lorenz is noted for his studies on
   a. prenatal marking.
   b. mating behavior.
 * c. imprinting.
   d. habituation.
   e. insight learning.

E 9. Imprinting is a(n)
   a. response to a stimulus.
 * b. learned behavior that occurs during a critical time period.
   c. fixed action potential.
   d. decline in the level of a response to a nonthreatening stimulus.
   e. instinctive behavior only.

E 10. Newly hatched goslings follow any large moving objects to which they are exposed shortly after hatching. This is an example of
   a. homing behavior.
 * b. imprinting.
   c. piloting.
   d. migration.
   e. none of these

D 11. Studies of _?_ in young animals could lend support for arguments that human parents and babies need to spend as much time together as possible.
   a. conditioning
 * b. imprinting
   c. habituation
   d. insight learning
   e. latent learning

M 12. Bird song
   a. has to be heard before a bird can sing it.
   b. is learned during early life.
   c. is specific for each bird species.
   d. has a genetic component.
 * e. all of these

E 13. Altruistic behavior is
   a. selfish.
   b. sexually directed behavior.
 * c. self-sacrificing behavior.
   d. aggressive behavior.
   e. nonreactive, such as freezing at the sign of danger.

E   14.   After starlings build a nest, they add branches with
            living leaves
            a.   as a form of camouflage against predators.
            b.   as a form of insulation.
     *   c.   to repel parasites.
            d.   to prevent other birds from using the nest.
            e.   for reasons that are currently unknown.

COMMUNICATION SIGNALS

M   15.   Pheromones are
     *   a.   used in nonverbal communication between
                 members of the same species.
            b.   found only in the invertebrates.
            c.   signals to members of other species.
            d.   types of internal hormones that control
                 maturation.
            e.   substitutes for hormones.

E   16.   Pheromones are advantageous because
            a.   they work in the dark.
            b.   they are often unique to individual species.
            c.   they sometimes act as sex attractants.
            d.   they do not trigger a response in other nontarget
                 species.
     *   e.   all of these

M   17.   Social behavior among insects such as bees depends
            on
            a.   genetic similarity.
            b.   bonding early in youth.
     *   c.   communication.
            d.   diversity.
            e.   polymorphism.

E   18.   Social behavior is most obviously the result of
            a.   genetics.
     *   b.   communication signals.
            c.   environmental influences.
            d.   parental upbringing.
            e.   learning.

M   19.   Even though the termite can detect the scent of an
            invading ant, this is not considered a form of
            communication between termite and ant for which of
            the following reasons?
            a.   The scent is not sufficient to cause a response in
                 the termite.
     *   b.   Communication must benefit both the signaler and
                 the receiver; the termite is an illegitimate receiver.
            c.   The ant does realize it is giving off a scent.
            d.   The scent is not sufficient to cause a response in
                 the termite and communication must benefit both
                 the signaler and the receiver.
            e.   The scent is not sufficient to cause a response in
                 the termite, communication must benefit both the
                 signaler and the receiver, and the ant does realize
                 it is giving off a scent.

E   20.   A termite that intercepts the scent of an ant is called
     *   a.   an illegitimate receiver.
            b.   an exploiter.
            c.   an illegitimate signaler.
            d.   smart.
            e.   a thief.

E   21.   Which scientist won the Nobel Prize for his research
            on the behavior of bees and the discovery of the way
            bees communicated the location of a food source?
     *   a.   Karl von Frisch
            b.   Nicholas Tinbergen
            c.   Konrad Lorenz
            d.   Skinner
            e.   Pavlov

E   22.   Bees learn the direction to a distant source of food by
            a.   following the foraging scout.
            b.   following a trail pheromone.
     *   c.   observing the tail-wagging dance.
            d.   observing the round dance.
            e.   observing the tail-wagging dance and the round
                 dance.

M   23.   Bees use which information for locating food and the
            hive?
            a.   local topographic features
            b.   odors
            c.   magnetism
     *   d.   the angle of the sun
            e.   distance between plants

M   24.   Communication by means of visual signals has a
            minimum requirement of
            a.   daylight.
            b.   short distance.
     *   c.   a clear line of sight.
            d.   keen eyesight.
            e.   sharp hearing.

MATES, OFFSPRING, AND REPRODUCTIVE SUCCESS

M   25.   Which of the following is mismatched?
            a.   male bison—engage in combat during breeding
                 season
     *   b.   male hangingflies—lek
            c.   amphibians and reptiles—parental care
                 uncommon
            d.   fiddler crab—attractive single large claw
            e.   male midwife toad—wraps developing eggs
                 around his legs

M   26.   The key factor influencing a female's sexual
            preference is
            a.   how many eggs are fertilized by a male.
            b.   how many eggs survive and reach adulthood.
     *   c.   the quality of the mate.
            d.   how many sperm are produced by a male.
            e.   all of these

COSTS AND BENEFITS OF SOCIAL GROUPS

D 27. All EXCEPT which of the following are disadvantages to sociality?
   * a. predator avoidance
   b. cannibalism
   c. food depletion
   d. contagious diseases
   e. parasite infestation

D 28. The presence of the strongest competitors in the center of a group of animals may qualify the group for status as a(n)
   a. altruistic society.
   * b. selfish herd.
   c. kin group.
   d. dominance hierarchy.
   e. community.

M 29. In the selfish herd, there is an advantage to
   a. being on the outside.
   b. being near the front.
   * c. being in the middle.
   d. being isolated.
   e. Position is of no advantage.

M 30. The example used to demonstrate that competitive interactions lead to the formation of dominance hierarchies involved
   a. albatrosses.
   b. a honeybee colony.
   * c. baboon troops.
   d. greylag geese.
   e. all of these

WHY SACRIFICE YOURSELF?

D 31. Whatever the motivation of self-sacrificing behavior on the part of nonhuman animals is, we know it is NOT
   a. genetic.
   b. the result of selection.
   * c. derived from conscious reasoning.
   d. a result of dominance hierarchy.
   e. any of these

D 32. Which of the following statements is FALSE?
   a. A communication signal has benefits for both the sender and the receiver.
   b. Under some circumstances, solitary individuals may leave more descendants than social ones do.
   * c. Social animals must exhibit altruism.
   d. Not every environment favors the evolution of social life.
   e. Altruism means helping others, which may mean sacrificing personal reproductive success.

E 33. Parental support of offspring is an example of
   a. artificial selection.
   * b. kin selection.
   c. natural selection.
   d. negative selection.
   e. stabilizing selection.

D 34. Researchers attempt to explain the persistence of altruism by the theory of
   a. self-sacrificing behavior.
   b. dominance hierarchy.
   c. social behavior.
   * d. indirect selection.
   e. being a fool.

M 35. Indirect selection refers to
   a. predators.
   b. dominance hierarchy.
   * c. altruistic behavior.
   d. the development of harems.
   e. symbiotic organisms.

D 36. If an individual for whatever reason cannot pass on its genes to offspring, the best alternative is to show altruism to
   * a. relatives.
   b. strangers.
   c. neighbors.
   d. other species.
   e. no one.

M 37. In highly integrated insect societies,
   a. natural selection favors individual behaviors that lead to greater diversity among members of the society.
   b. there is scarcely any division of labor.
   * c. cooperative behavior predominates.
   d. patterns of behavior are flexible and learned behavior predominates.
   e. all of these

M 38. In a bee hive, altruistic, sacrificial, behavior is shown by a
   a. king.
   b. drone.
   * c. guard.
   d. queen.
   e. worker.

M 39. Naked mole-rat colonies of 25 to 300 individuals
   a. are eusocial.
   b. show a high level of inbreeding.
   c. demonstrate a high degree of genetic diversity among different colonies.
   d. can be genetically characterized by comparing samples of DNA molecules of various individuals by genetic fingerprinting.
   * e. all of these

A LOOK AT PRIMATE SOCIAL BEHAVIOR

M 40. Which of the following is NOT typical of bonobo behavior?
   a. adult males are related
   b. females bond with each other
   c. live in groups
   * d. infanticide
   e. females sexually receptive any time

HUMAN SOCIAL BEHAVIOR

D   41.   In human behavior, adaptive does not mean
             a.   self-sacrifice.
             b.   altruism.
             c.   judgment.
       *   d.   morally right.
             e.   stupid.

Matching Questions

D   42.   Matching. Choose the one most appropriate answer
             for each. Some letters may not be used.
             1. ___ altruism
             2. ___ insight
             3. ___ instinctive behavior
             4. ___ imprinting
             5. ___ lek
             6. ___ learning
             7. ___ Lorenz
             A.   imprintings in goslings
             B.   capacity of an animal to complete complex,
                  stereotyped responses to first-time
                  encounters to key stimuli
             C.   problem solving without trial-and-error
             D.   an adaptive change in behavior
             E.   communal display ground
             F.   occurs during a sensitive period in which a
                  following response or social attachment
                  becomes fixed on a particular moving object
             G.   self-sacrificing behavior

Answers: 1. G   2. C   3. B

                 4. F   5. E   6. D

                 7. A

Classification Questions

Answer questions 43–47 in reference to the four kinds of social
behavior listed below.
             a.   cooperation
             b.   altruism
             c.   dominance hierarchies
             d.   cooperative predator avoidance

M   43.   When worker bees guard the entrance to the hive and
             sacrifice themselves to repel intruders, this is an
             example of _?_.

E   44.   Dominant males and females of a wolf pack are an
             example of _?_.

M   45.   Australian sawfly caterpillars collectively rear up
             writhing from a branch. This is an example of _?_.

M   46.   Wolves and lions who live in social groups and
             cooperate in hunts are considered examples of _?_.

M   47.   When a woman raises her brother's children, this is an
             example of _?_.

Answers: 43. b   44. c   45. d

                 46. a   47. b

Selecting the Exception

M   48.   Four of the five answers listed below are
             characteristics of behaviors that are inborn. Select the
             exception.
       *   a.   modified by the environment
             b.   stereotyped
             c.   performed the first time stimulus is presented
             d.   innate
             e.   automatic

M   49.   Four of the five answers listed below are pheromone
             signals. Select the exception.
             a.   sex attractant
             b.   alarm or attack
             c.   territory
       *   d.   social communication
             e.   physiology

M   50.   Four of the five answers listed below are activities of
             the same type of bee. Select the exception.
       *   a.   lay eggs
             b.   feed larvae
             c.   guard hive
             d.   clean and maintain nest
             e.   forage for food